The Family
ENCYCLOPEDIA
of General Knowledge

The Family
ENCYCLOPEDIA
of General Knowledge

WINDWARD

Edited by Christine Casley

Copyright © Instituto Geografico de Agostini S.p.a. 1982
Copyright © This arrangement and translation
The Hamlyn Publishing Group Limited 1982
London · New York · Sydney · Toronto
Astronaut House, Feltham, England

Published in this edition by Windward, an imprint
owned by W H Smith and Son Limited. Registered No 237811 England.

Trading as WHS Distributors, St John's House, East Street,
Leicester, LE1 6NE

ISBN 0 7112 0228 1

Printed in Czechoslovakia

51164

Contents

Science, Technology and Transport

Bridges Roads across the void

There are many types of bridges. One of the simplest is the light wooden construction held up by strong ropes, which in films always seems to cross a deep canyon and sway frighteningly under the feet of someone crossing. In contrast are the ancient Roman aqueducts, supported by stone and brick arches on top of tall pillars, which carried water across valleys to the towns. Then there are the tall, graceful viaducts in reinforced concrete which carry motorways in the mountains, and the suspension bridges which, hanging from steel cables, make "leaps" of more than a kilometre without any support from below. An example of this last type is the Verrazano-Narrows bridge which links the suburb of Brooklyn to Staten Island, in New York Bay.

A bridge can be defined as any structure which spans an obstacle such as a valley, a watercourse, a railway or a road. On the bridge there can be a simple footway, a railway, a road or even the basin of a canal.

Bridges may be built of wood (pine, larch or oak), bricks, stone, reinforced concrete or steel. Wood, stone and bricks dominated the construction of bridges (and every other type of building) without competition from other materials for thousands of years. In the last two centuries, as a consequence of the introduction of more durable and resistant materials such as steel and (later) reinforced concrete, they have been almost completely abandoned. Experiments continue with new materials and new solutions to constructional problems. In Quebec, in Canada, for example the Pierre Laporte Bridge, opened in 1970, was built of aluminium. The light weight of aluminium is an advantage, but it has not yet been widely used in bridge construction because of its elasticity and

This is the George Washington Bridge, over the Hudson river in New York. Built in 1931, it is one of the largest suspension bridges in the world.

cost. When these problems are solved its use is likely to become more common.

In any bridge, two basic parts can be identified: the superstructure and the foundation. The former includes the road, railway or canal basin and the structure immediately supporting it. The foundation is the part which takes the weight of the superstructure and anchors it to the ground. It consists of the abutments (the end foundations) and the piers (the intermediate pillars) on which the superstructure rests. The distance between two supports is known as a span.

Many long bridges have numerous piers instead of long spans. Among these is the bridge over Lake Pontchartrain, in Louisiana (United States), which is almost forty kilometres long. When it is not possible to build the intermediate piers close together (because the bridge is very tall, because it has to cross a very turbulent river, or for other reasons), it becomes necessary to use large spans.

Bridges with trusses

The superstructure supported by the piers can be either trussed, arched or suspended. The trussed superstructure is the simplest. Probably the first bridges were of this type. The construction is essentially one in which horizontal beams are held up by vertical piers.

The horizontal trusses are made of reinforced concrete or steel, but wood is also a suitable material, although it is no longer used, except perhaps for temporary bridges. The load they bear tends to make the trusses sag in mid-span, much as happens to library shelves when they are too long or have too many books on them. This structure is usually, therefore, adopted only for small spans of a few tens of metres. There are, nevertheless, some large examples of this type, including the bridge in Louisiana already mentioned.

The trussed bridge offers the great advantage of exerting only a vertical

Above, two very famous bridges. Left, the Rialto, in Venice: initially built in wood in the thirteenth century, then rebuilt in stone about 1590. Right, the famous bascule bridge, Tower Bridge, a soaring symbol of London.

Viaducts are aqueducts "without water": they have many piers and take traffic across valleys or other traffic routes. Left, a viaduct forming part of the Salerno-Reggio motorway in Calabria, Italy.

thrust down on the piers and abutments, without introducing horizontal stresses. Such bridges are suitable where the ground is not very firm.

Arched bridges

Trussed bridges cannot be built out of blocks of stone or bricks, because these materials are not able to resist tractional stresses (they do not sag, as happens with library shelves, but crumble instead).

How, then, was it possible to build large, sturdy bridges in ancient times, when only stone and bricks were available? The problem was solved thousands of years ago by resorting to the arched structure, one of the most important inventions in the history of construction. When the arch is used, all the material is in effect squeezed together and thus even stone and bricks will serve as supports.

Many of the most beautiful bridges, such as the Rialto Bridge in Venice, or the Sistine Bridge in Rome (both in Renaissance style), have stone and brick arches.

One of the most famous arched bridges of the Middle Ages was the Old London Bridge. This was the first stone bridge with masonry foundations to be built in a swift, tidal river. Built in 1209, it had nineteen pointed arches and carried a street of shops and houses.

The arch can be used also for modern materials such as steel and reinforced concrete. The first iron bridge in history, built by Thomas Telford at Coalbrookdale, Shropshire in 1779, was an arched bridge. The load-bearing surface of such a bridge is supported on top of the arch, either by means of small pillars, or by tie-beams fixed to the structure of the arch.

The bridge across the Parramatta, in Sydney, with a span of about 305 metres, is built of blocks of pre-fabricated reinforced concrete and uses the former method. The Bayonne Bridge which links Staten Island (New York) to New Jersey, has a central arch, made of steel girders, with a span in excess of 500 metres and uses the latter method. For greater spans the "suspension" system is used.

The world's principal suspension bridges

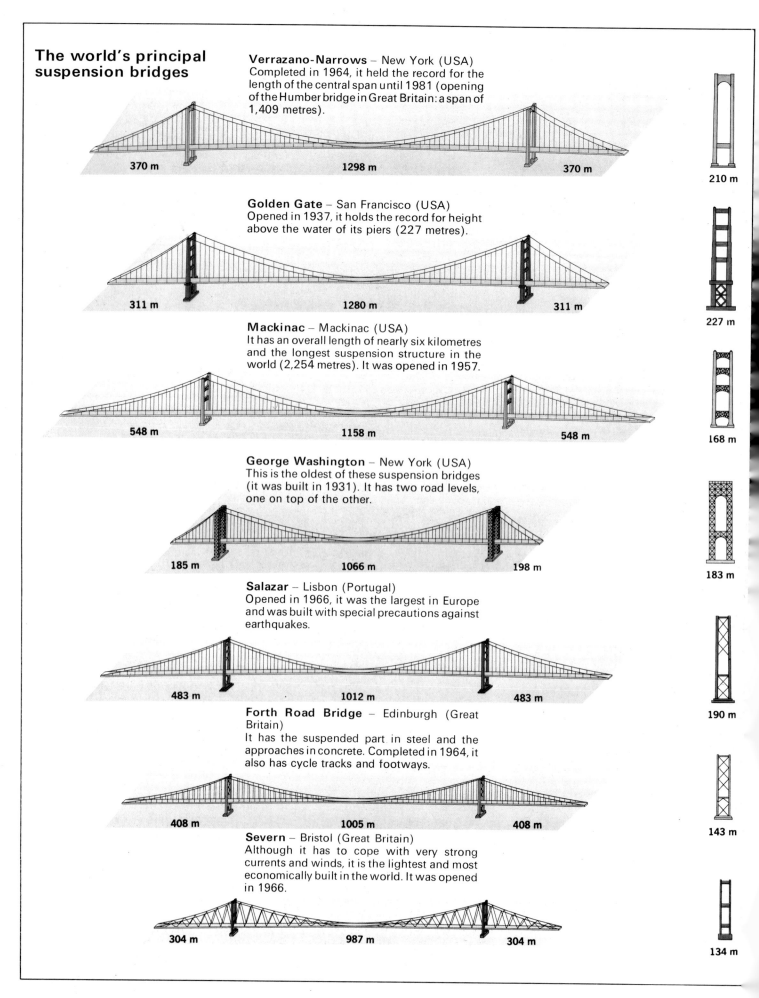

Verrazano-Narrows – New York (USA)
Completed in 1964, it held the record for the length of the central span until 1981 (opening of the Humber bridge in Great Britain: a span of 1,409 metres).

370 m   1298 m   370 m

210 m

Golden Gate – San Francisco (USA)
Opened in 1937, it holds the record for height above the water of its piers (227 metres).

311 m   1280 m   311 m

227 m

Mackinac – Mackinac (USA)
It has an overall length of nearly six kilometres and the longest suspension structure in the world (2,254 metres). It was opened in 1957.

548 m   1158 m   548 m

168 m

George Washington – New York (USA)
This is the oldest of these suspension bridges (it was built in 1931). It has two road levels, one on top of the other.

185 m   1066 m   198 m

183 m

Salazar – Lisbon (Portugal)
Opened in 1966, it was the largest in Europe and was built with special precautions against earthquakes.

483 m   1012 m   483 m

190 m

Forth Road Bridge – Edinburgh (Great Britain)
It has the suspended part in steel and the approaches in concrete. Completed in 1964, it also has cycle tracks and footways.

408 m   1005 m   408 m

143 m

Severn – Bristol (Great Britain)
Although it has to cope with very strong currents and winds, it is the lightest and most economically built in the world. It was opened in 1966.

304 m   987 m   304 m

134 m

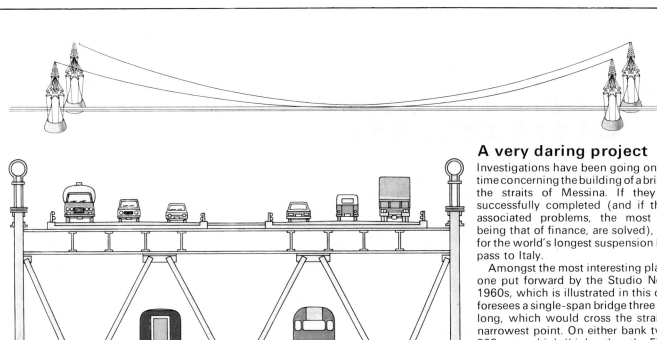

A very daring project

Investigations have been going on for a long time concerning the building of a bridge across the straits of Messina. If they are ever successfully completed (and if the various associated problems, the most important being that of finance, are solved), the record for the world's longest suspension bridge will pass to Italy.

Amongst the most interesting plans for it is one put forward by the Studio Nervi in the 1960s, which is illustrated in this diagram. It foresees a single-span bridge three kilometres long, which would cross the straits at their narrowest point. On either bank two towers 392 metres high (higher than the Eiffel Tower or the Empire State Building) would have to be built and linked by two bundles of steel cable more than a metre in diameter. Two levels are envisaged (road and railway) about thirty metres wide. More than 100,000 tonnes of steel would be needed.

Suspension bridges

The characteristics of the material are not fully exploited in arched bridges built of iron. Only the capacity to sustain compressional stresses is utilized, while the ability to resist traction is not. A century ago, engineers began to design steel bridges "made to measure", the extraordinary suspension bridges. Certainly, the idea was not new. The footbridges of wood and rope or those made wholly from lianas are in fact suspension bridges. But it was a new concept to bestride enormous spans with constructions which could take the weight of heavy motorized traffic.

Telford designed the 177-metre Menai suspension bridge in Wales in the 1820s, but the first major wire-cable suspension bridges were built by John Roebling. His Brooklyn Bridge in New York, completed in 1883, has a span of 486 metres. These days, as a result of research, significantly stronger bridges are being planned and built.

Let us see how suspension bridges are constructed. The bridge at Verrazano-Narrows, one of the most famous, has two pairs of steel cables of almost a metre in diameter, which, anchored to one bank by enormous blocks of concrete, pass up and over the top of the first pier, then curve downwards under their own weight (as happens with any metal bar fixed at its two ends) and pass over the second pier, which is close to the far bank, to drop to an anchorage in further blocks of concrete. To the two pairs of cables are linked a large number of vertical ties which support the load-carrying surface, which is literally "suspended" from the steel cables. The two piers, slender and graceful, are 207 metres tall and 1,298 metres apart. The 229,300 kilometres of wire from which the cables are made would stretch more than halfway to the moon.

In recent decades, bridges have been built which, though still defined as suspension bridges, have a very different shape from the classic bridges of this type. These are "multi-span" bridges. The structure consists of pre-stressed concrete beams supported by trestles below and by tension cables above. There is such a bridge, with a span of 236 metres, across the lagoon at Maracaibo, in Venezuela.

Movable bridges

There are other solutions to the bridge problem, apart from those dealt with so far. Bridges, for example, can float on the water and structures of this type are actually built, at least to satisfy temporary needs in special cases. A good example occurs in war, when it becomes necessary to ferry a convoy across a river and then remove the bridge to prevent the enemy from using it. Buoyancy provided by floats and rafts or by suitable wooden or metal boats is what keeps the platform afloat.

Mobile bridges are also fairly widely used. These incorporate a mechanism for raising them (like the drawbridges in medieval castles) or, alternatively, for causing the central portion to rotate. When the bridge is open, free passage is provided for those ships which would be too tall to go underneath.

The wind problem

The planning of important constructional works, such as a very high bridge for a motorway or a steel suspension bridge, entails detailed research and experiments on scale models. The solutions often call for a great deal of ingenuity. For example, the pressure of the wind can cause the structure (especially if it is a suspension bridge) to oscillate and even to fall down, as happened in 1940 with the bridge at Tacoma, in the United States, which had a span of 853 metres. A few months after its completion, it collapsed from the force of a wind which blew at only seventy kilometres per hour.

It is easy to understand, then, why "aerodynamic" shapes are of interest. These may offer a smaller wind-resistance and thus be subjected to less stress from wind pressure.

Building
The technique of construction

Is it more difficult to build a pyramid or a skyscraper, a stone aqueduct or a steel bridge? It is impossible to answer. All great civilizations have produced their own marvels.

Every child tries, sooner or later, to build something resembling a hut which his imagination marvellously transforms into a fort attacked by Indians, a space station, or whatever building his game requires. Children who live in the country or have gardens, use logs or tumbledown sheds or even try to make a hiding-place in the branches of a tree. Less fortunate children have to make do with "buildings" constructed with the aid of old blankets thrown across armchairs and tables. It is imagination, not necessity, that makes children unwittingly imitate their long-distant ancestors in something like the activity of building.

In the fullest and most modern sense of the term, building is the technology and art of constructing buildings and artifacts of every type (barracks or skyscrapers, cottages or palaces, dams or bridges). It has evolved a great deal over the years and progressed with the history of mankind. Primitive man was certainly not a good house-builder: on the contrary, in the earliest times he did not build at all; it was enough to find a place where he could shelter from bad weather and protect himself from wild animals. The safest and most comfortable havens were caves and the largest and dryest of these had their walls decorated with drawings and paintings. The cave was both a dwelling-place and a store-house in which the hides and meat of the slain animals were kept.

The next step took place when man changed from hunting to agriculture, abandoning the nomadic life at the same time. He built shelters from straw and reeds, sealed with clay to make them watertight. Not till a long time afterwards, with the use of bricks and the ability to shape wood, stone and tiles, did building begin to be the expression of a true craft.

supply of perforated bricks

tipper truck

tower crane with rotating arm

modular metal wall-sections

automatic concrete-mixer truck

concrete-mixer

cate truc

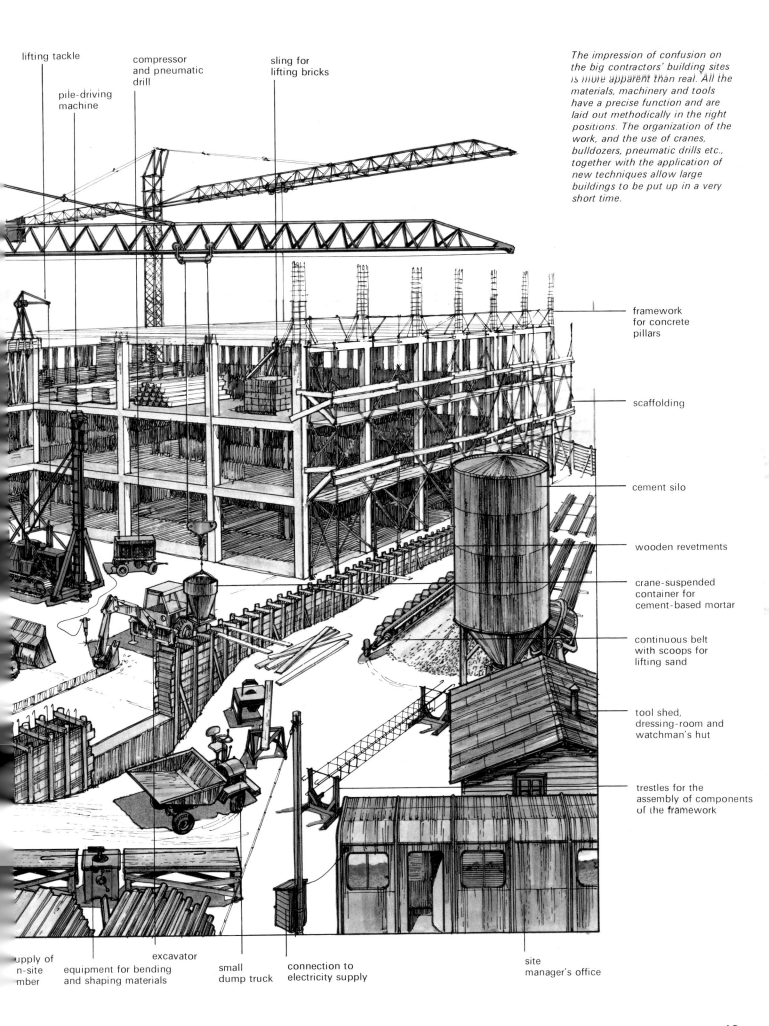

lifting tackle

pile-driving machine

compressor and pneumatic drill

sling for lifting bricks

The impression of confusion on the big contractors' building sites is more apparent than real. All the materials, machinery and tools have a precise function and are laid out methodically in the right positions. The organization of the work, and the use of cranes, bulldozers, pneumatic drills etc., together with the application of new techniques allow large buildings to be put up in a very short time.

framework for concrete pillars

scaffolding

cement silo

wooden revetments

crane-suspended container for cement-based mortar

continuous belt with scoops for lifting sand

tool shed, dressing-room and watchman's hut

trestles for the assembly of components of the framework

supply of on-site timber

equipment for bending and shaping materials

excavator

small dump truck

connection to electricity supply

site manager's office

Tireless builders

The accolade for the most important builders of antiquity goes without doubt to the Romans. Today, we still admire their monuments and temples, and also the bridges, roads and aqueducts (such as Tarquin's aqueduct in the photograph). These are the peak of civic architecture and are found in some form wherever Roman civilization penetrated.

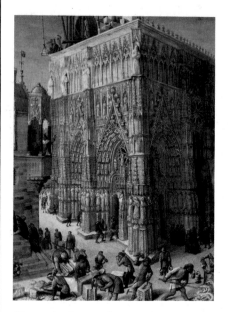

Centuries of work

Work on the Gothic cathedral at Bourges, in France: it was not finished until eighty years after the foundation stone was laid. Centuries have been taken over the building of other churches: in such cases, craftsmen from one generation have handed over to their successors in the next: from architects to stone-masons and from painters to craftsman-carpenters.

Bricks and arches

As long as five thousand years ago in Egypt and Mesopotamia, quite a few buildings were made from bricks, which in earliest times were dried in the sun, but later were baked in rudimentary kilns. The Egyptians utilized clay from the river Nile mixed with straw to make their bricks and with them built single-storey houses, boundary walls and monuments to the dead. For building the pyramids and larger temples, they preferred to use large blocks of hard stone (limestone, sandstone or red granite). These they quarried from the cliffs by marking out the top and sides of the intended block with a metal implement and then forcing wedges of dry wood in at the base of the block which had been squared off. When soaked in water the wooden wedges would expand and shatter the rock sufficiently to free the block.

The buildings which survive bear witness to the skill and perfection of their constructional techniques, but when building over an empty space, the Egyptians usually employed the elementary technique of beams. They used two vertical supports with a third long one (made of stone or wood) resting on them and bridging the gap, but it tended to sag and so was not suitable for large spans.

The Sumerians developed the arch, vault and dome in Mesopotamia as early as 2800 BC. The arch was basic in the Etruscan and Roman civilizations and has remained, despite considerable changes in materials and techniques, an important part of building technology to this day. It is able to span a greater distance than a beam, since it is a much sturdier structure overall, and the load it has to bear is redistributed onto the supports at the sides. The Mesopotamian civilizations also developed the use of mortar, to provide a better grip between the bricks. The ziggurats, colossal terraced towers, were built of bricks held together with bitumen.

The techniques of the Romans

From the towns, temples, theatres and stadiums of the Greeks (the first people, perhaps, with the notion of someone building on behalf of the state, that is to say a contractor), evidence of beauty, harmony and refined technique has come down to us: Doric, Ionic or Corinthian columns, whole buildings in marble and fortified walls. The Romans, as their successors, encouraged by the efficiency of their administration and by the need to unify the territories and peoples they had conquered, spread the Roman style of life and government with its palaces, temples, stadiums, theatres, baths, streets, bridges and aqueducts throughout the world as it was then known.

The first Roman aqueduct, the Appia (312 BC) was sixteen kilometres long and most of it lay below ground. Less than 150 years later, conduits of terracotta reinforced with bronze and able to transport water at 200 litres per second were being built. The first stone bridges built in Rome (the Gianicolo Bridge, today called the Sistine Bridge, and the Milvio Bridge) date back to 200 BC and although they have been restored to some extent, survive to this day.

During approximately the same period as Rome's power and splendour, in Central America and Peru Incas, Aztecs and Mayas were erecting temples in the shape of stepped pyramids and made of sun-dried bricks. The pyramid at Cholula, was fifty-four metres tall and at its base covered an area of eighteen hectares. Meanwhile, as Rome and its already disintegrating empire collapsed under the onslaught of the barbarian attacks and the shadows of the approaching Middle Ages darkened, the Byzantine civilization was creating the great basilicas of Constantinople and Ravenna and in the bold lines of the Arab mosques was foreshadowed that architectural and technical miracle which Brunelleschi and Bramante were to work some centuries later during the Italian Renaissance.

Religious and military architecture were the main objects of building in the Middle Ages. The most characteristic building was the castle, built at first in wood and later from square stone blocks or bricks. In the towns and villages, the ferment of the age and vigour and importance of the building guilds brought new blood into building and gave life to the splendid architectural masterpieces of the Renaissance. In 1436, Filippo Brunelleschi completed the great dome of Santa Maria del Fiore, in Florence, the first built entirely of masonry, eighty-nine metres tall and with an internal diameter of forty-two metres. This feat of lightness and balance marked an important step in the history of building.

The Industrial Revolution

Building faithfully reflected the history, culture and habits of its time, and from the eighteenth century on, it also reflected the profound changes arising from the emergent Industrial Revolution. While the French revolution was bringing down, both literally and metaphorically, the bulwarks of the past, a new type of building was coming to maturity in England: that used to build factories

Modern building takes advantage of new techniques and new materials such as steel, aluminium, glass and plastics. Instead of the highly gifted masons of former times, capable of building cupolas in brick or palaces in carved stone, today technicians and specialized workers are needed who, just as ably, move about inside the shells of buildings under construction.

warehouses and workers' houses. New materials were used, notably cast iron. New machines were employed in the building trade. By the mid-nineteenth century, for example, bricks were being made by machine and at more or less the same time the first steam-roller made its appearance. Meanwhile, something very important had happened – the "discovery" of cement.

In the second half of the nineteenth century, reinforced cement (or, more accurately, concrete) was developed. The first clear record of an attempt to use reinforcement in concrete was an experimental arch built in 1832 by Sir Marc Isambard Brunel in connection with his construction of a tunnel under the Thames. Other experiments followed in various countries, but it was not until the 1880s that the practical development of reinforced concrete occurred.

On the building site the fantastic can sometimes become the bizarre: all over the world, buildings with strange and unique shapes are going up. For example, the appearance of this hotel in Tunis is almost unbelievable, halfway between a ship and an upside-down pyramid.

In 1885, the American architect William Le Baron Jenney constructed the Home Life Insurance Company's building in Chicago. An internal metal frame (part cast iron, part wrought iron) supported the weight of the ten-storey building, eliminating the need for massive foundations and thick bearing walls. Many skyscrapers were built during the following years and in 1889 steel celebrated a triumph with the Eiffel Tower (300 metres tall), built to commemorate the Paris Exhibition. The Eiffel Tower remains today a great, though rather conventional, tourist attraction.

Steel and reinforced concrete together with stronger and larger plate-glass windows are the characteristic components of modern buildings. Functional considerations tend to outweigh the aesthetic and speed of erection can be at the expense of accurate planning. These objectives are pursued by the improved use of these materials, and by prefabrication, a new technique which is coming into ever-wider use. Prefabrication meets the increasing need for new houses, schools, institutions and public buildings in general, by allowing them to be built quickly and with appreciable savings in cost.

Prefabrication

As far as building is concerned, prefabrication means doing the construction work by fitting together parts mass-produced in factories, or sometimes produced in smaller numbers on site. The

elements which go into the making of house, for example, (such as walls window and door units, ceilings, stair cases or whole rooms complete wit fixtures and accessories) are produced b specialist industries, transported on sit and incorporated into the building und construction by means of powerfu cranes (or even helicopters), rivetting machines, welding-machines, etc.

The erection itself can be either "wet or "dry", depending on whether trad tional types of mortar are to be used. If th dry method is used, the components hav standardized dimensions so accurate tha individual components can be replaced required. This technique allows th building of whole housing estate schools and bridges as a sort of fantast and colossal jig-saw puzzle.

For some projects using pre fabrication, even steel, aluminium an

The construction of a big, new building complex in the centre of Essen (West Germany).

In the photograph below, we see something quite different: a detail in the formation of the steel skeleton for the reinforced concrete walls of the Millstone nuclear power station at Waterford in Connecticut (United States).

pre-stressed reinforced concrete (''new'' materials *par excellence*, since they lend themselves to assembly-line production and erection) are threatened by competition from other products such as plastics, which are lighter, easy to transport and less expensive.

Even though the wholesale application of laminated plastics in building does not at present go far beyond the pre-fabrication of ''light-weight'' bungalows for summer tourist sites, it is perhaps possible to foresee in the not-too-distant future the introduction of houses which are not merely pre-fabricated but literally ''stamped out'' to measure. In these ''dwelling-blocks'', even sanitary and electrical fittings and essential furniture will already be included.

The building site

Although a building project is conceived on the planner's desk and receives an appreciable contribution from many industries such as engineering, steel-making, and mining, it only comes into being on the site.

The site complex, however large or small it is, generally includes piles of essential building materials, areas for unloading them and for manoeuvring and parking the vehicles and machinery (cranes, concrete-mixers, bulldozers, excavators, etc.), and temporary buildings for the work-force. The more difficult the project in hand and the further from centres of civilization, the greater the tendency of the site to become self-sufficient: in other words, it turns into a small village dedicated to the building of a whole housing estate, dam, power station or factory, and for month after month serves as a real community for workers and technicians.

Every day another piece is added to the project in hand, adjusting the structure and the work on site to meet the particular demands of the place and the type of construction employed. The large sites for road-building, for example, are mobile and move along as the road advances; there have to be different arrangements on site for building, say, a bridge from those required to build a house or an airport.

When building a house using traditional techniques, the first parts to go up are strong pillars of reinforced concrete resting on deeply dug foundations. These are made by embedding a steel foundation in cement. Around the load-bearing pillars, the walls are built, usually from bricks, which may or may not be solid, and the flooring is laid for each storey. For the roof-covering, various materials are used, from corrugated iron or steel to earthenware tiles. Finally doors and windows, water and gas mains and the electrical wiring are installed.

The completion of a building always causes pleasure and excitement, and an important building is opened by a well-known person amid general celebration. In some countries it is still the practice even today to fly a flag from the roof of the completed building, or more simply, to tie a leafy branch to it. This is a good luck symbol as well as an acknowledgment that the task is finished.

Cities

How a village can grow into a city

Only a century separates these two pictures: Turin in the nineteenth century and Paris today. Yet they seem to belong to two different planets. A new name, megalopolis, has been coined for the new cities, which seemingly lack any well-defined boundary.

Different countries and ages have variously defined a city. In Britain, it is a town which has a cathedral or has been given a royal charter. Today, however, a city is generally regarded as an urban centre provided with public services and other amenities which contribute to an organized social life. It is not so much its size which determines a city as its structure, suited to promoting various human activities: industrial, scientific, commercial, religious, artistic and cultural. It is possible for a city to be smaller than a large country town, but it is more important in a civic sense. Since the first cities were founded between three and four thousand years before Christ, they have played an extremely important part in the history of civilization.

The period of the village

Villages existed before any cities grew up. These date back to the time when man became a farmer and settled down in a fixed dwelling-place. In those times, all the men of the village co-operated with each other; later when agricultural production outstripped demand, division of labour developed. Some people became craftsmen, others became priests and others oversaw the work of the rest and established themselves as leaders. In this way the chiefs of tribes, and even kings, arose. The structure of the village became more complicated: it became diversified by the demarcation of a sacred area, by a temple and by the building of a fortified citadel for the king to occupy. This was how the more complex and interdependent structure of cities came into being.

One characteristic, almost invariable throughout history, was that of a surrounding wall; we see it in the cities of ancient Mesopotamia, in Egypt, in the lands of the Maya in Mexico and Guatemala, and in Europe. These enclosing walls were a defence against outside enemies and at the same time a means of controlling the population. During periods of peace at home and abroad, the walls were not built and the result was an open city. This happened under the pharaohs, who unified Egypt not by force but by religious belief; it happened at the beginning of the Roman Empire with Augustus' peaceful policies; it was the same at times in England and Japan because they are islands.

Athens and Rome

There are cities which have grown up spontaneously and others which have been deliberately planned and laid out. Great urban centres like Athens and Rome did not at the outset have a regular layout; they developed naturally from clusters of dwellings. Geographical position very often accounts for the unplanned formation of cities. In Athens, the *polis*, roughly the "city-state", was born almost casually, on a hill called the Acropolis, a high, fortified city, the seat of religious and civil government. Archaeologists think that Rome was formed from the merging of the small villages on its seven hills and the layout of the city was, as a result, irregular and uneven. Though the structure of Rome itself was unplanned, the cities founded by the Romans had a very formal town-plan, like a network or like the chessboard pattern of the Roman military camp. The town-plan of Turin, whose streets intersect at right angles, bears witness to its Roman origin. Most modern cities have been planned on this rational model; an example is New York with its street-plan of right angles only.

Where do cities spring up?

Cities always started in places geographically suitable for their development: in fertile valleys drained by rivers (Mesopotamia, Egypt), at places where trade-routes crossed and where travellers could rest on their journeys; where commerce was engaged in; and on estuaries and coasts (ports like Venice and Amsterdam, with important trading links and magnificent urban centres); and on high ground, difficult of access, and therefore easy to defend. The nature of the city shaped the lives of those who lived
(continued on page 22)

Over-population is a problem which many modern cities have to face. One of these is London (below, map and a view of Trafalgar Square).

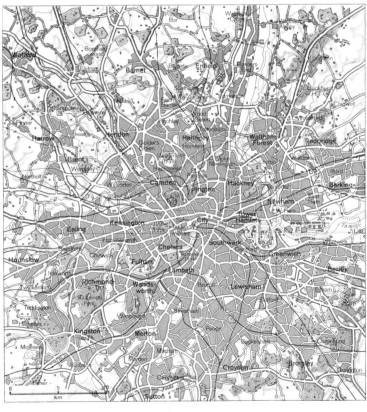

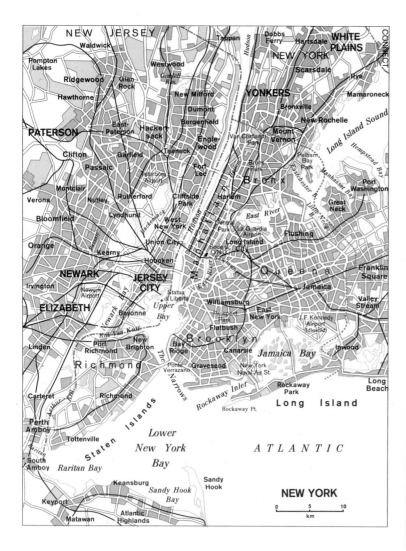

Some of the biggest cities in the world. Left, New York, the most highly populated metropolis in the United States. Situated in a fortunate geographical position (as can be seen from the map), it has five boroughs, the Bronx, Brooklyn, Manhattan (in the photograph), Queens and Staten Island. Below, an area in the industrial belt, shaped curiously like a ring, of another American city, São Paulo in Brazil.

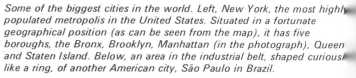

Let us go down to Australia and in particular to Melbourne (left), after Sydney the country's second city both in population and in importance. The photograph shows Swanston Street, the city's principal thoroughfare; in the background, the Mausoleum dedicated to the dead of the First World War. Tokyo (below and at bottom), an enormous sprawl of houses and streets: even in the eighteenth century it was claimed to be the most populous city in the world.

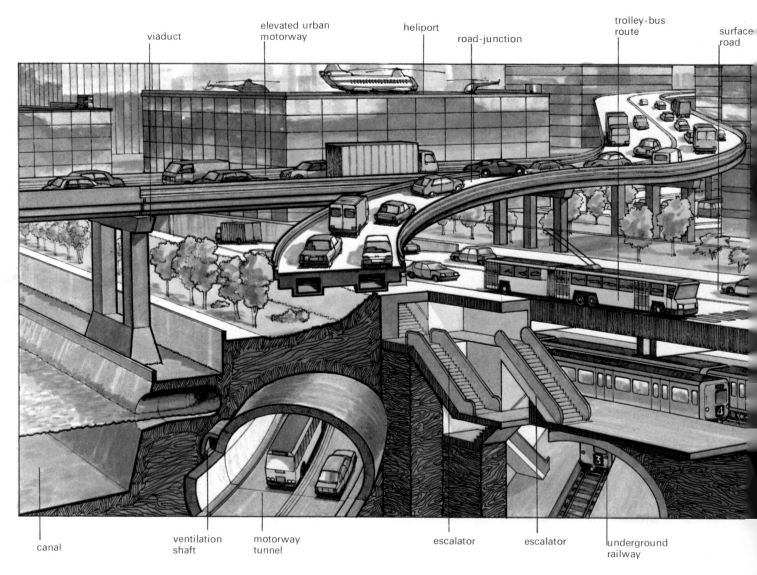

viaduct · elevated urban motorway · heliport · road-junction · trolley-bus route · surface road

canal · ventilation shaft · motorway tunnel · escalator · escalator · underground railway

Some of the largest cities in the world

Tokyo, Japan: 11,615,069 inhabitants; **Shanghai**, China: 10,000,000 inhabitants; **Buenos Aires**, Argentina: 9,677,200 inhabitants; **Mexico City**, Mexico: 8,941,912 inhabitants; **Peking**, China: 8,706,000 inhabitants; **Seoul**, South Korea: 8,367,000 inhabitants; **Cairo**, Egypt: 8,143,000 inhabitants; **Moscow**, Soviet Union: 8,011,000 inhabitants; **New York**, USA: 7,149,300 inhabitants; **London**, Great Britain: 6,696,000 inhabitants; **Jakarta**, Indonesia: 6,506,740 inhabitants; **Bombay**, India: 5,850,000 inhabitants; **São Paulo**, Brazil: 5,241,232 inhabitants; **Rio de Janeiro**, Brazil: 4,315,746 inhabitants; **Chicago**, USA: 3,369,357 inhabitants; **Calcutta**, India: 3,141,180 inhabitants; **Los Angeles**, USA: 2,809,813 inhabitants; **Paris**, France: 2,050,500 inhabitants; **Philadelphia**, USA: 1,949,996 inhabitants; **Detroit**, USA: 1,513,601 inhabitants.

(*continued from page 19*)
there and it determined their choice of activities. For example, in Venice it was easy to become involved in the sea-borne traffic and in commerce; in the fortified medieval city, there flourished the craftsmen, the art and trade guilds, commerce and banking (more particularly when the city was not at war).

The shape and structure of cities retain some constant characteristics across the centuries. The grouping together of private dwellings, then public streets, a cemetery, a square where markets and meetings could be held, shops, the holy ground with its temple (which later became consecrated ground around the church), the store-house to hoard provisions (in the most ancient times, this was often next to the temple) and the fortified citadel, seat of the king and the government (from which, later, municipal corporations developed).

It is from the ancient fortified citadels that the basic model of the modern city comes. Within these citadels appeared, almost 2000 years before the birth of Christ, for example in the royal palace at Knossos in Crete, technical innovations which much later were incorporated in cities: paving, buildings in stone and bricks, sewers, sources of running water, public conveniences and gardens and open spaces for leisure activities. Over the centuries, cities incorporated all the comforts of the citadel. For a long time their structure remained unchanged in its general plan (though not, of course, in architectural styles), from Mesopotamian times, about 4000 BC, until the last century.

The industrial city

What was it that decisively changed the appearance, structure and life of cities? The answer is the Industrial Revolution, which began towards the end of the eighteenth century in England with the introduction of the mechanical loom. A further development took place with the advent of steam-engines, which quickly replaced manual labour and were then employed on canal barges and railways. As a consequence of these new inventions, specialization of labour and the building of factories, a new type of city

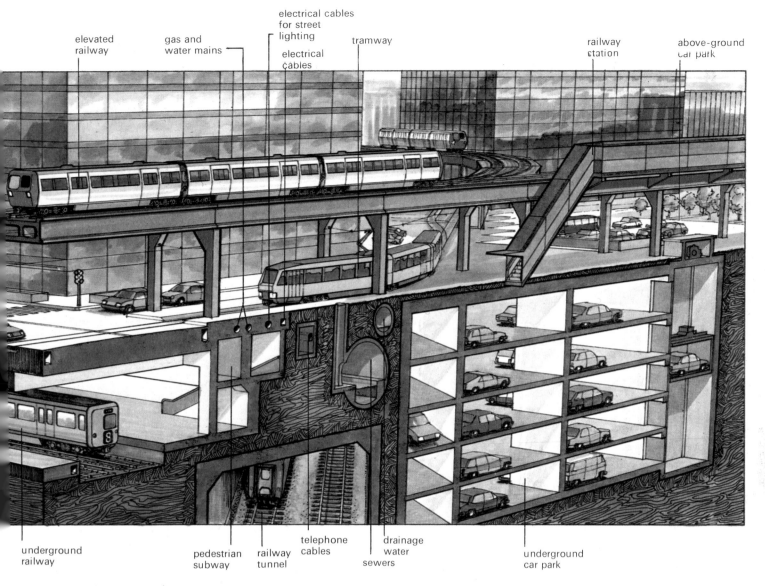

elevated railway · gas and water mains · electrical cables for street lighting · electrical cables · tramway · railway station · above-ground car park

underground railway · pedestrian subway · railway tunnel · telephone cables · drainage water · sewers · underground car park

came into being, characterized by chimneys, ugly industrial buildings and houses for the workers. Cities increased rapidly, both in size and number. The old city walls had lost their usefulness and in many cases were pulled down. Public transport became indispensable for the workforce, so horse-drawn buses, railways, trams, buses in the modern sense and underground railways gradually evolved. Lastly, the whole aspect of city centres was transformed by electricity (and the street-lighting it provided). The invention of the automobile and the increased use of cars, vans, lorries, etc., of particular significance since the Second World War, have profoundly affected the way cities look.

The modern metropolis

The modern city has grown upwards to dizzy heights to take maximum advantage of its central areas which are still regarded as of prime importance. Skyscrapers spring up first in the city's historical centre and then in adjacent areas. Steel and reinforced concrete allow bold, new architecture, using ideas that were unimagin-

able or impossible to realize before these technical innovations came in. Cities are becoming congested, with traffic chaos everywhere, so remedies have to be sought. New traffic arteries (by-passes and ring-roads) are being built away from the city centre and fly-overs and multi-storey car-parks are springing up. The city is acquiring more facilities so that its structure is becoming increasingly complex.

The complexity and problems of city life result from a series of contradictions. The modern metropolis, that is a city covering a large area with good communications and transport, on the one hand promotes a style of living which, in many respects, is more convenient than in the past. With all its "comforts" and public services, life is undoubtedly richer in cultural opportunity (museums, exhibitions, theatres and entertainments of all kinds). But overcrowding, the difficulty of human relationships, noise, pollution and the absence of open spaces lead to tension.

Attempts have been made to remedy this by setting up satellite towns with

The diagram shows an imaginary city, but it has real components which are by now easy to find in many large cities. As you can see, to avoid traffic paralysis with services grinding to a halt, development has been planned at different levels.

good transport links to the city. For example, "new towns", offering many of the facilities of a city, have been created around London. However, it is true that the urban centre, with a tradition and a history going back for hundreds of years, has a greater attraction. Yet the old established cities are very close to bursting at the seams.

We are witnessing a singular phenomenon for in some areas cities are merging together into a continuous mass. For example, the entire eastern coast of the United States, from Maine to Florida, is joining up into one enormous city: the metropolis is becoming a megalopolis, in which the peripheral areas, often monotonous stretches of semi-detached houses, alternate and contrast with the vertical scale of the city of skyscrapers, big business and entertainment.

Fishing

The men who make a living on the sea

The many ways in which man tricks and catches fish are often surprising. Nowadays, with even newer techniques, it is thought better not to catch as many fish as possible, because of the danger that soon there will be no more fish to be caught.

There is, perhaps, no human activity older, more varied, or more strange than fishing. Man catches fish in still lakes and in mid-ocean, in a thousand different ways, even with his bare hands or with the harpoon guns used in whaling. In some places even birds and dogs are employed.

The birds sometimes used for fishing are cormorants, trained by Chinese fishermen. These large flying creatures, plunging beneath the water, catch their prey in their beaks and bring it back to their owner's boat. Normally they would eat it themselves, but a ring inserted in the throat prevents this. The fisherman takes the fish and sends the cormorant back to capture another.

Dogs, on the other hand, are the "secret weapon" of some Japanese fishermen. When a shoal of fish is sighted on the surface, the dogs leap into the water and thrashing about furiously drive the fish towards the nets which are ready to receive them.

Another curious technique is practised in the extreme south of the island of Sri Lanka (previously Ceylon). The fisher men stand on tall poles driven into the bottom of the sea some thirty or so metres from the beach. They spend the whole day there, skilfully manoeuvring rod and line in a position which would seem to us impossible to maintain for more than ten minutes.

Catching fish with bare hands is the most primitive kind of fishing, but

hooks were among the first things he made.

The varying conditions presented b sea and coast, rivers and lakes in different parts of the world, offer many diverse opportunities to fishermen. One may fish on one's own with a rod, use a boat to go a few miles offshore or even risk the dangers of fishing far out to sea. Consequently, there is also a large range of instruments and methods: from bare hands to the most sophisticated electronic apparatus.

The forms of life which inhabit the seas and rivers are just as diverse. Apart from fish, there are crustaceans such as crabs, lobsters and shrimps, molluscs which include snails, oysters and mussels, and large cetaceans like the whales. Sponges and corals are not edible, but they have always been sought by men.

The equipment of the fishing boats

The system most used today, or the one which produces the biggest share of commercial fish, is known as trawling. The boat trawls by towing a large bag-shaped net whose mouth can be kept open by three different methods: a beam can be placed across the head of the net; two boats can be used, one at each side of the net, to tow it; or two wooden kites, or otter boards, can be attached to the sides of the mouth. The beam trawl is only used

(continued on page 28)

requires great skill. It is still practised, especially where fish are trapped in the ditches along the bank at low tide.

Whatever form it takes, fishing has always presented man with a challenge. He has to pit his wits against an unseen opponent, using his judgement and skill with techniques which have been developed over thousands of years.

As well as his hands, prehistoric man used the harpoon both for hunting and fishing. He drew pictures on the walls of his cave of the fish he caught as well as of the animals he hunted. Gradually the fish-hook was developed. At first it consisted of a sharp bone, a thorn or a piece of wood which the fish swallowed with the bait. As man's skill with metal developed, fish-

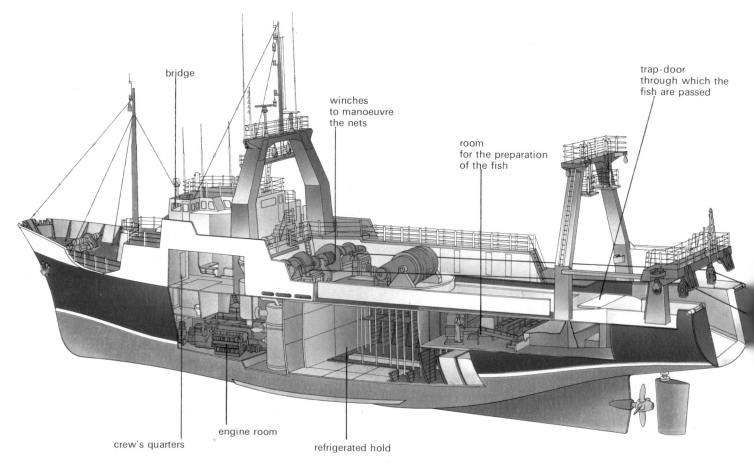

bridge

winches to manoeuvre the nets

room for the preparation of the fish

trap-door through which the fish are passed

crew's quarters

engine room

refrigerated hold

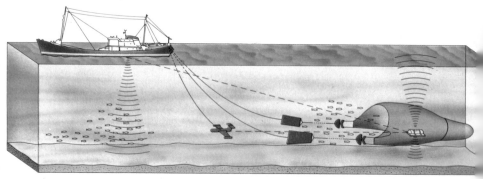

Above, the lay-out of a motor fishing vessel used for trawling. It is fitted out with special areas for the preparation and the refrigeration of the fish. Left, a small fishing vessel in a very small port and fishermen dealing with their catch. Above, a system of fishing using echo-sounding electro-acoustic equipment which enables shoals of fish to be located out at sea. This illustration shows how the fish are guided through a complicated system of corridors into the right passages.

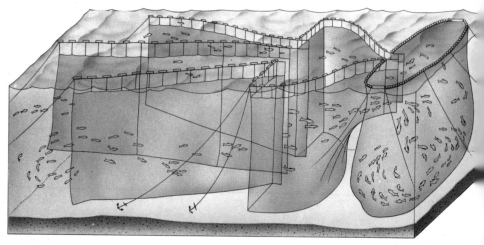

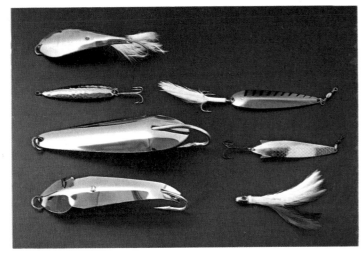

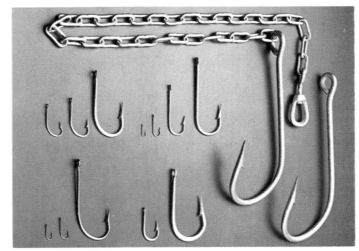

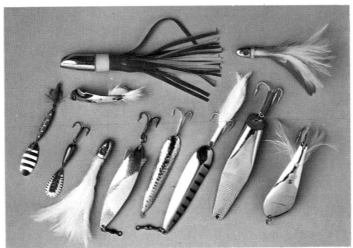

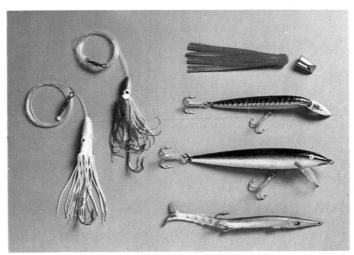

Fishing for sport is nearly always with rod and line. On this page are some types of artificial bait and fish-hooks of various sizes. Almost all the fishing-rods are equipped with a reel, which allows even long lengths of line to be wound in by means of a crank. Often small lead weights are hung on the end of the line to keep the line well below the water, with a float to signal when the fish takes a bite. The photographs show, left, a fisherman on the banks of a torrent and below, the fishing with lines which is done on the island of Sri Lanka (Ceylon). The fishermen are lashed to tall poles.

The cold northern seas provide rich fishing grounds for modern trawlers.

(continued from page 25)
on a few small fishing craft and pair trawling is used to catch hake and herring off the bottom of the sea. The otter trawl is the most widely used method and is employed on almost all but the smallest trawlers. The net gathers in everything which it meets including the fry, or newly hatched fish, the eggs, plankton and algae. Consequently, this system is very destructive and is causing an alarming impoverishment of the sea. Even relatively small fishing boats, equipped with diesel engines, and a crew of five or six, fish in this way. The net is pulled on board, closed like a sack, and the catch poured into the hold where it is covered with ice.

In the larger fishing boats, which operate in the North Sea or the Atlantic and undertake voyages which may last for weeks, the fish is also processed on board. In most cases, the ship is equipped only for refrigeration and freezing; in others, however, there is the equipment to complete the whole process: cod, for example, is gutted and salted; tunny is frozen in blocks, filleted or canned immediately.

Sometimes an entire fleet of fishing vessels is headed by a large factory ship fitted out just for the processing of the catch. A single "sweep" of the net often takes in tens of tonnes of herrings and this gives some idea of the quantity of fish which can be caught in the richer seas. Herrings, together with sardines and anchovies, account for 18 per cent of the world's catch. Another surprising fact is that 40 per cent of the fish caught in all seas are converted to meal or to oil and are used to feed animals.

The largest fishing vessel in the world is a factory ship. It is Russian, the *Vostok*, displaces 43,500 tonnes and carries on board fourteen motorized fishing boats which are lowered in mid-ocean and then taken on board again at the end of the fishing programme.

Today the large motor fishing vessels are fitted with sonar, or echo-sounding equipment, a device originally developed to detect the presence of submarines but which serves very well indeed to locate a shoal of fish. It gives out sound waves below the surface of the sea and registers the echoes caused by the presence of an obstacle. A large shoal of cod, for example, represents a mass at least as easy to detect as a submarine.

The trawling net is the most widespread system of fishing on the high seas, but it is not the only one. There is the drift net, for example, designed specially to catch herring. Each herring net is about fifty to sixty metres long and fourteen metres deep. Fleets of as many as eighty-five nets may be placed in the water at a time from one vessel.

The purse-net is used to catch fish which live in the upper regions of the sea. It is lowered from the ship in the neighbourhood of a shoal of fish and then closed like a sack and hauled back on board.

Along the coast of southern European countries, something of the sort, but on a small scale, is done with a lamp. This is a net which is closed so as to give a funnel shape and which is lowered into the sea at night. The fish are attracted by the acetylene lamp (the "lamp" which gives its name to this type of fishing-net) mounted on board one of the boats.

These are some of the many methods used in commercial fishing. The most widespread always belong to one of the three basic categories: fishing with the net, the fish-hook or the harpoon.

Flying Nature and man in the air

The ability to fly, that is to move freely through the air, is a feature of various animals (such as birds, bats and many insects) which have special organs, namely wings, that can transmit a given thrust to the body and keep it up in the air. Other animals which are wrongly called "flying" animals have less sophisticated organs and can at most glide downwards. The flying-squirrel has a special fold of skin down both sides of its body (known as a *patagium*). As it leaps between trees, this fold of skin spreads out between its front and rear legs to form a sort of parachute, enabling it to cover over 65 metres in a glide. The "flying dragon" (an attractive Malaysian lizard) has two wing membranes on the thorax and can glide over a distance of about 10 metres. "Flying fish" can span as much as 200 metres in a single glide by using their pectoral fins to hover in the air.

Birds' flights

Birds can fly much greater distances because of their physical structure. They fly by flapping their wings, steering mainly with their tails. When flying they reduce all air resistance to a minimum. Moreover, they are extremely light because their bones are hollow and their wings arch upwards, acting as very effective carrying surfaces. Whilst the lower concave part of the wing compresses the air and creates an upward thrust, the upper convex part causes a depression in the air which tends to pull the wing upwards. By these two effects (known as "lift") of the wings, various large birds such as, for example, eagles and falcons, can glide over long distances by taking advantage of upward air currents to rise to a higher altitude. The "flapping" technique is much more

A seagull flying over the North Sea. This bird has very large, strong wings which are incredibly light when compared to the rest of its body and enable it to fly over long distances.

complex and in this case the bird's wings move it forwards as well as keep it up in the air. This dual function is due to the different elasticity in the various parts of the wing. In fact, the front edge is stiff because of the presence of a bone and therefore provides an upward thrust when the bird flaps it downwards. At the same time, the rest of the wing, which consists of long elastic feathers (known as "flapping quills") performs the same function as a diver's flippers; the feathers became curved and transmit a forward thrust to the bird. During the opposite movement, gaps are formed between the flapping feathers and let the air through so that the bird can bring its wings back to the thrust position without encountering a great deal of resistance. Birds can modify their flying altitude and direction by changing the position of their wings and tail or by lengthening or shortening their neck or limbs to alter their centre of gravity. The "take-off" phase is also particularly interesting in birds. Small birds like sparrows can start flying by simply flapping their wings once, whilst large birds must run a short distance or let themselves drop. Flying ability varies

29

widely among birds and different types of wing go with different types of flight.

The way in which bats fly is very similar to that of birds although less effective. The flying organs consist of wings and membranes that start from the forelimbs, and extend as far as the hind limbs and tail, forming a large carrying surface. In this case, too, the front edge of the wings is stiff whilst the back edge is flexible.

Insects' flight

Insects have every possible type of wings which range from the large and rather impractical ones of butterflies to the minute wings of midges which they can flap more than 1,000 times per second. Their wings consist of very thin cutaneous membranes, strengthened by a dense set of ribs which form an integral part with the thorax and become stiffer around the front edge.

The back part of the wing is rather flexible and becomes curved when flapped. The way in which insects fly has only been studied fairly recently. There have been immense developments in ultra-rapid filming techniques. It has been possible to establish that good fliers like bees and mosquitoes make full use of the flapping movement and ensure that no breaks occur which could slow down their speed.

When flapping downwards, their wings move across forwards as well as downwards so as to keep the body in a horizontal position and therefore create an upward thrust. They then move their wings perpendicularly with regard to their flying direction and as they bring them upwards they use them as an "oar" to move forwards. By suitably applying these movements, it is possible for some insects (among them, bees) to hover in the same place and even fly backwards over short distances. Insects have no organs that they can use as a rudder and in order to change direction when flying they must flap their wings more quickly or more slowly on one side of the body, and alter the angle that their wings form with the thorax.

The first flying machines

The Icarus legend shows that since ancient days, man has tried to create devices that would enable him to fly. The simplest type of flying machine is the air balloon which consists of a large bag or envelope of impermeable material such as cotton or rubberized silk, filled with hydrogen or helium. These gases are lighter than air and therefore lift the balloon which carries a basket for passengers up into the air. The balloon also carries ballast, some of which is

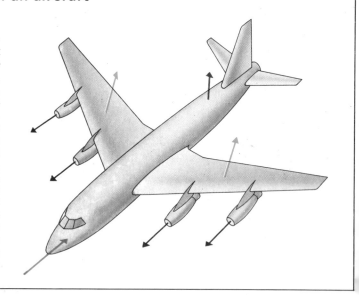

Forces acting on an aircraft

The forces on an aeroplane during a flight are the weight of the aircraft (shown in red), air resistance (green), the thrust of the motors (black) and the "lift". This force is due to the difference in pressure between the top and lower part of the wings. While the aircraft moves forwards, the wings compress the air below them and at the same time create a low pressure zone above them. This prevents the aircraft from falling.

jettisoned as the balloon leaves the ground. As the balloon rises into the atmosphere, it becomes surrounded with increasingly rarefied air. Its upward thrust, therefore, decreases until it reaches a given height when the balloon stops rising and is suspended in the air. This system has no engine and the pilot has to change altitude (by getting rid of the ballast or some of the gas) to find an air current that will take him in the desired direction.

The same principle allows airships to remain suspended in the air. These are, in fact, balloons which are tapered in shape and by a propeller system can move even in the opposite direction of the wind. They are also fitted with suitable rudders that allow them to keep to the altitude and direction required.

This sequence of photographs shows how birds fly. When the wings move upwards, air travels through the feathers without encountering any resistance. When they move downwards, the gaps between the feathers disappear and the wings can compress the air, producing an upward thrust.

Above, a solar energy aircraft. Photocell batteries can be seen on the tail unit and wings. These batteries convert solar light into electrical energy, thereby supplying the engine. In 1981, one of these aircraft succeeded in flying over the Channel. Left, the "airscrew" designed by Leonardo da Vinci.

Aeroplanes

The way in which aeroplanes fly is different for they can remain suspended in the air by the lift of their wings, that is the upward thrust which acts on the wings when the aeroplane moves. They make use of the same principle as that of birds when gliding. This should not, however, lead us to associate too closely the natural flight of animals and that of man-made machines. An animal's wing is an organ that keeps it suspended in the air as well as moves it forwards. In aeronautics, these two functions are performed by two distinct parts of the aircraft, namely the wings and the engines, either jet or propeller, which are operated and controlled by devices in the cockpit.

Although at first sight the main controls of an aircraft may seem much more accurate and sophisticated, they are very similar to those of a car. They consist of a control stick, a pair of pedals and a dial to regulate the flow of fuel to the engine. To take off, the pilot must drive the aircraft to the beginning of the runway and accelerate at full speed. Once the appropriate speed has been reached to allow the wings to create sufficient lift, the pilot pulls the control stick slightly towards him and the aircraft takes off, pointing upwards.

As soon as the aeroplane reaches a predetermined speed, the pilot reduces the output of the motor and pushes the control stick forwards, thereby bringing the aircraft into a horizontal position. This is when the wings are parallel to the flying direction and the engines can then be put on minimum because the wings encounter little air resistance.

Descent

To descend, the pilot has to move the control stick forwards. In this way, the elevators (small horizontal wings on the tail of the aeroplane) move downwards, the tail rises, the nose goes down and the aircraft starts to dive. To gain altitude, the pilot must pull the control stick towards him; the elevators then move upwards, the tail goes down and the aircraft points upwards starting to "pull-up". During this manoeuvre, the aircraft pulls up and the wings gain greater lift because they are at a steeper angle of inclination to the flight direction. Air resistance also increases and it therefore becomes necessary to increase the power of the engines to keep the aircraft at the same speed.

When pulling up, the aircraft should not be made to rise too quickly because if the wings are at too great an angle to the flight direction, the flow of air above them becomes uneven and turbulent and there is no depression above the wings to keep the aircraft stable. The aircraft will suddenly lose lift and start stalling (that is, it starts oscillating dangerously) and will tend to fall. To deal with the stall, the pilot must move the control stick forwards, accelerate and start to dive. The aircraft will then gain the speed required to keep flying and after a short descent the pilot can pull the control stick backwards to restore normal conditions.

Turn

The procedure for turning an aircraft is slightly more complicated. It is necessary to operate both the control stick and the pedals. If the pilot wants to turn left, he must move the control stick to the left and at the same time press the left-hand pedal. The control stick causes the flap, or aileron, on the right wing to go downwards and the aileron on the left wing upwards. In this way, the aircraft will start tilting and turn. The aileron on the right wing, which is outside the curve and must therefore move more quickly, is positioned downwards and encounters greater resistance than the aileron on the left wing. The aircraft thus tends to "bank", or tip sideways.

The pilot then presses the left-hand pedal and this turns the rudder (which is on the tail of the aircraft), towards the left. The air then tries to push the rudder back, so moving the tail of the aircraft to the right. This means that the nose of the aircraft goes to the left, and so the aircraft turns left.

When he is coming in to land, the pilot must reduce the engine power to a minimum and arrive at the beginning of the runway gradually after a long descent. At a few metres above ground, he must slowly pull the control stick towards him as if he wanted to pull up. In this way, the lift of the wings increases, the aircraft remains parallel to the runway and its speed decreases.

At a few centimetres above ground, the aircraft starts to stall and touches ground with its main landing gear (the wheels under the wings). The nose is still up but slowly goes down and after a few seconds the front landing gear also touches the concrete runway. The aircraft can then taxi to a halt.

A Glider
The silent wings

Gliders are aeroplanes without engines and can only proceed along a downward path. In practice they work in the same way as paper planes. Sometimes, paper planes can also fly upwards, but only if there is a wind (or, of course, if they are thrown upwards). The same applies to a glider, and the pilot's skill consists in taking advantage of air currents to descend as slowly as possible or to soar higher.

Gliders were invented before aeroplanes and can be compared to birds soaring without flapping their wings. Among the most famous pioneers of gliding were the Englishman, Sir George Cayley, who built the first man-carrying

glider which flew and crashed in 1853, and the German, Otto Lilienthal, who began his experiments in 1867. Aeroplanes were invented in 1903; basically an engine was added to a glider and this made it fly.

Gliders require help to reach a given altitude before starting to fly. In the past, this was done by launching them from the tops of hills, but nowadays an aeroplane is normally used to tow the glider up into the air. A strong nylon rope about fifty metres long and with a steel ring attached at each end, is sufficient to pull any type of glider to the required altitude. Once launched, the pilot must immediately find a rising air current if he wishes to soar. Huge gliders

were built during the Second World War to carry materials and soldiers. They were released over enemy territory and would quietly descend to a pre-arranged point. An American glider of this particular type, carrying a load of 1,500 kilos, was towed across the Atlantic for over 5,600 kilometres. However, the use of gliders for military transport was too risky (there were fewer risks with parachutists) and they were soon abandoned. Aeroplanes without engines became a means for practising one of the most exciting and thrilling sports: gliding. In the United States, the sport is called soaring, and the aircraft, a sailplane. Gliders today are made of light alloy and plastic, often with a wing span of more than twenty metres and fitted with retractable wheels or simply a skid under the fuselage for take-off and landing.

Their very light weight (about half that of a small car) and their particular aerodynamic shape, enable gliders to fly one kilometre with a drop in altitude

only twenty-five metres even if the air is perfectly still and they receive no help from air currents.

The best proof of the excellent performance of gliders flying under favourable conditions, is given by the world records achieved over the last few years: the distance record is 1,460 kilometres and the altitude record is 14,102 metres (as a comparison, aeroplanes on scheduled flights usually travel at an altitude of about 10,000 metres). Finally, the flight duration record is 56 hours and 15 minutes. This was set up by a Frenchman, Charles Atger, in April 1952. Later pilots were killed falling asleep while trying to beat his record, and duration was dropped as an official record. However, in the summer of 1961, the Hungarian pilot, Geza Vass, and his American co-pilot, Guy Davis, flew over the Nuuanu Pali in Hawaii for 71 hours 5 minutes.

Icebreakers
Cracking a problem

The hull of an icebreaker is made entirely of welded plates (not bolted or rivetted), and the line of the bow is characterized by a very special line, rounded and receding, making it easier for the ship to rise up above the ice slab barring its passage.

For icebreakers do not carve a passage by cutting the ice with their bows, as if using a knife. Rather, propelled by a powerful engine (diesel-electric engines are normally used), they rise up with their rounded bows and literally climb onto the ice, which may be as much as six metres thick but which will break under the weight in the end. So the bow of an icebreaker is always going up and down in a constant rocking motion.

Along the water line that separates the submerged part of the hull from the part out of the water, there runs a metal band, a real armour-plated belt, up to six metres wide and five centimetres thick. In addition, the plating on the ship's sides is specially shaped to diffuse upwards the pressure brought to bear on the sides by the surrounding ice. This is especially important when the ship is stationary and the ice-floes set together around her, gripping her in a vice.

To make them easier to manoeuvre in such an arduous environment, icebreakers are short, rather ill-proportioned vessels – they are about one-fifth as wide as they are long. In addition to three screws aft, they are often equipped with an extra propeller at the bow, which they use when they need to retreat out of an over-narrow passage. There is also a whole system of "heeling tanks", consisting of compartments at either side of the ship that can be flooded by pumping water from one to another, enabling the ship to rock free of the ice. Some of these tanks are located forward, to make the bow heavier and thus increase the force of the blow when the ice is particularly thick.

A doughty "trail-blazer"

What use is an icebreaker? During the winter season in cold seas, shipping is often greatly hampered by the presence of ice-floes. This happens a great deal in North America and the Soviet Union. It is to guarantee continued shipping in these conditions that the icebreaker is used to open passages for merchant ships, which follow in line behind her, passing along the channel opened by the armour-plated bow. This is why an icebreaker must have a wide hull, for she must carve a path large enough to allow other ships to pass.

This is the icebreaker's main task, but there are other jobs, too, that are far more difficult and exacting – voyages of research and exploration in the polar regions, for instance. It is here that we find exploits that are among the most memorable in the history of geographical exploration and scientific expeditions.

The idea of building armoured ships that could sail amid the polar ice first occurred to the Russians, at the very beginning of the age of mechanized propulsion. For Russian ports, both in the Baltic and to an even greater extent in the

Arctic Ocean, are completely blocked during winter. The first ship of this type was the *Ermak*, built in Britain for the Russian government in 1899. She had three screws aft and one in the bow, 38-millimetre steel-plating at the waterline, over 10,000 horsepower and displaced 10,000 tonnes. She proved so successful that she became the prototype for all the icebreakers that have followed. From then on, the Russians devoted themselves unceasingly to building ships of this kind. Some of them earned fame during the polar expeditions of the 1920s and 1930s.

The current Russian fleet has more than thirty icebreakers, their displacements varying from two to twenty thousand tonnes. One of the largest is the *Lenin*, which is nuclear-powered, 134 metres long, 27.63 metres wide and displaces 16,000 tonnes. She was built in Leningrad in 1957 and, in open sea, can travel at the remarkable speed of 18 knots. She has three screws and her atomic-steam-turbine-electric power plant gives a total of 44,000 horsepower. She is fitted with three atomic reactors, one of which acts as a reserve.

Left, an icebreaker under way. The diagrams below show a comparison between an icebreaker of 1958 (above) and one that dates from 1898. Both have an additional propeller at the bow. In the photograph below, right, another icebreaker at work.

The *Lenin* was the first ship in the world to be fitted with nuclear propulsion which is, among other things, especially suitable for an icebreaker, for nuclear power means a remarkable degree of independence, and a cruise can last for two or three years without the need to refuel. This is very important, since a ship navigating in Arctic waters may well get stuck and be unable to return to base until the following year.

Other countries including Poland and Japan have fleets of icebreakers, but it is the United States Coast Guard which controls the largest fleet outside Russia. During the extremely severe winters of the mid-1930s, the Coast Guard began breaking up the ice in northern rivers and harbours. In 1936, this was made one of its official duties. Ever since, it has kept open the northern ports in winter months.

Use of helicopters

Today's large icebreakers are equipped to carry helicopters, used for observation purposes – especially to spot where more easily navigable channels are opening up between the ice-floes.

Among more recent voyages of exploration carried out with icebreakers should be noted the Antarctic expeditions which began after the Second World War.

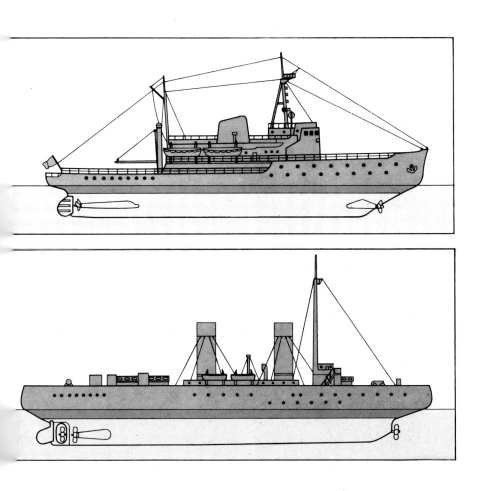

Industry Craftsman to mass production

The word "industry" immediately conjures up the picture of a large factory bristling with smoking chimneys. This image can be right, at least as a symbol, if we are thinking of a single industry or a single industrial establishment. However, if we wish to give a more general meaning to the word, if, that is, we are talking of industrial activity or industrial production or even of industrial civilization, then the image of chimneys gives us a false, or at the least very limited, notion of the reality.

To understand properly what industry really is, and understand it as a phenomenon of our own time, we must first of all establish a precise definition of the term. If we look it up in a dictionary we will find explanations of this type: "all the undertakings which produce a given type of merchandise, taken as a whole" or even "every activity whose objective it is to extract, produce and process raw materials to turn them into useful goods".

By these definitions, industry was in existence even in the distant past, even in prehistoric times. In the Stone Age, spearheads, for example, were a "given type of merchandise", they certainly were "useful goods" and flint (the material from which they were made) was without doubt a "raw material".

In effect, industry was born at the same time as the human race, even before agriculture. The original meaning of the word confirms this: it is the Latin *industria* which simply means being busy. Industry, then, has existed since man began to "transform" the materials which nature supplied into tools and other objects which were either necessary or decorative. In fact another definition of the term is just this: "activity of transformation". Our palaeolithic forefathers, like the craftsmen of the Middle Ages or the skilled workers of the Renaissance, were engaged in an activity of transformation.

However, when we employ the term "industry" today, it suggests a break with the world of the craftsmen. It is clear that what we mean is modern industry, an extremely complex phenomenon, which is certainly based on the transformation of raw materials and on the production of "useful goods", but which is characterized above all by a new method of production: a method so different from those of the past as to change profoundly and rapidly the whole of society.

Modern industry

The story of modern industry starts more than two hundred years ago, in Great Britain, with the invention in 1738 of the first automatic spinning machine. Improved versions of this, introduced in the 1760s, allowed the processing of cotton yarn to be greatly speeded up. The consequences of using these water-powered machines and others invented

Two pictures of the food industry: below, a stage in the preparation of spaghetti in a modern pasta factory; left, compressors for the deep freezing of horticultural produce in a refrigeration centre.

in the same period for weaving, were so important that someone called them revolutionary. Thus the evolution in methods of working (not only, as we shall see, in the textile field) and everything which sprang from this eventually came to be called the "Industrial Revolution".

This great leap in civilization has been compared to the profound changes which took place in the long-distant past when man "invented" agriculture and turned from being a nomadic hunter to a settled tiller of the fields. However, it was not only the increasing use of machines which brought about this "earthquake". The eighteenth century, as we know, was a century of great ferment and convulsion in all fields of human intellect, from science to philosophy. It ended with another great revolution, the French revolution, which, in the government of nations, opened the doors to newly emergent forces (above all the bourgeoisie) and totally changed the western world.

It was in that climate, so favourable to sudden change and the acceleration of progress, that Great Britain (the richest, politically most stable and most dynamic country of the time) put real vigour into modern industry. Conditions were very favourable to the British. They had readily available raw materials, energy at low cost provided by the coal mines, an expanding trade with the outside world and a well-developed banking system.

The dominating characteristic of this first phase of industrialization was the ever more widespread use of the factory system. Based on the use of the machine as an adjunct to or even as a replacement for manual labour, this system gradually supplanted the small craftsmen's workshop, causing grave social problems as it did so.

The first industry in which this process was employed was the English cotton industry. This had previously been based in the country, where the cotton was spun in the homes of the spinners. This method was no longer able to satisfy demand, so an attempt was made to improve the system of spinning, by looking for technical solutions which might allow greater quantities to be produced. The automatic spinning machine of 1738 was followed in 1764 by Hargreaves' spinning jenny and Arkwright's spinning or water frame. In 1779, Samuel Crompton combined the best features of both in his "mule". These machines unleashed a violent reaction from the small producers, who saw themselves threatened by the new inventions, which were available only to the larger and richer producers. Matters got so far out of hand that some of

We move on to the clothing industry: here on the right, shoes in position for drying out under special lamps; below, an automatic textile machine in which human intervention is limited, for practical purposes, to occasional checks; bottom, a large department in a factory producing ready-made garments.

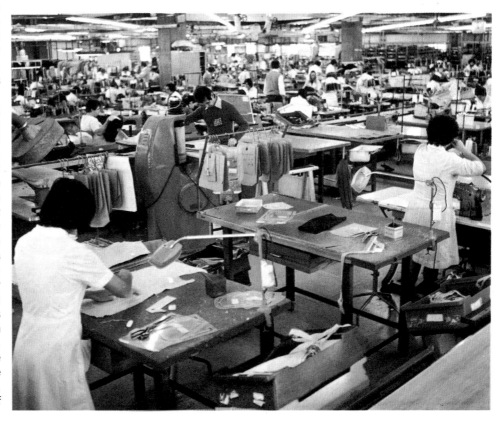

Above, the gloss-painting of petrol-tanks in a motor-cycle factory; above right, the welding shop in a French car factory. The first large company in the car industry was Ford, in the United States, founded in 1903.

Many engineering industries (in the photograph on the right we see one phase in the work) produce tools and machines destined for use in other industries, for example all machine-tools.

In the steel industry (photograph above) the most modern equipment brings together in one enormous complex all the different processing stages required to convert the various types of pig-iron into special steels.

industrial primacy to those countries rich in coal and iron.

The introduction of Watt's steam engine was decisive: from its initial use in the mines to pump water out of the galleries, it rapidly acquired more extensive use. It soon replaced, with notable advantages and relatively lower costs, the traditional source of energy from water-power. This meant, among other things, that it was possible to build new factories (which at first had been located on river banks) in economically more favourable places, for example, near the big towns and ports. This reduced the transport costs of the goods and made the recruitment of labour easier.

Between 1720 and the end of the century, British exports increased five-fold, and the country's prosperity was immeasurably improved. The industrial system had set off a process of growth in production, consumption and external trade in manufactures and raw materials which led in turn to a growing accumulation of capital available to fund new initiatives.

Alongside the extraordinary effects on the economy, which on balance were positive, the Industrial Revolution caused grave problems, mainly social in character. The new entrepreneurial class, which had invested huge amounts of capital (their own or loaned by the banks) in setting up the factories, sought to recover their money in the shortest possible time. Therefore they utilized the machinery to the greatest possible extent and exploited the workers. It was only through the efforts of the reformer, Robert Owen, that an Act was passed in 1819 limiting the age at which the children might work and their working hours to seventy-two per week.

The machines meanwhile were becoming faster, which made the conditions of labour even more burdensome. To induce the workers to increase their output, the system of piece-work was introduced in place of payment by the hour. The workers, with the sole exception of those capable of installing and repairing the machines, became easy to replace, since no particular specialization was required in their work which consisted always of simple, repetitive tasks.

This made it possible to take on unskilled staff at low wages. There was, in any case, a large and constant surplus of labour due to the influx into the towns of masses of peasants in search of work. It was again machines that were responsible for this exodus from the countryside. Introduced into agriculture, they had enormously reduced the need for manual labour.

the new factories were burnt down, but the craftsmen were fighting a hopeless battle. Industry was thrust forward by technological innovation and by the accelerated growth of production which the machines brought about.

Steam-powered machines

Other production sectors soon followed the lead set by the textile industry, in an unstoppable spiral of technical progress whose effects rapidly overflowed into other industrial processes. For example, in the steel industry coking coal was used first to replace charcoal in the furnaces, and then (following James Watt's invention of the steam engine in 1769) to provide motive power. This allowed steel to be produced in abundance, when before it had been very scarce and expensive. This in turn promoted the development of the mechanical engineering industry and gave economic and

Naval dockyards can also be thought of as industrial establishments. Above, an oil-tanker in dry-dock for repairs; left, the lifting of an enormous ship's screw.

The growth of modern industry

Half-way through the nineteenth century, the "classic" phase of the Industrial Revolution was drawing to a close and a new period of development was beginning, in a greater number of countries and fields of industrial activity. In France, Germany, Belgium and the United States, the economic and social structures were by now able to support the growth of modern industry.

The steel industry assumed growing importance in this second phase (the high temperature furnaces for converting pig-iron into steel were introduced between 1850 and 1860). At the same time the engineering industry capitalized on technological innovations and increased productivity several times over in all sectors. These developments coincided with others which, by analogy, are called the "transport revolution".

Steamships set out to replace the sailing ships and the first railway age began. Continually expanding industries found growth in transport to be a further important factor urging them on, and this resulted in a widening of the market.

Product availability and supply of raw materials grew in volume and flexibility, making it possible to buy and sell in more distant countries and in a shorter time. These improvements in their turn stimu

Another important industrial sector is printing, which in recent years has received a new lease of life thanks to the application of electronics. Right, the running off of a roll of paper just printed and, below, the leaves of a magazine ready for binding.

ated still further growth in production, profits and investment.

The coming of electric power

At the end of the nineteenth century, a third phase was ushered in with the birth of the great chemical industry. This at first concentrated on a few products (fertilizers, dyes and explosives), but later extended to iron-founding (the introduction of new alloys) and even to the creation of new materials (the first artificial fibres). But the "revolutionary" nature of this period was accentuated by a major step forward in the field of energy. Following water-power and steam-power, electricity was introduced into industrial processes, as a result of the perfecting, from 1880 on, of the techniques for "transporting" electric current over great distances.

The tempo of modern industrial advance became faster. At the turn of the twentieth century the first Fiat factory was opened in Turin. A few years later, Henry Ford introduced for the first time, in his automobile factory in Detroit, in the United States, the "assembly line". This system, which has generated enormous increases in production levels, has also aggravated those social and human problems (monotonous tasks and the stupefying effect of repetitive work-rhythms) which are typical of the man-

machine relationship and have not yet been overcome.

Scientific and technological development

After the Second World War, the exceptional nature of the new directions taken in the preceding phase was overshadowed by extraordinary scientific and technological events. These included amazing developments in transport on land and in the air, the utilization of nuclear energy, the application of synthetic materials coming from the petro-chemical industry, electronics and automation.

These technological innovations produce almost every day thousands of "revolutions", both large and small, in the economy, in the dissemination of information and in patterns of life. They also produce enormous problems, such as the vast scale of urban sprawl, pollution, an imbalance between production and consumption, a widening of the prosperity gap between rich countries and poor, the over-stretching of energy sources and a thousand other things. But progress is not coming to an end: indeed our civilization must learn, if it is to survive, to "direct" itself along better lines. This must be the real goal of the new phase, the phase of "maturity", in the Industrial Revolution.

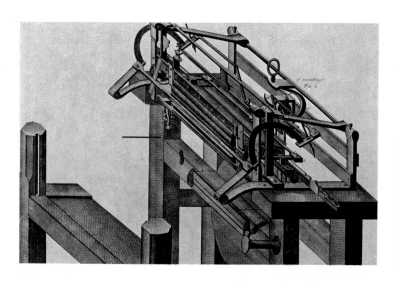

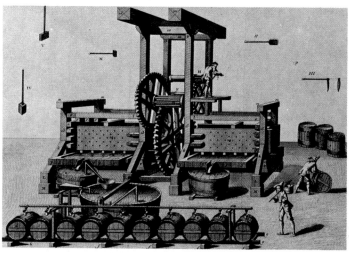

Machines
Ingenious devices

What does a bicycle have in common with a calculator, a movie camera with a car or a crane with an electric train set? They are all "machines". Each one of them is capable of performing a specified task and all of them consist of a combination of parts, some fixed and some moving. A car, for example, is made of a large number of parts, such as the wheels, the suspension and the engine, and each of these in turn is made up of many other parts.

Another characteristic common to all machines is that they can perform their allotted tasks only if they are provided with energy: the calculator, the movie camera and the crane work only if they are connected to a supply of electric current; the motor car will only move if there is fuel in its petrol-tank; and the bicycle is "fed" by the energy of the muscles of its rider.

At one time, it was usual to distinguish between two classes of machines – "motive" and "functional". All types of engine (electric motors, heat-engines and so on) came under the first heading, and under the second went all those which did the actual work. For example, according to this classification, in a car the engine is the motive machine while the gear box, the transmission, the wheels and so on, together make up the functional part. Nowadays, however, many machines are so complex that sometimes it is difficult to distinguish the motive part from the functional part and this classification has therefore been abandoned.

Anatomy of a machine

A machine dismantled into its smallest components, that is into a collection of screws, springs and cogs, resembles a lifeless organism. Yet even these simple components are very important. By examining them, one finds out that the proper working of a machine, sometimes so complex as to seem almost incomprehensible, is the result of the concerted action of a number of pieces, large and small, each of which performs ·an elementary task.

Many of these have a long history, since

These eighteenth-century drawings illustrate three machines of the period: above left, a loom for weaving stockings and, right, a wine-press (both taken from the Encyclopédie *of Diderot and D'Alembert); below, a hydraulic pump.*

they are the result of a gradual evolution from those "simple machines" (like the wheel, the lever, the inclined plane and the pulley) which have been known since ancient times. The word "machine" itself has a very ancient origin and probably comes from the Greek term *makhana*, which means expedient or handy. Let us examine some of these highly important parts and describe what they do.

We begin with screws. When it is "screwed in", that is, rotated, the screw advances in a straight line. Thus it converts the rotary motion given to it into rectilinear motion. Likewise it returns from the position it has reached only if it is made to rotate in the opposite direction. It is not possible to remove it simply by pulling it out (at least if breakage is to be avoided). For these reasons, the screw has uses in many machines. It is also used to join together two pieces which might otherwise come apart.

The ball-bearing (or roller-bearing) is also a basic component of machines. It was only introduced recently, but is really little more than an application of the much longer established wheel. It consists of two concentric cylinders between which a number of metal spheres are placed. When the two cylinders rotate at different speeds or in opposite directions, they glide along on the metal balls instead of dragging against one another. The amount of friction is thus greatly reduced and as a consequence, the motion made much easier. In other words, the same result is achieved as transporting an object by mounting it on wheels rather than dragging it along the ground.

Some famous machines of the nineteenth century: above left, the lathe of Sir Joseph Whitworth, one of the most talented inventors of the age; above right, the Monotype type-casting machine by Tolbert Lanston; left, the machine for countersinking by Eli Whitney; below left, the boring machine of John Wilkinson, which made it possible for James Watt to build his steam engine; lastly, below, a model of the first steam-powered sledge-hammer conceived by James Nasmyth.

How man is built, what his average bodily dimensions are, what the colours he notices most readily are, or what sort of movement he makes best: these are some of the things we study in ergonomics. The information is used when designing the most modern machines. Ergonomics is the study of the relationships between man and machines, especially in the working environment (the word "ergonomics" comes from the Greek *ergon*, that is work, and *nomos*, that is standard or rule).

The cog is a composite application of the wheel and the lever. When it is made to rotate, its teeth press against the teeth of the adjoining cog, thereby transferring its motion to that. So the adjoining cog also starts to go round: faster if it is smaller, slower if it is bigger.

Let us now pass on to a "mechanism", that is a group of interdependent components of a machine: it is the cam mechanism which converts a rotary or oscillating movement into a forwards and backwards straight-line movement (sometimes called "alternating motion"), or vice versa.

Of course, many other components and mechanisms exist, but it is impossible to describe them all. However, from the small number of examples considered, it is already possible to perceive what sorts of tasks they perform. We have described components and mechanisms which transmit motion, and modify it in so doing, like the screw (converts rotary to rectilinear motion), the cog (transmits rotary motion) and the cam system (converts rotary motion to alternating or vice versa); or even those which improve the performance of the machine, like the ball-bearing (which reduces friction) and the screw (which makes the machine easy to dismantle).

As well as the mechanical parts, in many modern machines there are also electrical and electronic components and in some of these, that is electric machines and electronic machines, these are the most important components.

Science, technology and invention

How does one set about designing a new machine? First of all, it is necessary to know exactly what components are already available and the physical laws on which their functioning is based. It is also necessary to be able to evaluate materials fully and understand the sources of energy available. Knowledge of these factors, however, is not enough. One needs the ability to invent in order to arrive at a solution which combines in different ways the components already in existence, or, if this is not sufficient, to create new components and mechanisms.

The design stage is done by making more and more precise drawings, which show even the smallest components in the minutest detail. Sometimes operational tests are also made using accurate scale models.

Today the machine is no longer simply, as the Roman architect Vitruvius defined it, "a coherent union of material parts which offers very great advantages in the carrying of loads": some modern machines are capable of completely replacing the human worker, often doing things which a man on his own would find impossible.

Moreover machines are now in such widespread use that our whole lives (not just our working lives) are affected by their presence: we need think only of the important functions of electrical equipment in the home or the motor-car. The ever-increasing role of machines in our society gave birth, a few decades ago, to a new science, ergonomics, which studies the relationship between men and machines.

Initially ergonomics confined itself to analysing the working capacity of men, so as to design machines which were easier and safer to use; by now its terms of reference have been significantly enlarged and include comparative studies of men and machines so as to be able to make a more rational distribution of work between the two. Machines, which are subject to neither boredom nor fatigue, are suitable for performing repetitive tasks and can be more powerful and quicker than people.

People have, however, a unique quality which cannot be reproduced: a brain capable of invention. Men and machines, in other words, are complementary. But a machine is only as good as its operator. So to that extent man will always remain its master.

The Parachute
How to jump 10,000 metres

When the parachute is open, the velocity of fall is about six metres per second. With recent models that have an open canopy with slits (as in the picture above), the descent can be regulated by manipulating the cords. During free fall, the velocity can be reduced if the person adopts positions that increase resistance to the air.

The parachute has a very long history. As long ago as the twelfth century, Chinese acrobats are said to have given displays of high diving using devices similar to parachutes. The first person to study the parachute scientifically and draw detailed designs, was Leonardo da Vinci, around 1514.

Leonardo's designs remained as fascinating theories, however, and were never actually put into practice. It is more than two centuries later that the first parachute jump took place when Louis Sébastian Lenormand made a jump from a high tower in 1783. Another Frenchman, André Garnerin, is thought to be the first to use a parachute regularly and successfully. In 1797, he made five "braked" jumps from a balloon in Paris (according to records of the time, one of his jumps was of 2,400 metres). The story of the parachute as a means of saving lives began in 1808 when a Polish balloonist used his parachute to jump out of his balloon which had caught fire in mid-air.

The invention of the aeroplane in 1903 led to discussion of the practicability of using parachutes for escapes from aeroplanes. Parachutes were improved in Germany and towards the end of the First World War (in about 1917), German pilots used them extensively. The American and British air forces adopted them a few years later.

As air travel became safer, the parachute began to be used for other purposes and was no longer regarded solely as a saving "umbrella". Parachuting became a widespread sport, and a new military division was born – parachute troops. Today, parachutes are used to drop supplies from the air in peace and in war, to reduce the speed of spacecraft as they re-enter the earth's atmosphere or of aeroplanes which have to stop in a short distance, as well as to decelerate the descent of bombs and mines.

The distinguishing feature of the parachute is that it slows down the fall of an object which, on its way to the ground, is subject to acceleration because of the effect of gravity. In free fall, a man would hit the ground at the fatal speed of around 200 kilometres an hour. Wearing a parachute, his velocity at the moment of impact is reduced, on average, to between 18 and 22 kilometres an hour.

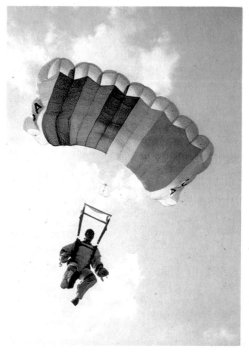

The point of parachute acrobatics is to see how much can be achieved (either individually or in groups, as in the picture above), before the descent is "braked". Left, the "sail" type parachute: its shape means that the descent is more like a gliding flight.

The parachute generally has the classic wide umbrella shape (known as a canopy) of seven to ten metres in diameter. The canopy weighs around fifteen kilograms and consists of twenty-four to twenty-eight triangular-shaped panels of extremely durable material (usually nylon) which are sewn together. Each panel is made up of smaller sections, so that a tear in the cloth will usually be contained to one section. Cords, called suspension or shroud lines, are fixed to the seams which join the panels. Each shroud line runs from the harness, over the centre of the canopy, back to the harness. If the parachute is for a person to use, then the harness consists of a series of belts and webbing to hold the human body.

Before use, the parachute is packed in a bag. In a parachute jump, it can either be opened manually by the parachutist, or it can open automatically. A small parachute comes out of the bag first (called the "extractor" or "pilot parachute"); it quickly inflates and the main parachute is pulled out of the pack. By tugging on the cords the parachutist alters the shape and inclination of the canopy and changes direction and speed.

The sport of parachuting uses parachutes with large slits, or holes, which are more easily manoeuvrable than other types, because they allow the air to escape and drive the parachute in the direction opposite the hole. Parachutes with ribbons have been found the most successful for very heavy loads. They have a canopy consisting of a series of strips, or ribbons.

Among the more spectacular parachute jumps on record was that made in 1960 by Captain Joseph Kittinger of the United States. He dropped 25,816 metres from a balloon at 31,330 metres.

Roads From paths to electronic tracks

Roads that will automatically "drive" cars are for the time being just an idea, almost in the realms of science fiction.

Roads were first built when trade started. Before that there were footpaths. The shortest, easiest or least dangerous route was found after many attempts and was eventually marked on the ground as a result of being walked over again and again. However, to transport goods on pack animals or carts it was necessary to improve paths by widening them, leveling them, removing large stones and filling any holes. This is how first mule tracks and later roads were created.

In the old days, tracks covered long distances but were rarely marked. Among the longest of these early routes, must have been that along which silk was brought from China to Rome. Large road networks were created in the territories conquered by the Romans and linked the capital with all corners of the empire. The most distant areas could be reached quickly to deal with any uprising, administer justice or carry out the governor's orders. This was not, however, a feature peculiar to the Roman Empire since major routes also existed across China, Mesopotamia and Persia.

These incredible road systems were achieved sometimes by connecting and improving existing paths and mule tracks, sometimes by planning entirely new routes. Along the roads, there were guest houses and post houses where people could rest and, if necessary,

These three pictures illustrate the development of roads. The two at the top represent "birth" and "childhood", a grass path with a rudimentary stone fencing on either side and a section of the Appian Way built in Roman days. The stage of "maturity" can be seen in the complex motorway intersection in Duisberg (Federal Republic of Germany). But this is not the end, as experts are already talking of electrified roads and automatic tracks, although on a purely theoretical level.

A section of the Milan-Genoa motorway and a small mountain road in Piedmont. Apart from bends, which are almost non-existent on motorways but which are particularly numerous on mountain roads, the main difference is the width. A motorway usually has three lanes on either side and can be up to 32 metres wide. A normal road can measure less than 10 metres in width (4 metres in the case of a one-way street).

change their tired animals. For example, the "kings' route", which was built in Persia during the fifth century BC under the Emperor Darius, linked the two old centres Sardis and Susa over a distance of 2,400 kilometres and included a great number of "service stations". The slow caravans needed months to complete the route, but the emperor's messengers, who galloped on horses which they often changed, could cover the whole distance in a week or little more, travelling at a speed which was quite exceptional for those days.

After the fall of the Roman Empire, there was a drastic drop in trade traffic. The road network in the western world was progressively abandoned and there were no technical innovations or new road constructions of any significant value for more than a thousand years. Traffic only started to increase again in the seventeenth century. Coaches and carts

became so numerous that the first traffic regulations had to be enforced, especially in cities. Many ancient roads were re-used and new ones were also built. Times had changed. In the eighteenth century, the first road and bridge government department was set up in France, and was soon followed by the first road engineering institute.

During the eighteenth and nineteenth centuries, there were many innovations, particularly in methods of paving. However, the most significant change in road construction has taken place during the twentieth century. This has been a result partly of the application of new techniques and the introduction of fast motor vehicles, but also of the very large increase in traffic. To accommodate this, it has become necessary to build wider and more numerous roads, producing an extremely dense network in all industrialized countries.

Preliminary studies

Nowadays roads are built for many reasons; for example, to facilitate new industries in a particular area, to increase tourism, to speed up the traffic on an already congested road or to make it possible to cover long distances more easily and quickly. Whatever the reason, in advanced countries the decision to build a new road is taken only after studies have ascertained that it will prove useful and will fit into the area.

At the beginning, surveys are carried out to establish what the traffic volume will be and what it will consist of (the percentages of heavy vehicles, buses, cars). The ''basic'' speed for the road is then determined, that is the speed which will not lead to accidents under conditions of good visibility and little traffic.

With these facts in mind, experts then establish the characteristics of the road and in particular the dimensions and number of lanes, the maximum gradient and minimum bend of curves and the arrangement of intersections (whether on the same or on several levels). The

Various types of roads: a junction in the centre of Stockholm (Sweden); a motorway viaduct in Liguria (Italy); and a straight road in Honduras (Central America).

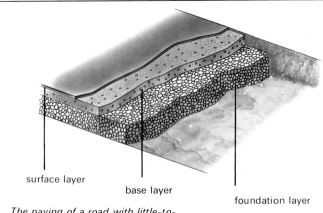

The different bituminous macadam paving layers. At the bottom there is a foundation layer consisting of broken stone, then two layers of bituminous macadam known as "base" and "surface" layers. The maximum size of the gravel, percentage of bitumen and thickness of layers depend on the climate, type of soil and traffic on the road.

The paving of a road with little-to-medium traffic in an area with a temperate climate. The total thickness is about 50 centimetres.

the "finished product". The engineer then enters on the layout both bends and straight lines, ensuring whenever possible that there are neither too many bends nor narrow bends at the end of straight lines (where vehicles will gain speed).

When the alignment of the road has been determined, its "vertical cross-section" must be prepared. In fact, if it is to have a satisfactory gradient, the road cannot continuously follow the original configuration of the surface. Use must be made of viaducts and tunnels. In his study of the road's cross-section, the engineer must endeavour to ensure that the route is safe and easy and must avoid depressions which are too deep and inclines which are too steep. Mountain roads used by heavy vehicles must include sections with gentle slopes so that large lorries may "recover".

Bearing in mind the layout and vertical section, the engineer then goes on to plan the actual roadway. He indicates where there should be excavations, retaining walls or walls to protect the road. The layout, alignment, vertical cross section and transverse cross sections are basic data for the project. To these must be added the "finishing touches". For example, the passage from straight sections to bends is eased by means of gentle transitional bends, junctions are examined and so on. The paving of the road (also known as the superstructure) must be studied. The surface used by vehicles must be even, water and ice must not damage it and the weight of the traffic on the ground must be evenly distributed. The paving aspect is so important that it constitutes a chapter on its own in the construction of a road.

minimum bend of curves depends on the basic road speed, because a vehicle which travels along a circular trajectory tends to go off the road and the force which pushes it (known as centrifugal force) increases with the speed of the vehicle and bend of the road. Therefore, design engineers plan sufficiently wide bends to ensure that vehicles travelling along them at the basic speed do not go off the road.

Engineers use large scale ordnance survey maps. Large scale maps are essential, as small scale maps cannot be used to draw the route because an error of a fraction of a millimetre on the drawing (and errors cannot be avoided) is in fact an error of several tens of metres on site. Large scale maps are not the only source of information on the topography of an area. Aerial surveys and measurements are also used to determine the characteristics of the zone in more detail.

An accurate survey of the geology of the whole area is also required because, if at all possible, the route must avoid dangerous terrain such as marshland or areas subject to landslides or that where the construction of the road would prove too long and too expensive. Finally, engineers determine points at which watercourses should be crossed (and where bridges will be built) and study access roads for the new venture, to establish the most suitable points for junctions.

The project

When all preliminary studies have been carried out, the actual project is started. The initial layout, which is a rough draft of the route, is first prepared. A good project depends on the initial layout. Like a rough drawing or the plan of an essay, the layout contains much basic information about

Methods of construction

In ancient Mesopotamia, a road consisted of blocks of stone or bricks covered with bitumen. The Romans constructed their roads from up to four layers of different materials, sometimes amounting to a metre in depth altogether.

During the eighteenth and nineteenth centuries, the road surface was reinforced and waterproofed by covering it with a series of well compacted layers of resistant stones. Foremost amongst those who developed these methods were the British engineers, Thomas Telford and John McAdam. These superstructures were based on the resistance capacity of the underlying soil, which was therefore treated and compressed before being laid. This type of paving was, however, too uneven, dusty and noisy to lend itself satisfactorily to car traffic. Road surfaces had to be studied further and research continued into the problems created by

Danger points

Here are the thirty-two possible danger points of a junction in a country where traffic drives on the right: they are the points where cars going in different directions can cause problems and even accidents.

There are points where the traffic flow diverges (empty circles), points where it converges (circles with a dot) and intersection points (black circles). Most dangerous accidents occur at the last-mentioned points. In order to reduce the number of danger points, junctions are usually arranged on several levels or include lanes for dividing the traffic.

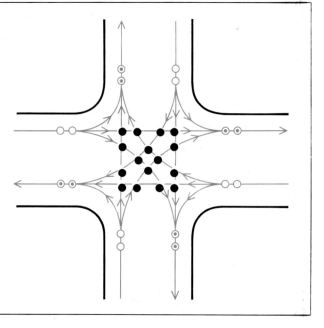

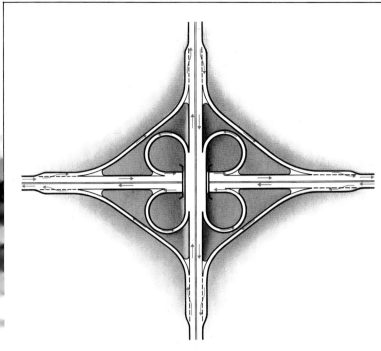

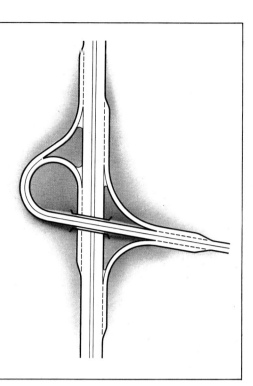

Cloverleaf and fly-over junctions. Two of the most common types of junctions. On the left, a "cloverleaf" junction, which is where two roads cross on different levels. The various flows of traffic do not meet and the danger points, where the two traffic flows diverge or converge, are made less dangerous by means of long lanes side by side. The same applies to the junction on the right, known as a fly-over, which routes the flow of traffic of a minor road to a main road.

the new forms of transport.

We have all seen the answer which the engineers found. The surface is covered with one or more layers of bituminous macadam (bitumen mixed with sand and gravel) or concrete. The sub-base and other layers under the surface are similar to those used in the past.

Innovations in this field over the last few years include the use of plastic materials. For example, in cold countries polystyrene blocks (up to one metre thick) have been inserted between the paving and sub-base to ensure that water and ice do not damage the road. There are also other less known as well as less common systems; for example, wood paving (blocks of hardwood held together by pitch), metal paving (triangular cast iron plates with grooved surfaces), rubber paving (concrete blocks covered with a layer of rubber which may be coloured and makes the road quieter). In cities, some roads still have stone pavings, made of cobbles, flagstones or paving stones.

Road construction

The construction of the road involves moving a great deal of earth. Soil is excavated at the higher points and is then used to fill depressions. The first step consists in marking out the alignments, that is the line of the road shown on the drawing is marked on the ground, using a series of stakes. Then the soil is "skinned" (the layer of grass is removed) bit by bit and depressions (points where the road is lower than the soil level) are prepared. If the soil which is excavated is suitable, it is loaded on to lorries and taken to

"embankment" sections (parts of the road which are higher).

Embankments are then compressed to ensure that the soil does not remain soft and can withstand the weight of the traffic. In earlier days, when machines were not available, the construction of a road required a great deal of time and a large number of labourers. During their work, labourers would walk over and over sections that had been levelled and the continuous and protracted trampling contributed to the formation of well-compacted embankments. This is now carried out much more quickly by machines such as road rollers. Walls, which were in the past built of bricks or stones, now consist of reinforced concrete structures. Particular care is given to the problem of the water (whether rain or a spring) to ensure that it does not get into the embankments or retaining walls and cause them to collapse. Finally, paving layers are laid on the sub-base. This is also done by appropriate machines, such as those that mix the bituminous macadam and spread it in layers of even thickness.

What will roads look like in the future? Plastic materials will certainly be used frequently and we may witness even more significant changes. For example, some experts believe that motorways will be electrified. Vehicles, which will have two motors (an internal combustion motor and an electric motor), will reach the motorway and be connected to the electrical supply, thereby becoming something like small trolley buses.

Other experts believe that motorways will become electronic tracks where

vehicles will get on tracks which will guide them automatically and will even allow drivers to go to sleep during the whole journey. However, for the time being, these are only ideas and even if the second sounds extremely attractive, it does seem somewhat fantastic.

Science
Why physics has become "top of the class"

In the last three centuries, starting with Newton, physics has reached the highest level of perfection, becoming a model for all the other sciences and even influencing philosophical thought. This supremacy, however, could pass to biology, which in recent years has made extraordinary progress.

The term "science" is derived from the Latin *scientia*, which means knowledge, or learning. Today this word is used to describe certain disciplines (such as mathematics, physics, biology, economics or psychology) which are founded on undisputed facts, ideas which have been critically tested and organized in a logical and rigorous manner. From these we expect reliable forecasts, satisfactory explanations, and whatever is necessary to understand the real world in which we live and to regulate our actions in the most suitable way.

Nowadays, scientific research is a specialized field, carried out in universities, institutions and large firms. This often has the effect of making it seem remote and beyond our understanding, something which exerts an outside influence on our daily lives. However, science is a part of human culture and includes (even though in abstract form) those ideas typical of the age and the society which produced it. Neither is there only one way to "do science": the term

applies to every form of knowledge which seeks to relate facts, to explain them and to forecast them. The lessons the ordinary man learns from his daily experience, represent an elementary form of knowledge, whereby the customs, beliefs and proverbs of popular tradition develop a function equivalent to that of the laws and theories of actual science. There is no radical distinction between common knowledge and scientific knowledge: the latter is simply an extension of the former with rigorous arrangement of facts. Seen in this light, science appears a natural activity for man, who detects a certain regularity in natural phenomena and studies them in the belief that understanding them will be to his advantage.

The first signs of scientific behaviour appeared many thousands of years ago when man realized that, for example, hunting and skinning his prey were made easier if he used a stone, especially one of a particular shape. He already knew how to recognize the connection between the function of a tool and its shape and soon

learned to chip away the stone to obtain the desired form. The two characteristic stages of the scientific method were present (even though unconsciously) in the development of this rudimentary technological activity: theoretical thought (imagining a tool designed for a certain purpose) and the experimental phase (making the tool, checking that it worked and making any necessary modifications). Alongside this, the idea of "magic" developed to explain nature. Man presumed that invisible forces existed to control the most important natural phenomena. These forces were thought to have a mind of their own but could be induced to behave in the desired manner by propitiatory rites performed by a sorcerer. Magic is not a very reliable basis for a system of laws, but in this naïve behaviour are found some very important characteristics.

Man does not submit passively to the whims of nature, but considers phenomena as effects produced by well determined forces which can be under stood and which he can influence. This ambitious notion led man to venture into space and to attempt to modify the genetic code of the cell.

Egyptian science

In prehistoric times, the various peoples all had the same basic level of scientific and technical knowledge. This was mainly because in those days innovations followed each other at such a slow pace that the many different races had time to learn them and to integrate them into their own culture. This situation began to change at the beginning of recorded history when the progressive drying up of large areas led to the wide band of desert which reaches from central Africa to the heart of Asia. The inhabitants of the drought-stricken lands emigrated to the humid areas close to the Nile, the Tigris, the Euphrates and the Indus, thus founding the first major civilizations.

Ancient Egypt is an example of this. The fact that the earth was fertile but liable to periodic flooding stimulated the development of the science of geometry and architecture just as the need of a fairly complex society for a code of laws and an elementary accounting system encouraged the development of numerical computation and writing.

In fact the mathematics of ancient Egypt was fairly rudimentary. They only had one sign (which represented unity) and they repeated this until the desired number was indicated. In arithmetic, they could only do addition and subtraction with any speed, while multiplication and division required complicated processes. Also their knowledge of geometry was fairly limited and was confined to basic formulas for measurement and to a few elementary principles of right-angled triangles and quadrilaterals which they worked out in order to calculate the correct fall of irrigation canals and to trace the boundaries of fields swept away by the periodic flooding of the Nile.

These people, however, made a notable and substantially original contribution to the science of the measurement of time. The Egyptians were the first to determine the length of the year as 365 days. The day and night were each divided into twelve hours, but since the day was measured sometimes from sunrise to sunset and sometimes from the appearance of daylight to its disappearance, the length of day and night varied through the year. The ancient Egyptians also made very accurate medical and astronomical studies. Their architects, too, had elementary notions of balance and hydraulics, while in the copper mines of Sinai the techniques of metallurgy were perfected.

Galileo was the father of the "scientific revolution" of the seventeenth century. He asserted the need for direct, accurate observation and the proof of hypotheses. On the opposite page, Galileo demonstrates the falling of weights in the presence of Giovanni de' Medici. Alchemy (an ancient study that attempted to transform various metals into gold) could not be considered a true science, even though it made an effective contribution to the development of modern chemistry. Right, a picture of an alchemist's laboratory.

This vast collection of knowledge might give the impression that the Egyptian culture, like that of other great civilizations of that time, had reached an advanced level of science. In reality, this knowledge was confined to the priests who were inclined to see divine intervention in natural phenomena. This type of explanation satisfied the requirements of society and they did not see the necessity to reorganize the mass of information at their disposal in a critical and rational manner.

The discovery of rationality

We find a totally different attitude among the Greek philosophers of the sixth century BC. These men were not priests but ordinary citizens and had the good fortune to live in a cultural environment which valued free discussion and criticism. In this climate of tolerance, abstract reasoning finally appeared as a fundamentally important instrument in the process leading to knowledge. The Greek discovery of rationality was a radical advance in the development of scientific thought.

In order to understand the importance of this innovation, remember that the Egyptian geometricians had discovered a long time ago that in certain right-angled triangles the square on the hypotenuse was equal to the sum of the squares on the other two sides. But they never asked themselves whether this was a general property, valid for all right-angled triangles, nor did they try to prove it by general and abstract reasoning. However, this is precisely what the Greek Pythagoras did when proving his famous theorem.

Furthermore, the Greek thinkers rejected the idea that natural phenomena were regulated by the intervention of the gods and maintained that everything that happened in nature could be explained by the properties of the original elements from which the universe was made. Their purpose was, therefore, to construct a rational, perfect and universal science which could be applied to all reality in the same manner. In the field of geometry (for example, in the *Elements* of Euclid), they effectively succeeded in reducing all the properties of geometrical shapes to a few basic principles by means of a process of logical and rigorous reasoning (the proofs of the theorems). This method was not so effective in the case of the natural sciences, where the attempt to deduce by purely logical means all the phenomena of the original elements, such as water, fire, the

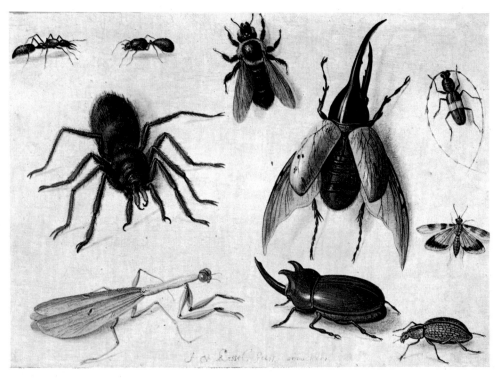

air, the earth, numbers or atoms, only led to a general interpretation of nature.

The Greeks did not consider this limitation as a failure: what they asked of a "true science" was principally to provide a total and rational understanding of reality. This attitude, which led them to undervalue the role of experience in the understanding of nature, was partly corrected by Aristotle in the fourth century BC. Besides writing a fundamental treatise on physics (which influenced scientific thought until the time of Galileo), this great thinker practised experimental research and dedicated himself to a study of biology (he described and classified some 500 creatures) and physiology, where he used the technique of dissection. In the same period, with Alexander the Great, Greek culture came into contact with that of the Orient and the sciences of astrology, alchemy and magic began to influence Greek rationality.

In the meantime, the cultural centre moved from Athens to Egypt, to Alexandria, where the study of optics, acoustics, geometry and astronomy (development of the geocentric model of the universe by Ptolemy) flourished, whilst with Eratosthenes the first geographers applied themselves to the problem of determining the shape and size of the earth. Notable also was the study of mechanics which, however, was generally directed towards the construction of war machines. An exception was Archimedes of Syracuse (the greatest physicist of antiquity) who, besides making fundamental discoveries in the field of mechanics (the laws of the

This illustration shows a seventeenth-century entomological plate. Entomologists are people who study insects.

lever and the concept of the centre of gravity), mathematics and hydraulics, dedicated himself to the design of a vast range of technological devices (the water screw which was a machine for raising water, the toothed wheel and tackle with moving pulleys) of obvious practical use in daily life.

From the Romans to the Arabs

In the meantime, however, the influence of the Orient grew stronger and the people tried to satisfy their own need for knowledge through those religions founded on ancient rites. All this certainly did not help to create a cultural environment which encouraged serious scientific development and the simultaneous rise of the Romans did not improve the situation. The Romans, in fact, were much more interested in the problems of social organization and preferred the applied sciences. Because of this, the Romans extracted from Greek science everything that was useful to them for navigation, the building of ports, aquaducts and roads and the design of war machines. Their practical sense led them to add their own original contributions, but regarding the natural sciences, they limited themselves mainly to compiling encyclopedias where knowledge was included with scant critical appraisal. In the first century AD, therefore, science thus embarked on a progressive decline.

In the first centuries of the Middle Ages, oppressed by invasions, wars and economic difficulties, the people of Europe forgot the ancient wisdom of the classical age and any knowledge of medicine, mathematics and geometry survived only in a few monasteries.

In the meantime in the seventh century AD, the Arabs conquered Arabia, Syria, Persia and Egypt and came into contact with the classical culture in the great libraries of Alexandria, Damascus and Baghdad. The classical texts were translated and assimilated by the Arabs who developed this knowledge and made original contributions. The two greatest mathematical achievements of the Arabs were treatises on arithmetic and algebra and these signalled the introduction into the Mediterranean area of the method by which today we write numbers and also the fundamental ideas of trigonometry which were learned from the Indian mathematicians.

Arab alchemists sought the elixir of long life and the "philosophers' stone" which would turn substances of low value into gold, and the numerous experiments which followed with this aim led to the isolation of various elements, the synthesis of new compounds and the acquisition of important new knowledge of chemical reactions. In this way, the experimental basis from which chemistry later sprang was formed.

After the year 1000, the first universities (communities of students and professors) began to be founded in Europe and the fierce theological disputes which developed there gradually revived the taste for discussion and logical reasoning. People were now less disposed to accept indiscriminately the traditional teachings. The rediscovery of the classical culture (which occurred through contact with the Arab world) led to a restoration of faith in reason and caused them to see nature as the environment in which man lived and on which he could exert his own influence.

From this new willingness to understand and, above all, to act, developed the need for knowledge. At first, science was still permeated with the ideas of alchemists, astrologers and magicians, but in the fourteenth century scientific thought was substantially freed from this influence, as the work of Leonardo da Vinci subsequently showed. The traditional concept of reality was superseded by the view of Copernicus that the sun was the centre of the universe and between the sixteenth and seventeenth centuries, with Galileo, it was already clear that in order to understand the laws governing a phenomenon it was necessary to formulate hypotheses, and to draw quantitative conclusions from them and test these by means of experiments.

Modern science

Towards the end of the seventeenth century, Isaac Newton expounded the first true, modern physical theory. He defined both the concepts he used (inertia, mass, force, acceleration) and the task of scientific research. He was not concerned with the intimate nature of things, but only to investigate how phenomena occurred. With Newton, the theory of physics attained the same level of rigour as the mathematical sciences and became a model for all the other sciences which had made considerable progress in the intervening period.

From the seventeenth century onwards, the spread of practical experimentation led to the invention of new measuring equipment, instruments of observation and their systematic use in scientific research. At the beginning of the nineteenth century, after the French revolution, there was a climate of great expectancy. Faced with the inability of the philosophers to reach definite conclusions, it seemed that the only way to understand creation was through science. This simplistic attitude was, however, shared by many great scientists who began to reflect on the real significance of the concepts they were using and asked themselves if it were permissible to consider a theory true just because it worked. The discovery that it is possible to have an infinite number of geometries besides those of Euclid increased this perplexity. An attitude of blind faith in scientific theories was common among the people, but many of those who had assisted in working these out considered them only as a particularly efficient method of co-ordinating what was known of natural phenomena. This attitude persisted, especially in twentieth-century physics. With the theory of relativity and quantum mechanics, physics could no longer rely on familiar concepts, but needed new ones of unusual significance and which could be apparently contradictory.

In order better to understand the development of scientific thought in the course of the last three centuries, we should look at physics because this is the experimental science which has reached the highest level of perfection during this period. We should also remember, however, the great progress made by other sciences (for example, biology) and the development of new disciplines such as psychology, sociology and anthropology.

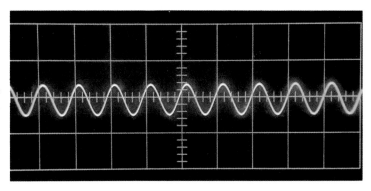

In recent years, science has made enormous progress with the aid of sophisticated apparatus. Above, a computer controls the culture of enzymes. Right, an oscilloscope records a sound wave. Below, a modern radar station.

Ships
Are the big sailing ships coming back?

The earliest pictures we have of ships are rock drawings made in Egypt about 6000 BC. They show vessels made from bundles of reeds, bound together and bent upwards to form the bow and the stern. By 3000 BC, the Egyptian reed boats were travelling across the Mediterranean to Crete and Lebanon. In 2900 BC, the Pharaoh Snofru sent forty ships to Phoenicia to buy cedar wood for shipbuilding. Two hundred years later, a sculptor carved a relief of an armed flotilla which the Pharaoh Sahure sent to harry Syria. This shows boats whose hulls were built by pegging together thick blocks of wood. Taut ropes gave further support. The ships had a mast and oars. Gradually, the Phoenicians took the lead in sea-faring, and it is believed that by the thirteenth century BC, their square-sailed boats had travelled as far as Britain.

In the shape of a fish

Phoenician ship design was taken up by the Greeks, the Etruscans and the Romans. The Greek triremes, with their three tiers of rowers, were swift warships but they could not carry much cargo because they had such large crews. Basically, they were no more than big rowing boats, and if we examine the line

Training ships (above, a Norwegian one) are generally sailing ships: for it is only by handling sails that one can become a skilled sailor. Below, a figurehead displayed in a museum in the Scilly Isles. These wood-sculpted figures (usually in the form of a woman) decorated the prows of ships in the olden days.

of the hull it is obvious that the designers took their inspiration from the shape of the fish.

But when the ancient ship-builders started to build real cargo ships, they had to forget the fish shape and develop new ones. Merchant ships became taller and fatter (they were a third or a quarter as wide as they were long), and they relied mainly on sails to help them along, thus reducing the number of oarsmen. The discovery of two Roman ships at the bottom of Lake Nemi in Latium, dating from the second century AD, has enabled their structure to be examined. These ships were just over seventy metres long.

The Roman ships were the ancestors of the Byzantine *dromon*, which was up to forty-five metres long, had one or two fighting towers and was rowed by a hundred or more men. From this the galley was to develop. The model for these warships (which had pointed rams on their bows, to ram into enemy ships) was still the same fish shape. But the merchants of the time continued to develop their cargo vessels and gradually a ship emerged with a more rounded shape, carvel-planked (smooth-sided), with two or three masts and "lateen" (triangular) sails. This type of vessel was

The fast-moving Phoenician war biremes had an elongated hull ending in a pointed beak at the bow. Between the oarsmen's benches, a narrow walkway ran down the centre of the ship. The square sail could be used only with a following wind.

called the *nef*.

Meanwhile, the influence was beginning to be felt of another kind of warship — the *drakkar* (or longship) which the Vikings used in the seas of northern Europe. This had an extremely elegant, long, tapering construction; it was open and lay low in the water, with overlapping planks.

Around AD 1200, came one of the most important developments in seafaring — the invention of the stern rudder. This was in general use by the end of the fourteenth century, and by the end of the fifteenth another revolution was taking place. Ships were becoming three-masted. The invention of "shrouds" during the Middle Ages was also extremely important, since it meant that a crosswind could be used to advantage.

However, it was to be some considerable time before oars disappeared altogether, because enough was still not known about all the possibilities offered by sails. It was the battle of Lepanto (in Greek waters in the Gulf of Patras) on 7 October 1571, between the fleets of the league of Christian states and the Turks, which finally demonstrated the superiority of sail and signalled the end for the large, oared vessels.

The galley family

The galley, with her crew of two or three hundred men, of whom two-thirds were rowers, is the head of a large family, which includes the larger galleass. By the seventeenth century, the largest galleasses were up to sixty metres long and fifteen wide; they had three masts and were completely decked, to make it easier to manoeuvre the sails. The banks of oarsmen were confined below decks, while above decks, ranged along the ship's sides, were the cannon, whose significance in battle had already been proved. The galleass had a very high stern, and in this resembled the galleon.

During the fourteenth and fifteenth centuries, the best features of Viking and Mediterranean sailing ships had merged in vessels known as carracks. The galleons were descended from these. They were massive ships, high in the water, with a wide cargo hold, numerous artillery pieces ranged on two or three decks, three or four masts but no oars at all. The two foremasts had all kinds of square sails, and the one or two astern usually had "lateen" sails.

Towards the middle of the seventeenth

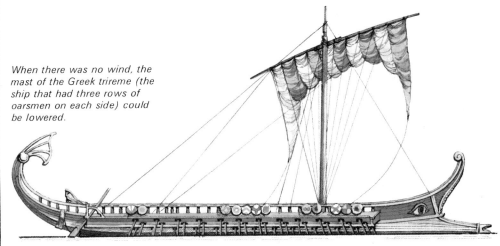

When there was no wind, the mast of the Greek trireme (the ship that had three rows of oarsmen on each side) could be lowered.

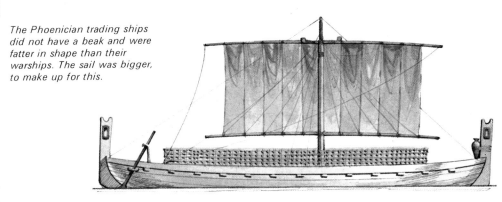

The Phoenician trading ships did not have a beak and were fatter in shape than their warships. The sail was bigger, to make up for this.

The Roman trireme had a gangplank for boarding enemy ships, allowing the soldiers to fight at sea exactly as they did on land.

This is the leader of the line of the Dukes of Savoy used at the Battle of Lepanto (7 October 1571). She had two masts with lateen (triangular) sails, and a low, slender hull.

century, the galleon gave birth to the full-rigged ship, a decided improvement both in shape and in proportions of hull, as well as in armament and sails. The general structure differed from that of the galleon mainly in that the superstructure was less high, in particular the "fore-castle" on the bow. The number of cannon varied, according to the ship's size, from around fifty to over a hundred. The famous *Victory*, the ship of the great British admiral Horatio Nelson (1758–1805), was armed with 102 guns.

A ship of this "class" (ships were now being divided into groups or classes, on the basis of armament or numbers of decks) had a crew of around 800 men and was about sixty metres long and seventeen metres wide. Displacement (the weight of the ship without cargo) was around the 2,000 tonne mark. Like all other ships of the time, the full-rigged ship had a hull made of oak wood (the common oak), while the masts and yards were of fir. To build one medium-sized full-rigged ship, many hundreds of top-grade tree-trunks were required.

Engines and steel

In the late eighteenth century and first decade of the nineteenth, various inventors, including John Fitch, William Symington and John Stevens were experimenting with steam-driven boats. However, it was an American, Robert Fulton, who designed the first commercially successful steam-driven vessels. The merchant marine rapidly went over to the new type of propulsion, which became widespread. In the military sphere, the sailing ship played out its final

In the sixteenth century, sails had almost completely replaced oars. The "jewel" of this period was the four-masted galleon the Henry Grâce à Dieu *(below), built by King Henry VIII of England in 1514, and rebuilt in 1536–9.*

scene with one last battle, the battle of Navarino in the Ionian Sea, which took place on 20 October 1827 between the Egyptian-Turkish fleet and the Anglo-Franco-Russian alliance (the Turkish fleet was destroyed). With the introduction of metal hulls and mechanical propulsion, naval architecture became one of the most important branches of engineering. Ship-building techniques underwent major changes as time went by. The latest revolution is that today the hull is assembled by putting together prefabricated sections which are hoisted into their correct positions by enormous cranes.

Methods of propulsion changed as quickly as methods of construction. Steam boilers were followed at the end of the nineteenth century by steam turbine engines. Early in the twentieth century, these were followed in their turn by the diesel engines of the motor vessels. After

(continued on page 62)

Above, a print records the famous Battle of the Nile, at Aboukir Bay, near Alexandria in Egypt, fought in 1798 between the English and French fleets. The English, under Lord Nelson, were victorious.

The drawing below shows the third-class Spanish vessel, the Santissima Madre, launched in 1778. Ships of that time were divided into groups, or classes, according to their number of cannons: those in the third class, for instance, carried between fifty and seventy and were the most useful in battle, since besides being obviously very well armed they were agile at manoeuvring.

Sailing ships reached their peak with the "clippers". These were agile, rapid brigs with very high masts which could attain amazing speeds. They were used on trans-oceanic trading routes, mainly for carrying expensive merchandise. They often had epic races to be the first to reach port and sell their cargoes at the highest price. The clippers first appeared in the United States at the end of the eighteenth century, but achieved their highest development in England. The only clipper that still survives is English – the Cutty Sark (left), launched in 1869. After ploughing the seas for more than fifty years, she was given to the British government and is now earning a well-earned rest as a museum-ship.

This is the Great Eastern, one of the first transatlantic steamships. Launched in 1858, she was designed by Brunel and built at Millwall. She had an iron-clad hull and auxiliary sails.

The transatlantic liner the Mauretania, holder for twenty-two years of the "Blue Riband", the record for the fastest crossing of the Atlantic on the northern route.

The Rex, one of the largest transatlantic liners in the Italian passenger fleet. She was launched in 1932 and took the "Blue Riband" the following year.

Six masts and a smokestack

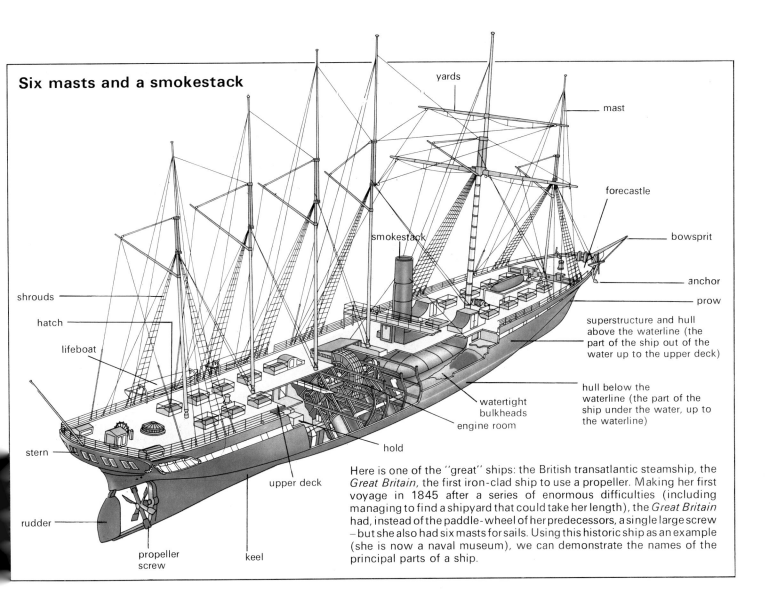

yards

mast

forecastle

bowsprit

anchor

prow

smokestack

superstructure and hull above the waterline (the part of the ship out of the water up to the upper deck)

shrouds

hatch

lifeboat

hull below the waterline (the part of the ship under the water, up to the waterline)

watertight bulkheads

engine room

stern

hold

upper deck

rudder

propeller screw

keel

Here is one of the "great" ships: the British transatlantic steamship, the *Great Britain*, the first iron-clad ship to use a propeller. Making her first voyage in 1845 after a series of enormous difficulties (including managing to find a shipyard that could take her length), the *Great Britain* had, instead of the paddle-wheel of her predecessors, a single large screw – but she also had six masts for sails. Using this historic ship as an example (she is now a naval museum), we can demonstrate the names of the principal parts of a ship.

Ships in modern naval fleets are very sophisticated. The Italian frigate the Lupo is equipped as an anti-submarine and missile-launching vessel, as a convoy escort ship and as an amphibious operations support ship. All the various weapons and equipment which she carries are computer-controlled.

One of the most advanced of merchant marine ships: the nuclear-powered Savannah.

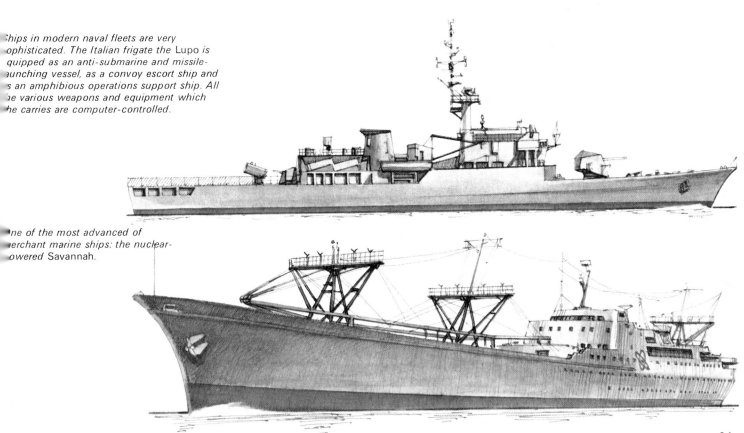

This cutaway of the United States ship the *Savannah* (1959) enables us to see the nuclear reactor installed in her. The *Savannah* was the first nuclear-powered merchant ship, but not the first overall: the submarine the *Nautilus* (also American) came earlier, as did the Russian icebreaker the *Lenin*. Another well-known and more sophisticated nuclear-powered merchant ship is the German *Otto Hahn*.

(continued from page 59)

the Second World War, came the gas turbine; and finally, the 1950s saw the launching of the first nuclear-powered merchant ship, the American *Savannah*.

The oil tanker is the largest

The huge progress made in civil aviation, particularly in the last twenty years, has meant the end of the "liner" for carrying passengers over long distances – and in particular it has meant the end of the transatlantic run which, in the hundred years of its life, had become ever more rapid, convenient and luxurious. Cruise liners have remained, however, and, of course, ferry-boats, which are capable of carrying cars too.

Once a ship reaches port, life on board does not stop. The time is used to carry out maintenance tasks. Our picture shows two sailors painting their ship's immense anchor.

Opposite page, centre, an Italian tanker ship; below left, a French shipyard; below right, a tug in the port of Genoa. This page, above, a ship being built at the La Spezia arsenal in Italy (military construction and repair shipyard). Right, the unusual equipment on board a French navy oceanographic research ship.

In the merchant shipping sector, we usually distinguish between "dry cargo" ships and tankers. The first include container-ships (where the goods are packed in standardized containers), barge-ships (with the cargo carried on motorized barges), bulk-carriers (for loose cargoes such as cereals or coal), ore-carriers (for minerals), and refrigerator and cement-carrying ships. Among the tankers (ships for liquid cargoes), the most common are the oil tankers, which recently have increased enormously in size: they can now be as large as 500,000 tonnes gross tonnage, more than 300 metres long, with engines totalling 50,000 horsepower. There are also tankers for carrying liquefied gases, like the methane tankers. "Working" vessels include tugs, icebreakers, large trawlers which also process the fish, whaling ships, cable-laying vessels, and dredgers which dredge up sand from the sea-bed.

As far as warships are concerned, those old monarchs, the battleships, have now disappeared. Their reign lasted from the Hampton Roads engagement (9 March 1862) to the battle of Okinawa (7 April 1945), when the magnificent Japanese ship, the *Yamato*, was sunk by aeroplanes without ever being able to open fire. Today's most important warship is the aircraft carrier, the appearance of which has meant the end of the large battleships with their powerful cannon (which have in their turn been overtaken by missiles).

With nuclear power, submarines too have become more efficient than they were at one time, while the torpedo vessels in use until the last war have more or less disappeared. Now we have frigates, light cruisers and destroyers, vessels specializing in carrying anti-ship and anti-aircraft missiles and helicopters hunting for submarines. Then there are landing craft, mine-layers, mine-sweepers, motor-vessels, hovercraft and what are known as "auxiliary" vessels, intended to back up and supply other ships.

And the ships of the future – what will they be like? The answer is surprising: they may be sailing ships. Designs are already under way, in America, Japan and Europe, for large sailing ships with four, five or six masts and enormous sails manoeuvred electronically, and requiring very small crews. They would sail almost as fast as the cargo ships of today, but with huge savings.

Work is also being done on other designs for ships that use wind energy, but not with sails: they have great high nets supporting huge bladed fans. The rotation of these blades is then transformed into motor energy for the propellers.

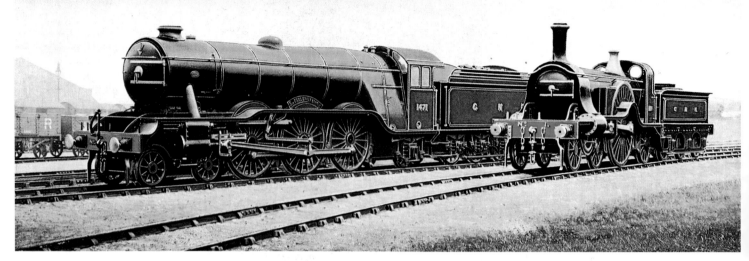

Trains
The power of locomotives

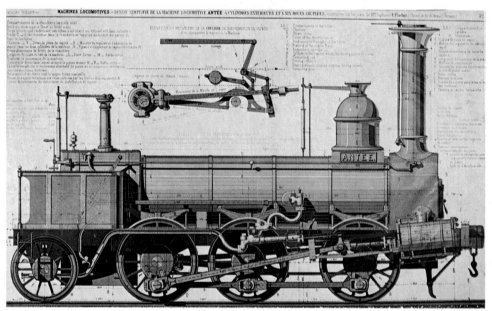

Trains were invented in Great Britain at the beginning of the nineteenth century. In 1803, Richard Trevithick built his first full-size steam engine at Coalbrookedale ironworks. He made a wager with the owner of a mine in Pen-y-Darren, South Wales that he could transport 10 tonnes of iron with no problems whatsoever with his steam engine. On 21 February 1804, his second steam engine left Abercynon with the load of iron as well as a passenger "coach" with seventy people. The whole route between Pen-y-Darren and Abercynon (about 16 kilomettes) was completed in four hours and Trevithick won the wager.

In spite of the success, the vast weight of the engine broke the rails, and the problem of supporting the weight of locomotives remained unsolved for several years. Trevithick was unable to perfect his engine and so demonstrate the obvious advantage that this new means of transport had over animal-drawn systems. This is why the invention of the train is often attributed to another Englishman, George Stephenson. During the following years, he succeeded in designing and building railway tracks, coaches and in particular locomotives that quickly ensured that the steam engines became a symbol of industrial progress.

Steam engines (on this page there are three British ones and a French one) were first used to transport passengers in 1825 and continued up to the beginning of the twentieth century when electrified lines became more common in Europe.

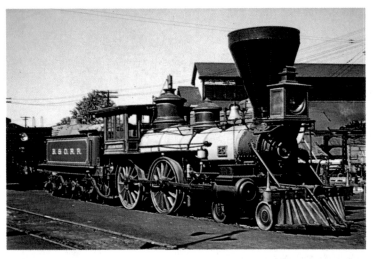

Top left, a steam engine of about 1840; it was used in the United States on the Baltimore-Ohio line which had been used ten years earlier by the first passenger train (animal-drawn). The picture clearly shows the typical front "cow-catcher" of the engine; it was used to get rid of any herds of animals on the line. Top right, a steam engine still in use in Java (Indonesia) for transporting passengers. The motor uses the steam twice, first in the high pressure cylinders and then in the low pressure cylinders. Above, two American steam engines used until the 1960s for transporting goods (left) and for station operations and sorting.

On 27 September 1825, Stephenson's "improved locomotive engine", *Locomotion*, hauled the train during the inaugural journey of the first real railway line in the world (between Darlington and Stockton) which was to be used for the transport of goods and passengers. Speeds of up to 24 kilometres an hour were reached. Four years later (1829), Stephenson won a competition, held by the directors of the Liverpool and Manchester Railway, with a new type of locomotive (the *Rocket*) which could travel up to 39 kilometres per hour. On 15 September 1830, the Liverpool and Manchester Railway was opened, the first to be operated entirely by steam.

An incredible development

Within the space of ten years, Great Britain passed from the 50 kilometres of the Liverpool to Manchester line to more than 2,000 kilometres of lines, including lines that were already operational and some under construction to link the most important centres of the country. The first railways in the United States were built in 1830, in France in 1832, in Belgium and Germany in 1835, in Russia in 1837, in Italy in 1839 and in Spain in 1848. Trains

were then introduced into countries as f[...] away as India in 1853, Australia in 185[...] Egypt in 1854, Argentina in 1857, Jap[...] in 1872 and China in 1876.

The development of railways was n[...] only due to the considerable improv[...] ment in the construction of locomotive[...] Trains were, in fact, the most obvio[...] result of the Industrial Revolution and th[...] growing success and importance [...] machines. They were also an essenti[...] part of a more rapid technical progres[...] steel plants had to work full time [...] produce thousands of kilometres of rai[...] new methods had to be invented to bui[...] bridges and tunnels quickly, to inst[...] rails, stations and appropriate syster[...] along the never-ending lines which oft[...] crossed areas of difficult access. Amon[...] the greatest ventures undertaken duri[...] that period by engineers, technicians a[...] workers, mention must be made of t[...] Mont Cenis and St. Gotthard tunnels; t[...] Simplon tunnel which allowed railwa[...] to cross the Alps; the 5,000-kilome[...] long trans-continental line in the Unit[...] States, between the Atlantic and Paci[...] coasts, which was inaugurated in 186[...] the highest line ever built in Peru whi[...] has 4,800 metres of tunnels and w[...]

How a modern electric locomotive works

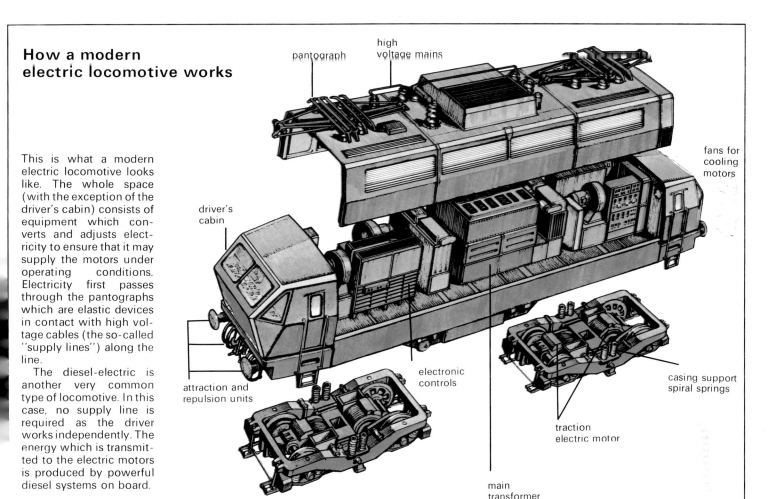

pantograph

high voltage mains

fans for cooling motors

driver's cabin

attraction and repulsion units

electronic controls

traction electric motor

casing support spiral springs

main transformer

This is what a modern electric locomotive looks like. The whole space (with the exception of the driver's cabin) consists of equipment which converts and adjusts electricity to ensure that it may supply the motors under operating conditions. Electricity first passes through the pantographs which are elastic devices in contact with high voltage cables (the so-called "supply lines") along the line.

The diesel-electric is another very common type of locomotive. In this case, no supply line is required as the driver works independently. The energy which is transmitted to the electric motors is produced by powerful diesel systems on board.

Left, a collection of electric and diesel-electric locomotives. The last one on the bottom right-hand side is Italian. The others are models currently used on railway lines in the United States.

constructed between 1870 and 1893; and, finally, the Trans-Siberian line between Moscow and Vladivostok, which was more than 9,000 kilometres long and was only completed at the beginning of the twentieth century.

Speed

Railways were not always welcomed with enthusiasm. Apart from the legendary attacks of Red Indians who considered trains as invading monsters used by "palefaces", there was also the hostility of those who believed that trains were a dangerous form of competition (from horse traders to stagecoach companies) and called them the most evil and dangerous creations of the machine age.

It must have been difficult, especially for those who lived far from the turmoil of large cities, to accept placidly the change from horse-drawn coaches to the shaking trains with their black locomotives driven by fire and belching smoke.

67

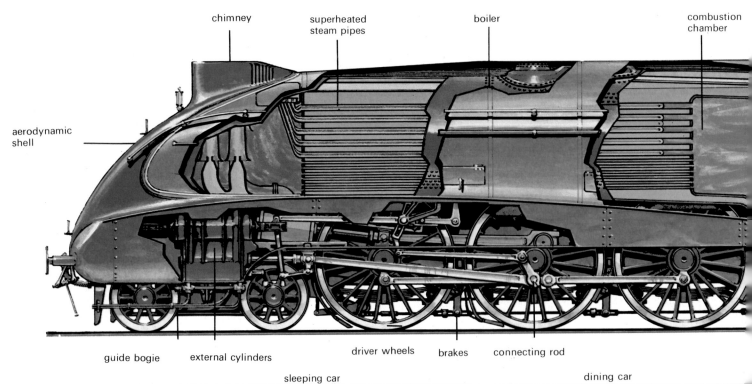

chimney

superheated
steam pipes

boiler

combustion
chamber

aerodynamic
shell

guide bogie external cylinders driver wheels brakes connecting rod

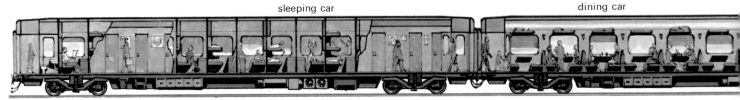

sleeping car dining car

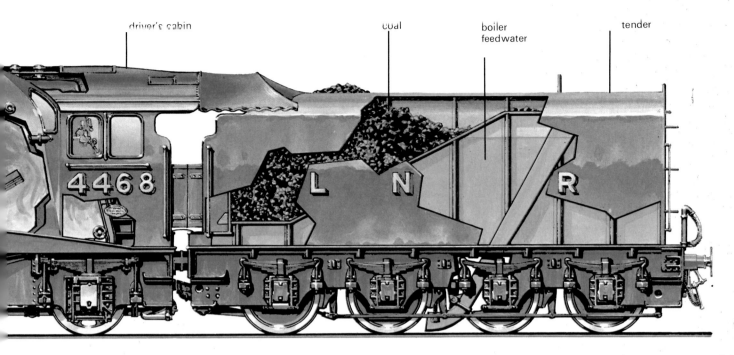

driver's cabin — coal — boiler feedwater — tender

4468

L N R

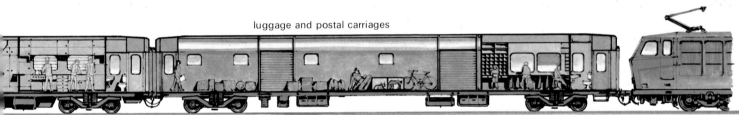

luggage and postal carriages

The two drawings above are a cross-section of one of the most advanced steam engines and of the carriages of a modern electric train. The steam engine is the famous British A4 Mallard which set the world speed record in 1938 by travelling at a speed of 203 kilometres per hour. This was the last incredible performance of the glorious steam engine as all steam engines were replaced by electric locomotives. However, there are very few locomotives which can travel at such high speed even today. The best results have been achieved by the French and Japanese railways. The picture on the left shows a TGV (high speed train and driver's cabin), which is an electric train connecting Paris and Lyon at an average speed of 260 kilometres per hour. It achieved the world record of 380 kilometres per hour in 1981 during a test run. The bottom left-hand picture shows a Japanese torpedo-shaped electric train.

In addition, there was the disturbing effect of speed. In 1850, trains were already travelling at more than 50 kilometres per hour and the fear of a disaster was by no means unfounded. When the first "sleeping cars" were brought in on the longer routes, passengers were advised to sleep with their shoes on, so that they were ready to jump up if an accident occurred. Some even claimed that by travelling at that speed there was a risk of suffocation because the air surged through the windows like a whirlwind.

However, the development of trains was so rapid that few fears or arguments had time to be noted. Locomotives became more and more powerful, the comfort and safety of passengers was improved with sprung carriages, buffers, covered sections between carriages, upholstered seats, toilets, lighting and heating.

These improvements, which at first were only available to first-class carriages, were gradually extended to the whole train. The railways gained universal approval and even farmers (who originally opposed them because they said that trains frightened their animals and prevented the cows from producing milk) finally accepted them.

Electric trains were introduced at the end of the nineteenth century. In 1881, the first public electric railway was started at Lichterfelde, near Berlin, and in 1883 the first part of Magnus Volk's electric railway was opened at Brighton. The City and South London Railway, opened in 1890, was the first electric underground railway. Initially, electric trains were used on shorter routes, for suburban or metropolitan railways in Berlin, Budapest, Paris and London, but by 1906 a number of electrified lines were operating all over Europe. Steam trains, however, continued to rule all over the world and it was not until the 1960s that they were completely replaced by diesel engines, electric-diesel engines and electric locomotives.

More recently high-speed passenger trains have increased in importance. In 1976 a long and expensive research programme resulted in the introduction of British Rail's High Speed Diesel Train (HST). The HST can reach speeds of 200 kilometres per hour, twice that achieved by the long distance steam trains. But research did not stop in 1976. British Rail has continued work on the Advanced Passenger Train (APT), which can reach speeds of 240 kilometres an hour, and first ran in December 1981.

Tunnels
How to dig through a mountain

Is it possible to build a tunnel right through the earth from one side to the other, a tunnel, for example, from Washington to Moscow? This extraordinary question fascinated an American scientist, the mathematician Paul Cooper. Having studied this imaginary tunnel, he declared that, according to his calculations, if a train were pushed into the tunnel at a sufficiently high speed, it could overcome gravity. Mr Cooper also stated that for such a futurist voyage to be successful, it would be necessary to

create a vacuum in the tunnel. The absence of air would then minimize friction. Next, a huge cooling system would have to be built in order to neutralize the great heat existing under the earth's crust.

All these problems are insuperable at present, even if use is made of the most sophisticated techniques available. For people who will be alive in the year 2000, the idea of a journey through the centre of the earth belongs to the realm of science fiction and Jules Verne.

Nevertheless, it is true that undertakings which at first seemed absurd and impossible have been achieved over the years. People have always tried to modify and dominate nature and have wanted to excavate and penetrate into the earth with their own hands, as well as break it up and reshape it. Defence and self-defence have been among the main aims of the many peoples and civilizations which have built trenches, including underground tunnels and even entire cities. The link with earth is very strong, almost instinctive.

The earth has always been considered as something good and positive. Many civilizations worshipped it in their rites as a bestower of life and a protector of precious things. This was the basic reason why huge underground structures were built. An example of this is provided by the Egyptians who excelled in the art of excavation. Some royal tombs were built in rock with intricate underground galleries, mazes of tunnels and rooms to guarantee eternal repose for the

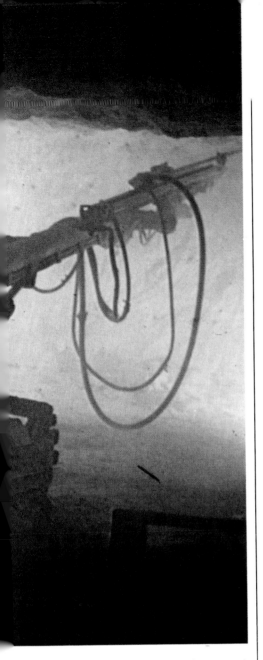

Past successes

Three illustrations of the history of tunnels. Above, a drill used for the construction of the Mont Cenis railway tunnel between France and Italy. The tunnel was opened in 1871 after thirteen years' work.

Left, a model of the timbering system with beams used for the Simplon tunnel (between Italy and Switzerland) which is almost twenty kilometres long. It consists of two galleries side by side. The first was inaugurated in 1906, the second in 1921.

Below, a section of a different type of tunnel, the London underground. The first section (Paddington to Farringdon Street) was opened in 1863. The underground passes under the Thames at various points.

pharaohs. Galleries were therefore used to protect the "next world" against outside dangers. For a similar reason, Christians buried their dead in catacombs which were excavated one on top of the other (up to seven, but usually four or five) and at a depth ranging between six and twenty metres below ground.

However, excavations were used mainly in civil engineering. Water was the basic reason for many undertakings. Egyptians dug deep channels which widened into chambers where jars full of water were stowed in the event of drought. Greeks and Romans built systems of pipes to convey water from rivers and lakes and to irrigate and drain dry areas.

The Greek historian, Herodotus, described the construction of an aqueduct on the island of Samos around 530 BC as "one of the greatest works to be seen in the Hellenic world". The conduit, which was used to collect rain water, had to cope with a hill. The architect, Eupalinos, who

was responsible for the works, solved the problem by having a gallery excavated at both ends at the same time.

The reasons for which tunnels are built nowadays include the overcoming of natural obstacles, the shortening of distances and more rapid communication systems. In fact, thanks to tunnels, roads can maintain specific characteristics of gradient and alignment both through mountains and under other roads, rivers or the sea. There are railway galleries with one or two railway tracks, whose width depends on the dimensions of railway carriages, the measurements of which have now been standardized. There are also road tunnels below river-beds or canals, where traffic regulations enforce very strict rules concerning time, speed and safety. These tunnels are linked to the main routes and vary in width depending on the number of lanes.

Hammer and chisel

These and other outstanding achievements in the history of tunnels are the more amazing when we consider the few primitive tools with which man tenaciously excavated through mountains and hills and under rivers and lakes. The fact that hammers and chisels were the tools which passed "from one hand to the other" gives some idea of the effort involved.

To make the manual work of the diggers easier, methods of crushing stones were invented. One of the oldest and most common methods was invented by the Egyptians and later used by the Greeks and Romans. A piece of rock was heated with fire and then immediately cooled with jets of water. The rock expanded and then contracted suddenly, crumbling as a result. However, this system filled the tunnel with smoke and steam, and the cooling process released dangerous fumes (mineral fumes containing sulphur or arsenic, which could kill). In fact, ancient civilizations were able to build underground structures largely because they had great numbers of slaves who could not protest about bad conditions or

danger to their lives. For example, to construct the 6 kilometre long aqueduct from Lake Fucino, the Roman emperor Claudius had to rely on about 30,000 men over a period of eleven years.

Excavation work in galleries changed completely with the use of explosives. They were first used in France during the eighteenth century and reduced construction time, although serious accidents occurred at first. A rational excavation system was used for the first time during the construction of the 6 kilometre tunnel of the Saint Quentin Canal in France in 1803 (opened in 1810). This system was based on an organized subdivision of the work. Engineers have since then established various excavation techniques some of which have taken the name of the country where they were created.

There are two basic methods: partial excavation, which is the oldest and which is used by the German and Belgian systems, and total excavation, which is typical of English and Austrian techniques. With partial excavation, timbering and lining follow each other for each element that makes up the excavation section or front. In other words, the teams first tackle the "roof" of the tunnel, then the "sides" and finally the main central part. With total excavation, the tunnel is dug, timbered and lined over a given length (ring) as a whole, with all three teams working at the same time.

The Mont Cenis tunnel

As a result of improved transport, trade between countries increased quite considerably during the nineteenth century. Railways shortened distances and put an end to many natural obstacles. However, by the middle of the century, the Alps, the most formidable rocky barrier in Europe, had still not been overcome. People travelling from France to Italy had to get off the train at Modane and continue by coach to an Italian railway station. Moreover, the alpine passes could not be used in winter. The idea of a tunnel linking Italy and France was first considered in

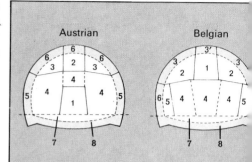

Excavation techniques and internal lining of a tunnel can vary by starting from the centre or sides and top or bottom. The choice can depend on the type of ground. These diagrams show the sequences (indicated by numbers) used in Austrian, Belgian, Italian and German systems.

1842, but the project seemed impossible. To excavate the tunnel through hard granite rock with nothing but explosives, hammers and chisels would have required a very large number of workers and taken at least half a century.

However, by the time the French and Italian authorities had agreed on a route and how the costs should be shared, the engineer, Germain Sommeiller, had perfected a pneumatic drill. So the first tunnel through the Alps, the Mont Cenis tunnel, was also the first built with the aid of compressed air drills. Excavations started on 31 August 1857 on the northern side of the Alps (Modane) and in October 1857 on the southern side (Bardonecchia). In 1860, machine drilling was introduced and the rate of progress improved from 15 metres to 81 metres a month. Throughout the excavation, two thousand men were used on each side. On Christmas Day of the year 1870, after thirteen years of uninterrupted work, the last section fell and the tunnel was opened to traffic two months later. The engineers' work was so precise that the difference in level between the two sides was only 30 centimetres and the difference in alignment only 45 centimetres, a record for those days.

The journey into the very heart of the mountain was a memorable experience for the first passengers. The ventilation system was rather rudimentary and passengers were almost "tortured". "The driver and the assistant wore gas masks and an inspector checked that all windows of the carriages were closed before the train entered the tunnel . . ." related a writer describing the journey in 1896. "Smoke got into the compartment

The construction site of one of the two parallel galleries which form the Gran Sasso tunnel.

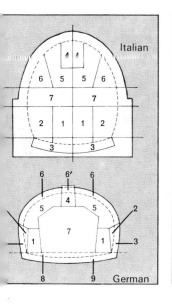

Italian

German

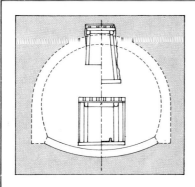
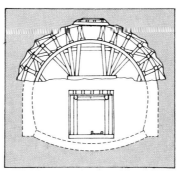
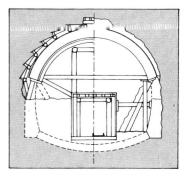

The three pictures above show in detail the main construction phases of a tunnel built using the so-called "mixed Belgian" system. Work starts by simultaneously excavating two separate small galleries one above the other. The top one is widened until the roof is formed, and is then reinforced with pillars and lined. The lower sides are then excavated and immediately propped and lined with stones or reinforced concrete.

through the narrow openings of the window to such an extent that we could not see each other. . . . The temperature continuously increased . . . and the smoke and noise produced by the engine were unbearable. When I got to the stage that I could not take it any more and that my only wish was to get out, daylight suddenly re-appeared."

The project

The layout of a tunnel is one of the most important elements in the success of its construction. First there must be topographical and geological surveys of the area. To avoid problems during the excavation and to prepare the techniques and materials to be used in construction, the engineers need detailed information on the composition of the ground and the presence of underground rivers. The route, which must generally be straight for long tunnels but may sometimes be curved or mixed, is marked on the map. Then the route level (altimetric profile) must be calculated with sufficient gradient to allow any infiltration of water to flow out. When this phase of the project is completed, work is carried out on site. Pits and openings are dug at various points of the route in order to use them as reference points during the excavation. In the case of mountain tunnels, the distance between the two ends is calculated, together with the difference in level, which is corrected on the basis of triangulations and geometric calculations.

The weary work of drilling, removal of rock and lining of the walls is now fully automatic. Nowadays all machines (drills, mechanical shovels, conveyor belts, systems for lining the walls with prefabricated materials) are carried together in a truck which acts as a mobile site.

Main railway and road tunnels

name	type	country	length in km	year in which it was opened
Dai-shimizu	railway	Japan	22.17	1979
Simplon II	railway	Italy-Switzerland	19.82	1921
Simplon I	railway	Italy-Switzerland	19.80	1906
Shin-Kanmon	railway	Japan	18.68	1975
Bologna-Florence	railway	Italy	18.50	1931
St. Gothard	road	Switzerland	16.30	1978
Fréjus	road	Italy-France	16.10	1980
Henderson	railway	USA	15.80	1975
St. Gothard	railway	Switzerland	14.90	1882
Lötschberg	railway	Switzerland	14.50	1913
Hokkuriku	railway	Japan	13.85	1962
Mont Cenis	railway	Italy-France	13.60	1871
Cascade Range	railway	USA	12.52	1929
Mont Blanc	road	Italy-France	11.69	1965
Arlberg	railway	Austria	10.27	1884
St. Bernadine	road	Switzerland	6.60	1967
Great St. Bernard	road	Italy-Switzerland	5.81	1964
Viella	road	Spain	4.96	1948
Kanmon	road	Japan	3.52	1958
Mersey river	road	Liverpool (GB)	3.36	1934
Holland	road	New York (USA)	2.88	1956

Food, Health and Welfare

Farming
The good earth

The history of farming ranges from the invention of the hoe to the invention of machines which are able to harvest cherries. Nowadays machinery and technology are essential to agriculture, for by the year 2000 the earth may have to feed almost seven thousand million people.

For about a million years, man lived by hunting, fishing and from the plants and fruits which grew wild. Only after centuries of effort did there finally emerge a new, revolutionary relationship between man and the land. Man learned that it was possible to produce food by cultivating plants and domesticating animals.

The earliest form of agriculture, which was very primitive, began in Asia Minor ten thousand years ago and seems to have been practised mostly by women, while the men continued to devote themselves to hunting. From the more fertile valleys of Palestine, from Syria and from southern Turkey, where the archaeological remains of the first rural villages have been found, agriculture spread along the valleys of the Tigris and the Euphrates in Mesopotamia and the Nile in Egypt. From here it arrived in Mediterranean Europe and, still later, between 4000 and 2000 BC, in central and northern Europe.

The first instrument for working the land was a simple stick sharpened at one end. This stick was the ancestor of the mattock, pick, spade and fork. The invention of the hoe was a great step forward. Another, more than three thousand years before the birth of Christ, was the plough, the first real agricultural machine. It was extremely simple in design, made of hard wood and in two parts: one part cut into the ground and the peasant held the other in his hands. Later the plough was pulled by oxen and buffaloes, at first harnessed by the horns and later attached to a yoke.

The plough: how it works

Primitive ploughs (left) were made of wood, and consisted only of a handle with one or two grips to steer by, of a beam to attach the draught animals to and of a share to break the earth. Later ploughs were made of iron and became more elaborate: the lead share turns the sod, the coulter cuts the ground vertically, the share proper cuts it horizontally and lastly the blade turns the sod to one side.

handle
beam
share
blade
share
coulter   lead share

Alternation and rotation of crops

The Greeks used the technique of alternation of crops to remedy the poverty of their own stony land. For example, a field was put down to grain one year and grass the next, and this rest period allowed the land to recover its fertility.

Another technique was the rotation of fields, which consisted of dividing a field into two parts, sowing a crop in one and leaving the other to rest. The uncultivated part is called fallow land, and is sown the following year when the first is left fallow. This system was passed on by the Greeks to the Romans who in turn spread it throughout the Roman Empire together with other farming techniques they evolved, such as pruning, manuring and the grafting of plants.

A more economical system of crop rotation which allows more land to be cultivated, came into use in central Europe at the end of the seventh century AD. It was triennial rotation or "three-field rotation". This method consists of

Even the soil becomes tired and worn out

In the meantime, man began to realize the importance of keeping his land fertile by applying manure. In early times, farmers had had to abandon their fields after only two or three harvests, because the land had become impoverished. They tried to restore fertility to the soil by allowing it to rest, either leaving the natural vegetation to grow or else growing different crops, for example pulses such as peas and beans. About 2000 BC, animal dung began to be used and became very valuable. Soon other materials such as compost, ground bones, wood ash, dried blood and fish were also used to enrich the soil. The big advance in the nineteenth century came when chemical fertilizers were discovered. Their use today ensures that the fertility of the land is easily maintained and increased.

There exist, however, types of land which are naturally fertile. In particular the valley of the Nile and the valleys of the Tigris and the Euphrates influenced early civilizations tremendously. The richness of that land gave rise to the splendid Egyptian and Mesopotamian civilizations. The grain produced in Egypt was of the best quality, as seeds found in archaeological excavations show, and belonged to the same species which is still grown today. In Mesopotamia, a large part of the splendid barley harvests was put aside for fermentation and an alcoholic drink very similar to beer was made.

dividing the land into three portions: in the first cereals are sown in autumn, in the second pulses are planted in the spring while the third is allowed to lie fallow. The following year, the cereals go in the second field which has been enriched by the ploughing-in of the pulses, the pulses are grown in the fallow field, while the field which produced cereals is left uncultivated.

The introduction of new fruits

From the ninth century onwards, the Arabs introduced new plants from the East and Africa, among them rice and citrus fruit, into the countries they conquered. They spread the cultivation of sugar cane throughout northern Africa and Europe at the same time as the Chinese were taking it to Java and the

Three types of cultivation: plains (right) are suitable for almost all types of crop; hillsides (below right) are sometimes converted into a series of terraces. To grow rice (below left) the fields must periodically be flooded.

Wheat above all else

The cultivated lands of the world cover about 1,500 million hectares (a hectare is 10,000 square metres). The figures given below (in millions of quintals: one quintal is 100 kilograms) are for 1977 and give the total world harvests for some of the most important crops.

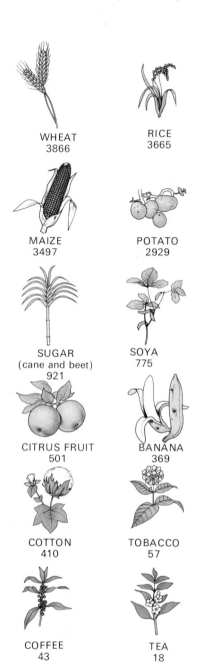

WHEAT 3866	RICE 3665
MAIZE 3497	POTATO 2929
SUGAR (cane and beet) 921	SOYA 775
CITRUS FRUIT 501	BANANA 369
COTTON 410	TOBACCO 57
COFFEE 43	TEA 18

The most abundant crop is wheat: the country which produces most of it is the Soviet Union (920 million quintals) followed by the United States (550 million). In the case of rice, China is top with more than a thousand million quintals.

Above, a combine harvester in a field of cereal. Below, a pea-vining machine for harvesting peas (left) and another machine for hulling grains of sweet-corn. Many agricultural jobs are by now done by machine: from ploughing to seed drilling, from manuring to harvesting. In the most developed areas, the wheels and belts of tractors have completely replaced draught animals in the fields.

Philippines. Columbus took it to San Domingo in 1493 and from there it spread to Cuba and the other islands of the Caribbean. Cortés and other explorers carried it to Central and Southern America, and by 1600 raw sugar production in tropical America had become the largest industry in the world at that time.

After Columbus had reached America, other unknown plants arrived in Europe: maize (or sweet-corn), the potato, the tomato, cocoa and tobacco. Maize was for the American continent what corn has been for Europe and Asia, that is the principal source of nutriment. It grew wild in Mexico and the people there were eating it five thousand years before Christ. Later the Indians discovered that maize grew easily and ripened in less than two months, so they cultivated it. They prepared a type of bread with the maize or else they toasted the individual grains in the fire, rather as is done today with popcorn.

Maize was not popular with the Europeans who discovered America and they took it back to their native countries as cattle fodder. It was not until the end of the 1600s that the poorer people of some European countries began to eat flour made from sweet-corn. In Italy, for example, around Venice and in Lombardy, maize flour was, until a few decades ago, the staple food of the peasants, and eaten instead of bread which was reserved for the rich, or for feast days.

The potato was introduced into Europe in the second half of the sixteenth century. It had a high nutritional value and produced a good yield and within one hundred years it had become a major crop in Ireland. Its popularity spread and it was widely grown in Europe, especially in Germany and the west of England. Today it is one of the eight main food crops of the world.

Like maize, the tomato also reached Europe from Mexico. The first variety was yellow, but by the end of the sixteenth century both red and yellow varieties were being grown in England, Spain, Italy and France. The first record of its cultivation in the United States is in 1781.

What is monoculture?

In America the European colonists laid out immense plantations where, with the cheap labour of millions of black slaves imported from Africa, they grew sugar-cane, cotton, tobacco and coffee. This was the beginning of monoculture, that is agriculture specializing in the production of one particular crop. To succeed it needed a lively international trade, with

The rearing of animals

The Romans word for money was *pecunia*, which comes from *pecus*, that is livestock: to them, obviously, nothing was more precious than their flocks. The raising of cattle, horses, pigs, sheep or chickens brought wealth and well-being to many people. From prehistoric time, man understood that by raising animals (as distinct from merely hunting them) he could obtain meat as food, skins as clothing and even help in his work in the fields.

Today stock-raising is done in different ways: firstly free grazing which is widespread in the less prosperous countries where only enough animals to satisfy the needs of a small community are reared. Then there is stock-rearing linked with the growing of crops, where, for example, forage for the animals may be obtained from the fields lying fallow. Lastly, there is intensive or industrial stock-rearing, which uses the most modern techniques. Chickens, for example, are kept in enormous sheds illuminated day and night to ensure that they sleep little and eat a great deal so that they produce as many eggs as possible. Modern intensive stock-raising is no longer linked to agriculture, but it is supported by many specialized industries: the chemical industry which produces special types of feed, heavy engineering which produces the machinery (such as incubators) and lastly the food industry which receives the products (meat and eggs) ready for sale.

POULTRY
6,961,564,000 head
UK: 120,264,000

CATTLE
1,212,017,000
UK: 13,534,000

SHEEP
1,083,954,000
UK: 29,967,000

PIGS
763,461,000
UK: 7,873,000

HORSES
61,830,000
UK: 140,000

one country buying from another the things which it did not produce itself. This was different from the attitude in medieval times, when communities tried to produce everything they needed, and commerce with the outside world was reduced to a minimum.

The mid-eighteenth to the mid-nineteenth century, the time of inventions and of the Industrial Revolution in Europe, brought profound changes to agriculture too. Industry was developing and needed more labour, so the farming population was progressively reduced, even though this made it increasingly difficult to produce enough food for the ever-growing population. For centuries, the countryside had been tilled using roughly the same methods as those in the days of the Roman Empire, such as the practice of leaving land to lie fallow. Now the land had to yield more. The moment of change had arrived; all the land was about to be exploited. Crop rotation was adopted on a large scale and fertility was maintained both by natural manuring and above all by artificial fertilizers which began to be produced by the newly formed chemical industry.

The new agriculture

The development of agricultural machinery is an example of the collaboration between industry and agriculture. From the middle of the eighteenth century onwards, mechanical scythes, seed drills and reapers drawn by horses came into use. In about 1850, steam engines were introduced as stationary power units to take the place of the treadmills worked by animals. Later in the nineteenth century, self-propelled steam engines were used to operate grain-threshing machines and other stationary farm machines such as corn husker-shredders and shellers. Farm mechanization has become even more important during the twentieth century, with the introduction of the internal-combustion engine tractor, the development of hydraulic-control equipment and the use of electricity for such operations as the automatic feeding of livestock.

The chemical industry has also revolutionized the agricultural world during the last hundred years. The fertilizers it produces provide every type of land with the nutrition it needs; the insecticides control pests; the weed-killers free the land from the many different weeds which infest it.

Modern technology offers much to help the modern farmer: tractors which can plough the land very deep; new systems of irrigation, including plants for the de-salination of sea-water; selected crop-strains more resistant to disease and harsh climate; machines which can perform almost all the agricultural operations, including the harvesting of fruit and vegetables.

As a result of these innovations the land produces much more than before and must continue to do so if it is to feed the seven thousand million people who may inhabit the world by the year 2000. However, the mechanization of agriculture has caused some problems. The use of excessive amounts of fertilizer or of certain pesticides, as well as the difficulty of disposing of waste from very large livestock operations, can cause serious pollution of our environment.

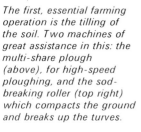

The first, essential farming operation is the tilling of the soil. Two machines of great assistance in this: the multi-share plough (above), for high-speed ploughing, and the sod-breaking roller (top right) which compacts the ground and breaks up the turves.

Nowadays machines are also used to harvest fruit. The centre photograph shows a "cherry-sucking" cannon which works like a dust collector. The bottom photograph shows a mobile gantry to lift people up to collect honey, safer and more comfortable than the ladder used in the old days.

Food
Carbohydrates, vitamins and minerals

Even while we sleep we use up energy: our body is like a machine perpetually in operation, but just any kind of "refuelling" is not enough.

The purpose of eating is to feed oneself, but a problem arises over the quantity and the quality of the food, whether one eats too much or too little, well or badly. If one does not eat, one does not live, as we all know. But a person may fall ill and die by eating too much as well as by eating too little or badly.

Statistics cannot show us how many people become ill through over-eating; but they can give some idea of how many are made ill or die through malnutrition. It is easier to establish this because the cause is frighteningly simple: in the under-developed countries, the poorest people cannot find enough to eat. It has been calculated that over 450 million people suffer severely from hunger. Every year, deaths from hunger amount to more than 4 million and of these, in India alone, one million children die. About one eighth of the population of the world, especially in Asia and Africa, suffer from hunger. Yet those who die "of hunger", do not die because they have no food at all, but because the absence of essential nutritive substances in their food has caused diseases which can only rarely be cured. Poor nutrition in childhood affects normal development and malnourished children are also less able to resist infections such as measles, which may kill the weakest.

One of the most terrible diseases, anaemia, is caused by lack of iron and insufficient quantities of red corpuscles in the blood and leads to fatigue and lethargy; kwashiorkor and marasmus are caused by a lack of protein; beri-beri by insufficient vitamin B; rickets by too little vitamin D; xerophthalmia by a shortage of vitamin A, and can lead to total blindness. These are difficult names, but we should try to remember that they are names for the hunger of the human race.

Food and air

Food, then, is essential. Without food, we would starve to death within six to twelve weeks. Our body demands care and if we wish to have the energy for walking, working, studying, playing or simply for living, we must first of all make sure that the body receives what it needs. To stay strong and in good working order, the body needs two things more than anything else: air and food.

Both are equally indispensable. The food we eat could not be transformed into energy without the help of the oxygen which we breathe from the air. This transformation is made possible by the process of digestion: the various substances which make up the food, that is proteins (meat, fish, eggs, milk and cheese), starches (bread, potatoes, rice and pasta), sugars (sweet things), fats (butter, margarine, lard and oil), vitamins, mineral salts and, of course, water, are absorbed into the blood and circulated to the organs of the body. The oxygen in the air is inhaled, absorbed into the blood supply and distributed to the various

This eighteenth-century painting shows a huge banqueting table in the house of a Venetian nobleman. At that time, the aristocracy held sumptuous meals for hundreds of guests who were served at table by platoons of footmen for hours on end.

Foods and styles of eating vary from country to country. They depend on local resources, climate, differences of culture and tradition and religion. Here are some examples: Indians, Iraqis and Argentinians (photograph above); Eskimos (left) and Chinese (below).

organs. When the two meet, they generate the heat and energy the body needs to grow or to replace its worn out parts, so that we can walk, work, study and play: in other words, live.

Nature prudently sets aside some of this energy as a form of saving. The organism draws on this saved energy when it needs it, for example when we are asleep, for even then, because of the unceasing activity of the respiratory muscles and the heart, energy continues to be consumed. This consumption is called basic metabolism. Its extent varies from one person to another, according to age, weight and brain-activity.

A good diet is always varied. A healthy person should eat some of everything. A sick person, on the other hand, requires a special diet, which meets his particular needs and excludes those items which the body cannot tolerate. Special diets are often recommended also for the elderly, athletes, expectant mothers and those who have been under great physical or mental strain. The dietician even advises students under stress of examinations to eat certain foods and avoid others. This shows that concern with what we eat is not only the responsibility of cooks, but also (and in some cases especially) of doctors.

Vitamins at work

Let us sit at the table and look at the food on our plate. Whatever it may be, tasteless or appetizing, exotic or ordinary, simple or elaborate, it consists of particular nutritive substances each of which has work to do in the interests of our well-being: potatoes with butter, steak and salad. The butter, as well as making the potatoes more appetizing, stimulates our digestive functions as all fats do, while the carbohydrates in the potatoes give mor strength to our muscles. The stea contains the vital, body-building pro teins: every day more than one millio cells die in the human body, but th proteins carefully rebuild them. The sala provides important vitamins, some o them very important indeed, to "con solidate" various parts of our body. Thes are also found in fruit where the natur; sugars work together in the ceaseles labour of "building" which is going o inside us.

Other substances play supportin roles: for example, the so-called miner; salts. Calcium, phosphorus and mag nesium are good for our teeth and fluorir in particular prevents teeth being eate away by dental decay. Calcium an potassium give vigour to our muscles; irc makes good blood. Besides these, there water: a person needs about three litre

What is gastronomy?

Gastronomy is the art of good eating – the rules, methods and customs of preparing food. It comes from two Greek words: *gaster*, which means stomach and *nomos* which means law, or perhaps *nomea* which means to lay down or establish standards. Gastronomy is also called the culinary art because in Latin *culina* means kitchen.

Not until the fifteenth century and the Renaissance did the gastronomic art begin to acquire importance in Europe. Before that, in the Middle Ages, the kitchen was still rudimentary. Whole carcases of wild boar and cattle were roasted on the spit, there were no dining-rooms as such in the castles and even the princesses ate with their hands and neither forks nor napkins were used. The scraps were thrown to the dogs who fought over them round the table. The left-overs went to the servants. Only in rare cases and in the most sophisticated courts were conditions a little better. All this shows that the great art of gastronomy is of fairly recent origin.

Primitive peoples have a very simple diet, based on the produce of their country, and what they can get from hunting and fishing. Above, two Dani women (New Guinea) engaged in cooking over an improvised brazier of leaves.

The photograph below shows a Bozo woman (Mali, in Africa) preparing her meagre daily food.

per day. Some of this is drunk and the rest is consumed with food.

On average, a person takes in more than 1,000 litres of water and eats 500 kilograms of food in one year. This seems a great deal, but the weight of the food alone does not give us a very good idea of its value, that is the amount of energy it provides. This is measured in special units, called calories. A calorie is the amount of heat required to raise one gram of water 1°C.

We "burn" more food when it is cold

The human body requires varying numbers of calories according to the work and conditions it has to cope with. A grown-up needs about 2,500 calories per day, but the requirement goes up if the person has a very tiring job, or lives in a cold climate. An Eskimo, for example, consumes more energy (more calories) than someone who lives in a temperate climate. This does not mean that he will have to eat more, but it does mean that he must choose those foods with a higher number of calories.

How can we know how many calories there are in a glass of milk or a bar of chocolate? These calculations can be made by a calorimeter or "heat pump", which is a container attached to a thermometer. When a small quantity of food and the right amount of oxygen are put into it at the same time, the ensuing reaction produces heat energy, which immediately registers on the thermometer. A rise of one degree means that one calorie has been produced.

That is how we can find out that a gram of fat produces nine calories and a gram of lean meat about four. In the same way, we learn that a hundred grams of bread corresponds to about 246 calories while an egg is worth ninety. From these figures, it is obviously essential to know the number of calories consumed during the day if we wish to lose or to put on weight: with a diet of cakes and sandwiches, that is sweets, starches and fats, we might well become obese – and we would almost certainly be ill.

Everyone has his preferences in food. Eating is not like taking medicine, and it cannot be claimed that all preferences are due to greed rather than bodily requirements. A small boy who eats bags of sweets may be obeying the demands of his body which needs sugar, but he may simply be a little glutton. However, it is sensible to eat the food we want and like: sitting down to a meal should be a pleasant, relaxing occasion.

Even a new-born baby, sucking his mother's milk, shows his satisfaction

sleeping	taking a shower	getting dressed	riding a bicycle	sitting down to study	walking	sitting down to eat	running	swimming
0 calories	**25** calories	**30** calories	**150** calories	**25** calories	**140** calories	**28** calories	**490** calories	**500** calories

  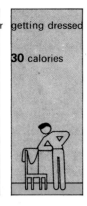      

Double consumption of energy

How much energy do we use in our everyday activities? The diagram shows the number of calories burned in an hour, but we have to add something to these figures. Even when we are doing nothing (for example, while we are asleep), the body needs a certain amount of energy to support the regular working of heart, brain and muscles, for breathing and digestion, and to make the blood circulate. This very important consumption is called "basic metabolism" and is not the same for everybody: it depends on weight, age and many other factors which vary from individual to individual. The basic metabolism of a boy is, very roughly, about 1,500 calories per day – about 60 calories per hour. Thus, in the course of one hour he will use up a total of 200 calories (140 for walking, plus 60 for metabolism).

clearly: it is not just the food which makes him content, but the protection and security provided by the proximity of his mother.

Food is a part of culture and human history. From the wedding feast to the business dinner, eating acquires various meanings: celebration, reunion, friendship and geniality. This has been so in every country and every age. It was a sign of good-will in many of the ancient civilizations for host and guests to break bread together. Today, if a friend calls, we offer him a cup of tea or coffee, or a drink – we may even invite him to a meal. The significance of the invitation remains the same.

Religions attribute certain values to food by recommending periodic fast days indicating that a moderate diet helps to ensure good health, and by giving some foods a symbolic value. Bread and wine are used in the Christian service of Holy Communion, and the apple has acquired great significance in the Old Testament story of the creation. From their food we may learn much of the history of a people, their habits and the geographical and economic conditions in their country. The Chinese eat a great deal of rice, not only because they like it, but mainly because their climate favours the cultivation of rice-fields.

Special foods are associated with particular festivities. We eat turkey, plum pudding and mince pies at Christmas, for example; hot cross buns are eaten on Good Friday, and often a special cake or biscuits are made for Easter.

The preservation of food

The increase in commerce and trading have led to better and more varied food and aroused a great interest in recipes from other countries. Transporting the food from one country to another, however, has brought problems in food-preservation which science has solved in different ways. The earliest methods were salting, smoking and dessication. Today, food can be refrigerated or deep-frozen and when it has thawed out, it regains most of its original freshness. Food can also be canned with added preservatives or dehydrated by removing all the water until just before use, when water is added.

Nowadays, most households have a refrigerator and "deep-freezers" are becoming even more common. These are particularly useful for those who produce their own vegetables, where the occasional "glut" of one kind of plant can be contained and it is possible to enjoy summer foods in the depths of winter.

Frozen foods are, too, a boon for the busy housewife. Convenience foods mean that she can perhaps go to work outside the home and still keep her family well and interestingly fed.

These problems are nothing compared with those which science must solve to support a growing world population. If the threat of hunger is to be removed, it is essential that the earth's resources should be increased and exploited, and that those areas, such as deserts, which were previously thought incapable of growing anything, should be made fertile and productive. Research is needed into new foods such as algae, which are rich in vitamins and mineral salts. Every avenue must be explored if people in all parts of the world are to be properly fed and survive into the future.

A nail and some water

Let us imagine ourselves "dismantling" the human body to see what it is made of. In a person weighing about seventy kilograms we find, amongst other things: twelve kilograms and a half of carbon (equivalent to the coal needed to run a stove for three days); one kilogram of calcium (enough to provide the mortar for a wall of ten bricks or to whitewash half a wall); seven hectograms of phosphorus and about two of sulphur (enough to make the tips for fourteen boxes of matches); a hectogram of sodium (a small packet of kitchen salt); four grams of iron (say, one of the small nails used by cobblers) and, in very small quantities, some other mineral substances. The main constituent of the human body is water: about fifty litres.

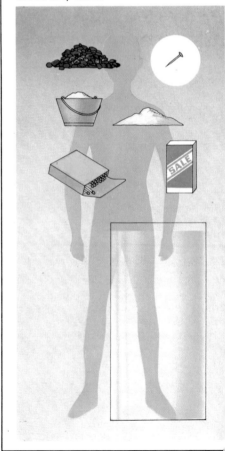

Health
Doing fine

The first thing you ask a friend when you meet him is, "How are you?" It is an important question, in fact one of the most important. "Well, thank goodness I've got my health!" we say when everything else is going badly. And the Latin saying *mens sana in corpore sano*, meaning "a healthy mind in a healthy body", has come down to us from Roman times. All the money in the world is of no use if your body is stricken with disease. Even a slight headache can ruin a whole day.

All the same, when we are fit and well, good health seems indestructible; we take for granted. We only think about it when something is wrong, when the body is not working properly or when it is growing old. This is a mistake – and leads to reversible errors. Every day we see the results of so-called "progress": smog, air and water pollution, adulteration of food and other such problems cause serious, sometimes extremely serious, illnesses. These are not chance accidents: they are the result of negligence and an unwillingness to pass laws restricting harmful practices.

We must all take direct, personal responsibility for our health and do what we can to protect it. Some illnesses are due to poor eating habits, smoking, too much alcohol, or overtaxing our mental and physical energies.

Prevention

Medicine steps in when the damage has already been done. It provides care and treatment and often cures. It would be far better, however, if health were constantly guarded and protected. There is much talk these days of preventive medicine which is basically an attempt to stop fit people from becoming ill. Even a child can practise "primary prevention" – by observing hygiene, washing thoroughly, not putting dirty hands or objects in his mouth, doing gymnastics and sports, and co-operating willingly at medical examinations and tests. "Secondary prevention", however, is the job of the expert, that is the doctor. It concerns people who are already unwell, but are at the beginning of their illness, before the symptoms have become very obvious. By a swift and accurate diagnosis, health can be restored before the illness grows too serious. It is to this second stage of preventive medicine that all the tests belong, the X-rays and the inquiries that are not connected to any particular disease but help the doctor to identify the danger in time and fight it.

"Tertiary prevention" is extremely significant from the social point of view, as it it deals with people who are already seriously ill. It involves all the tests and analyses that help to prevent the physical condition from deteriorating further, the illness becoming chronic or the patient permanently damaged. It is concerned only with the development of the illness and seeks to halt it at a tolerable point.

Health is, then, the aim of medicine, and the principal job of the health authorities is to prevent infectious diseases from spreading and causing epidemics. In many countries, vaccinations are given from childhood. They help to prevent serious contagious diseases, some of which have been almost wiped out for good. There are many other diseases which were once regarded as fatal but can now be treated and cured. In the last century, people died of tuberculosis, typhus, pneumonia; today, with modern cures, these and other diseases no longer arouse so much anxiety. The discovery of antibiotics (which are able to destroy bacteria) has lead to the control of infections – and for this we should be grateful to the great British scientist Alexander Fleming, who discovered penicillin in 1928. Antibiotics are chemical compounds and today most industrialized countries produce at least one antibiotic, and many produce several.

In every age, certain diseases are prevalent. There are still some today for which science has not yet been able to find definitive remedies. This is the challenge that faces research workers. We cannot know the forms or virulence of the diseases which may attack future generations. In past centuries, people died through lack of hygiene and drugs, and thus from infectious diseases spread by contagion. Today's main killers are heart attacks and cancer, two illnesses that may well be closely connected with the effects of our industrial civilization.

A delicate balance

"Ecology" is a word that has been much

Outdoor life and sport are especially helpful in keeping young people healthy. Mental health is just as important and this is encouraged by using our intelligence to the full and having a happy relationship with other people.

used recently. It is the name of the science that studies the relationship between living organisms (including man) and the environment. The health and well-being of all forms of life is affected by this relationship and by our respect for nature. If the balance of nature is changed, someone is responsible. It may be the industrialist who pollutes the river water with the waste products from his factory, or even the child who rips a plant out of the soil, preventing it from becoming a tree and helping to purify the air.

Health today depends on preventive measures and on health education to a far greater extent than it did in the past Correct attitudes and training must start a an early age. Periodic medical examinations (or check-ups), general tests regular dental appointments to keep th teeth in good order, are all essentia precautions. Alongside these is respec for one's body, which needs a regula routine, adequate sleep and nourishin food. Last, but not least, is the need t protect the nervous system from outsid aggression and excessive emotion: Psychosomatic illnesses (that is, wher the mental state affects physical health are on the increase everywhere. Ou civilization often strikes at the bod through the mind, causing irreparabl harm. The problem of the future is nc restricted to finding new drugs, but also t rescuing man from conditions of stres making medical advances available to a and restoring the balance of nature.

Medicine Major progress

A French miniature from the fourteenth century, taken from a manuscript on the work of Galen, a Greek physician who lived in Rome in the second century AD, and whose theories were followed for a thousand years.

Medicine is the study of diseases, how to cure them and how to prevent them in order to lengthen man's average life-span and increase his well-being. From the first definition, then, there is obviously a vast quantity of material to study. How could it be otherwise? Every person is different from every other and his well-being depends on varying conditions themselves determined by the place and time in which he lives, the work which he does and by many other factors. In that case, medicine becomes a real "science of man" and as such is exposed to continual "invasions of its territory", particularly by religion and philosophy. Besides, more and more often the doctor has to rely on the help of other scientists, experts in many varied disciplines. For example, biologists, chemists and psychologists work in a hospital while medical students study mathematics and physics as well as medicine at university. It is precisely to the collaboration of scholars working in such different fields that we owe the extraordinary possibilities opened up by modern medicine.

Help from technology

To diagnose a disease there is today a range of extremely complex equipment available to help us, such as X-ray machines, which can take photographs of the inside of the human body and pick out the diseased areas or in many cases even the specific disease which has afflicted the patient. It is also possible by using X-rays to see right through the skin and muscles of a person who is standing behind a screen so that only his skeleton appears on the screen. The X-rays can be taken in successive millimetre "slices" or planes right through the body until one obtains, after enlargement, a "complete picture" of the patient. This is called "serioscopy".

It is not just by radiology (the science which exploits the power of radiation) that one can look inside a sick person: there are also recent machines which produce a kind of photograph made up of dots which record how sound waves have been scattered and reflected in different ways by the different organs they encounter. The method is called "ultra-sonics" and it is possible, for example, by using it, to find out the sex of a baby at the end of the fourth month of pregnancy, five months before it is born, or to make sure even earlier that the baby has no deformities.

Optical instruments are so perfect that it is possible to film what is going on inside even the thinest veins and arteries by inserting long filaments ("optical fibres") finer than a human hair, but able nonetheless to transmit light and pictures. It is also possible to register the very tiny electro-magnetic discharges produced by heart and brain activity and make a graphical representation of them. The tracings which result from these investigations are called "electrocardiograms" and "electroencephalograms" respectively. Special devices have also been brought into use which work like extremely accurate thermometers and take the temperatures of different parts of the body, identifying those where the temperature is not as expected and which presumably correspond with a diseased area.

Progress in chemistry has made it possible, in addition, to make very detailed analyses of bodily secretions or of samples taken from the body by surgery. The level of perfection reached in electronic microscopes allows the samples under examination to be magnified thousands of times.

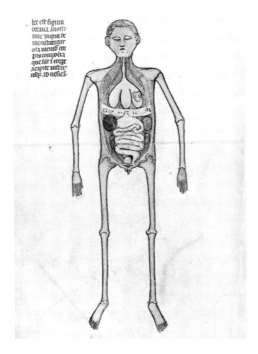
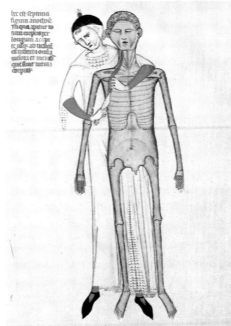

Far left and left, two curious illustrations from a book on medicine of 1345. Far left, a primitive anatomical diagram showing the internal organs; left, how to make an incision in the thorax.

With the aid of all this astounding equipment, diagnosis (the identification of the disease) by the doctor has become very much easier and more accurate than formerly. The doctor also has at his disposal instruments, not dreamed of even twenty years ago, to cure (or provide therapy for) the disease as soon as it has been diagnosed. Surgery, the branch of medicine which specializes in the removal or re-building of diseased or damaged organs, has made gigantic strides as a result of advances in other fields, for example in bio-engineering. This is the science which is concerned with designing and making surgical instruments and devices of ever-increasing ingenuity, capable of replacing the functions of heart, lungs or kidneys for long enough to repair the damaged organ and sometimes even to make it completely sound. Without this level of technical perfection, complicated and delicate operations like heart transplants and the implanting of "protheses" (that is man-made devices to do the work of the diseased organ or the organ to be taken out) could never have been attempted. The oldest form of transplant, without doubt, is blood transfusion: every hospital is equipped to transfer a donor's blood into the body of the patient who needs it.

Clinical medicine, which seeks to cure without resort to the scalpel, has also made great progress recently. It is closely allied to research and the pharmaceutical industry, which develops and produces new medicines.

Above right, an English print of the eighteenth century shows a physician examining the urine of a patient by looking at it against the light; below, the cures offered to a sick man in a drawing of 1480.

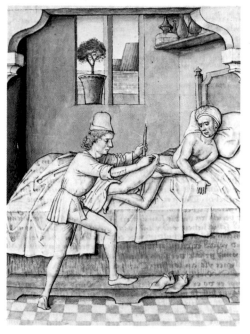

Before the diseases take hold

Despite the infinite resources of modern medicine, if someone contracts an ailment, whether serious or minor, the important thing is to identify it in time. The margin of error in diagnosis and in selection of the right treatment is still too great and this is often due to the fact that not all hospitals have the "advanced scientific" equipment we have been talking about and certainly doctors in general practice do not possess it.

An error in the initial diagnosis can be fatal, and a delay can have very grave consequences. In this fight against time, one branch of medicine has specialized in countering diseases before they appear: this is "preventive medicine", which recommends and sometimes, by legal sanction, enforces compliance with standards of hygiene and sanitation whose purpose is to prevent disease or to arrest it in good time. In many schools and places of employment, for example, students and staff have regular chest X-rays (to detect tuberculosis) and check-ups. Vaccination against certain diseases is strongly recommended. People who wish to travel to tropical countries are advised to have the necessary inoculations.

With the same aim of preventing disease, beef cattle and calves ear-marked for the abattoir are checked over by a veterinary surgeon and before the meat is sold it has to be certified as being free of any infection dangerous to man. Water supplies are periodically analysed and in the large towns the purity of the air is tested. The food industry has to conform to a series of measures concerning hygiene.

The beginning

Medicine has always been linked in two ways with the main requirement of every group of people, of whatever period or

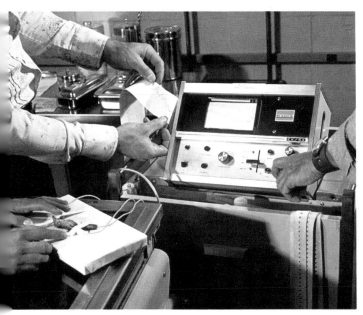

On this page, we see some electronic instruments used in a modern hospital. The application of recent technical discoveries in medicine has enabled surprising progress to be made in the space of a few decades. Computers are used to process patients' clinical data and contribute to the diagnosis of numerous diseases. Other electronic aids are the electroencephalograph, which detects the weak electrical currents produced in the brain, and the electrocardiograph, which registers similar currents from the heart.

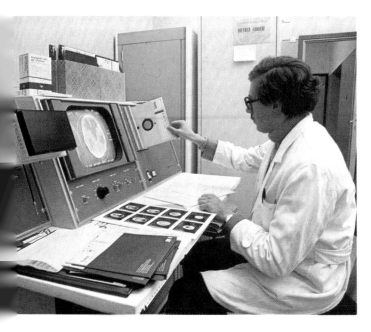

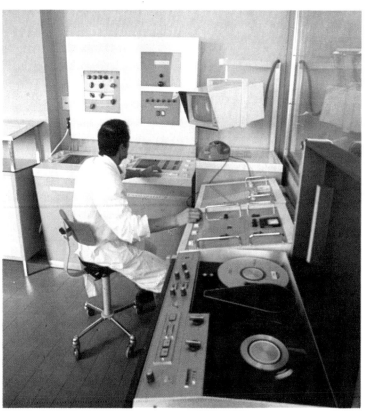

civilization – the preservation and reproduction of its own society. Archaeological excavations have revealed traces of surgical intervention, such as trepanning of the skull, from prehistoric times. Recently it has been established that the patients survived for some time after the operation. This surgery, however, performed by witch-doctors, was really an aspect of religious conviction, for the holes drilled in the skull were intended to allow the evil spirits responsible for the malady to escape.

Similar conceptions of medicine are still held today by some peoples whose development seems to have progressed little since the Stone Age. Strangely enough, some of their cures have been shown to be scientifically valid: for example, for centuries some South American tribes have prepared medicines from quichua bark, containing quinine, which is still used today to counter malaria. Examples of the extraordinary effectiveness of similar primitive cures, discovered by trial and error and passed on from generation to generation, are numerous even in the history of western medicine.

From Hippocrates to Fleming

The first medical research which can be called scientific dates back, however, to the classical Greeks and to Hippocrates in particular, founder of the school at Cos and father of modern medicine. Documents dealing with the medical art had been found from even earlier times. The great Babylonian code of Hammurabi (1700 BC) regulates medical activities and is so detailed that it lays down the payments that surgeons shall receive as well as their punishments in case of error. In the Egyptian *Papyrus Ebers* (1550 BC) over a thousand formulations, pieces of advice on hygiene and descriptions of types of surgery, are listed. Chinese medicine dates back to the earliest times of all and contains a great deal of extremely precise pharmacological information which is so sound that some of its medicines are still used today. Chinese medicine, however, did not allow, on religious grounds, the study of anatomy. Indian medicine was very advanced too, but documents about it are of a later date (fifth century) which suggests that it had been influenced by the Greek school.

Hippocrates was born on the Island of Cos in 460 BC and was the first to uphold the principle of observation. The doctor had to lie down beside the sick person, taking note of the symptoms (manifestations of the illness) with great accuracy. Hippocrates' descriptions of diseases are so precise that today's doctors have been

Homeopathic medicine

About two hundred years ago, at the end of the eighteenth century, a German physician, Samuel Hahnemann, had the idea of curing diseases with medicines which in a healthy person caused the same symptoms shown by the sick person. For example, if someone had a headache, Hahnemann gave him, in small doses naturally, medicine which would give a healthy person a headache.

Thus was homeopathy or homeopathic (from the Greek *Homoios*, like, and *pathos*, disease) medicine born, but a great deal of fierce opposition was aroused: there were some who held that these cures were not only hazardous, but totally pointless. Then it was discovered that Hahnemann, within limits, was right and so there are still today those who are cured by homeopathic methods.

able to identify the afflictions he cured: for example, tuberculosis, influenza and diphtheria. He wrote numerous theoretical works and the codex of medical practice, which to this day underlies the oath which is still taken at some universities by graduates in medicine: to use medical science for the benefit of the patient and not to reveal secrets learned while engaged on medical work. In the first century AD, there lived in Rome Aulus Cornelius Celsus, who made a compendium of Hippocratic teaching and other medical practice in his *De Medicina*. His work was rediscovered by the humanists and the modern medical terminology in use today has largely drawn its vocabulary from it.

The Greek Galen (second century AD) was the first to realize that the blood is contained in the arteries and veins. Many hundreds of years were to elapse before the English scientist, William Harvey (1578–1657), discovered that the blood actually circulated throughout the organism. After Galen, medicine had to endure a long period of stagnation. For eight centuries, in the western world, not only was no progress made, but, disregarding the teaching of Hippocrates, men believed that diseases might be caused by evil spirits punishing them for their bad deeds. As happened with many other disciplines, the task of ensuring that the results obtained in medicine during classical times were not lost, fell to the monks in the monasteries, who copied out the works of the classical writers for posterity.

In about the ninth century, the school at Salerno came into existence, but its principal fame dates from the tenth and

eleventh centuries. Scholars gathered there from near and far. One of the earliest was Constantine the African (c. 1020–87) who sought refuge there after years of wandering in the East. The school also produced a book, *Regimen Sanitatis Salernitanum*, which was written in verse by a number of people and has been translated into many languages.

During the Renaissance, studies of anatomy and the dissection of dead bodies began clandestinely, as they were actively opposed by the Church. The work of Leonardo da Vinci was very important. He produced accurate anatomical diagrams.

The invention of the microscope and the substantial improvements made to it later, allowed the identification of living organisms invisible to the naked eye, for example, amoebas, some of them responsible for disease. This opened up certain lines of enquiry and led to the discovery in the nineteenth century by the Frenchman Louis Pasteur that many diseases were caused by even smaller living organisms – the bacteria.

By the end of the preceding century, the Englishman Edward Jenner (1796) had brought into use a system of vaccination (against smallpox) but it was not until after Pasteur that more powerful agents were prepared.

An English surgeon, Joseph Lister (1827–1912), introduced chemical substances capable of killing bacteria to disinfect operating theatres, thus avoiding the infections which often broke out after operations. It was an American William Thomas Morton, who perfected systems of anaesthesia, using ether, a substance which sent the patient to sleep and so spared him the pain of the operation. Hygiene in hospitals improved rapidly and the role of the hospital nurse became even more important. In earlier times, nurses had been regarded as servants without any professional standing.

The most extraordinary invention, in pharmacology, comes from the present century: in 1928, the Scottish bacteriologist, Alexander Fleming, discovered penicillin. In 1945, with Lord Florey and Ernst Chain, he was awarded the Nobel Prize for medicine.

From then on, antibiotics capable of countering almost any infection were developed. During the Second World War, top priority was given to the commercial production of penicillin which therefore became widely available in a surprisingly short time. Science and technology work hand in hand with medicine and every day new inventions make the work of doctors easier.

Police investigation Looking for evidence

Much that we know about detectives comes from films and novels. We see the detectives checking every fact, often discovering the truth and thus the offender, from one particular detail. They patiently question people, follow them, spy on them, listen to them and observe their reactions. They can analyse appearances and perceive many other things that other people never notice. This is the romanticized portrait of most famous detectives of thrillers, whatever individual characteristics and idiosyncrasies they may possess, but detectives are real persons, professionals, people who can discover any sign of criminal activity. Unlike most heroes of thrillers, they can also go wrong.

The proof that a crime has taken place is called evidence. Sometimes it is very obvious, at others not so immediately apparent. Evidence may be an object such as a button found next to a dead body, footprints, a blade of grass still on the victim's clothes, lipstick on a glass, a cigarette end, a fingerprint, sand in the trouser turn-ups of a man who has been kidnapped and then killed.

The purpose of investigations is to identify and find the guilty persons and provide the authorities with evidence of their guilt. In fact, people do not always confess and provide sufficient evidence to convict those responsible for a crime. Moreover, it must be remembered that neither confessions nor evidence can be considered infallible. People can confess because they are afraid or because they want to protect someone else from the blame. Evidence from witnesses is often

Above, two pages of Cesare Lombroso's book Criminals in Relation to Anthropology, Criminal Law and Economic Factors. Lombroso was an Italian psychiatrist and criminologist of the last century. He maintained that he could identify a potential criminal through specific physical characteristics. Left and below, the Frenchman Louis-Adolphe Bertillon, one of the founders of the School of Anthropology in Paris, introduced the measurement of skulls and also analysed the relationship between crime and physical appearance. These theories have now been superseded.

affected by poor memory, too much imagination, dishonesty and other reasons. People used to say "evidence does not lie", but this is not completely true, because evidence is sometimes modified to cause confusion. A detective's task is therefore made more difficult by another problem: he has to be able to distinguish between real evidence and evidence that has been deliberately planted. He must analyse it and assess it.

Investigations are among the most important activities carried out by the police forces of every country. In 1923, the representatives of twenty nations met in Austria to discuss the problems facing them and the International Criminal Police commission (Interpol) was formed. The outbreak of the Second World War brought its activities to a standstill. After the war, however, an international conference was held in Brussels in June 1946 and the French government offered Interpol a headquarters in Paris to co-ordinate the various working methods for fighting crime and to encourage the exchange of information between countries. Since then Interpol has flourished and by the early 1960s ninety countries were represented.

Fingerprints

The first part of an investigation of a murder is a visit to the scene. The detective goes to the place where the crime was committed, collects all possible evidence, ensures that the body is photographed and examines every mark and detail. The visit must be made as quickly as possible after the crime to avoid any important evidence disappearing or becoming mixed up with evidence left at a later stage by other people. However, the detective must not come to the conclusion that an obvious piece of evidence is proof positive, for it cannot always be considered as indisputable proof of a person's responsibility. The first part of the investigation, which consists in gathering evidence, is followed by a second phase, which is just as important – the analysis of the evidence.

Fingerprints are one of the most revealing, as well as one of the most commonly used pieces of evidence. No two people have the same fingerprints. The impression made by the ridges on the end joints of the fingers and thumbs of every person is unique, and the arrangement of the ridges does not change as the person grows. Fingerprints cannot always be seen with the naked eye, but there are substances such as metallic powders and chemicals that can reveal them and enable police criminal labora-

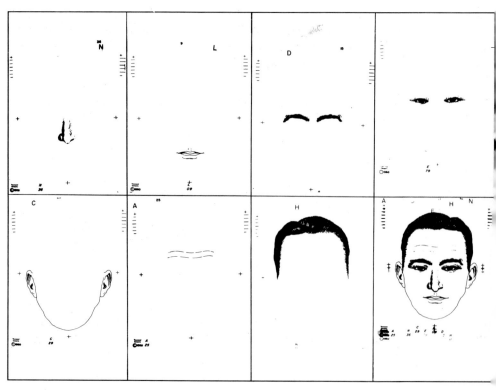

Above, the identikit is one of the most common means of identifying a person. The method consists of superimposing transparencies showing all facial details (nose, mouth and so on). Left, the card prepared by Bertillon on Vincenzo Perruggia, the man who stole the Mona Lisa. The card includes an identification photograph as well as fingerprints and physical features. This type of card is still used nowadays by modern detectives.

tory experts to "read" them, even if they are on surfaces that may appear unmarked. It must also be remembered that the same object may have been touched by many people, which means that the fingerprints are confused.

However, even if fingerprints are visible and unambiguous and can identify a particular person, they can only prove that the person was, at some stage, at the place of the crime; this is certainly a useful piece of information, but is not sufficiently decisive to identify the person responsible for the crime. Fingerprint cards are kept to record the prints of those convicted of a crime.

A murderer can leave many traces

behind him, as the readers of thrillers know. Without actually being aware of it, a criminal leaves an account of all his movements: a stain, a hair, the slight indentation made by his body on a settee, anything is sufficient to provide a clue. In this day and age and in the cities in which we live, the mark which is left behind is obviously not that of a savage on wet sand, and yet a footprint, the way in which a heel or sole is worn down, showing how a person walks, the shoe size, type of shoe all provide the detective with worthwhile information. Moreover, a footprint does not have to be on damp ground to be revealing. Information can even be obtained if it is on a carpet or a tiled floor and it is possible to tell whether the shoe was covered with mud, whether the murderer limped and whether the person was a woman, a man, an adult or a child. These are old methods, but even in our era of microphones, recorders and other electronic gadgets, they are still needed and used by detectives and criminal laboratory experts.

The marks left by criminals vary greatly. To remain on the subject of shoes: some years ago, the position of the slippers (which the victim usually left under the settee on which he sat comfortably watching television, and where he was later murdered) immediately showed that the murderer was a member of the family or a very close friend of the victim. Had the attacker been unknown to the murdered man, the latter would have had to get up and put on his slippers to open the door (and would have also probably switched off the television). Even before any hint was dropped or detail examined, the position of the slippers provided important evidence and reduced the search.

In other cases, as people who watch thrillers on television will know, cars can supply a great deal of information for the prosecution: wheels covered with mud, dents, marks left on tyres, drops of petrol from the tank. Sometimes the mark left by the teeth on fruit or a bun is sufficient to betray the guilty person. It may even be the victim who provides the prosecution with knowledge about the assailant. If there were a fight, for example, hair might be found under the victim's nails or the assailant might carry traces of evidence, such as blood stains. Some time ago, the soles of a suspect's shoes showed that he had been in the mill where the crime was committed, as they carried traces of flour. A very ordinary or even stupid circumstance can work against a criminal. For example, a murderer was found guilty because of his lice, as he had left some in the victim's room.

The experts

Laboratory equipment used by the police is extremely sophisticated and accounts of the detective's unaided talent and success are more fictional than real. Many people become involved in an investigation. There are even experts who determine the exact type of weapon used to fire a particular bullet, establishing the direction of the shot and measuring the distance from which the shot was fired.

Often the detective must also be able to distinguish between murder and suicide. If the victim is found holding the gun with which the shot was fired, the detective should not always accept what he sees and jump to the seemingly obvious

conclusion. The position of the body, the path taken by the bullet and many other factors must be taken into account, especially the death spasm, that is the muscular contraction of the hand which fired (or is thought to have fired) the shot. Murderers often try to make their crime look like a suicide by putting the weapon into the hand of their victim. Similarly, murderers have also attempted to make a premeditated crime appear as if it were due to an accidental shot. In these cases, too, the police must be able to determine the truth by looking at the weapon used for the crime.

There are many types of investigation and they are by no means always carried out because of a murder. Some people ask for an investigator (in this case private) to watch the activities of a wife or husband who has left home, or to identify the person responsible for revealing an industrial secret. Sometimes detectives have to deal with cleverly falsified documents with forged signatures, although no forger will ever succeed in tricking a good handwriting expert. The slightest correction, change to a number, superimposition or addition, can quickly be seen under a microscope and the ink used for the forgery will be clearly proved to be different from the original. Sometimes words have been rubbed out and then the detective must rely on an expert who is able to read what has been erased. It is also important to establish the type of erasure, that is whether the text was scraped off, rubbed out or washed off. An ultraviolet light positioned at a particular

Private detectives often co-operate with police detectives in solving a case. A well-known detective agency was formed in 1850 in Chicago by Allan Pinkerton (centre of photograph). Amongst his successes was the discovery of an attempt on President Lincoln's life by a Southerner.

angle can sometimes be sufficient to reveal the words that the forger wanted to remove. However it is usually necessary to resort to chemical methods and special photographic techniques such as infrared films to recover the text and detect the secret of the blank sheet.

Graphology is also used to establish whether someone's handwriting has been copied. By studying the general as well as individual features of the handwriting, the expert is able to determine whether the handwriting is original or not. In this case the shape of the letters as well as margins, spaces between words, thickness of the lines, dots and position of the lines, must be taken into account. The expert's methods are similar to those of the graphologist.

If an important document is found burnt, rolled up or very fragile, before it is touched it can be sprayed with a substance containing collodium and castor oil as this gives the paper a certain amount of flexibility. Without this treatment, the paper would dissolve into dust. Handling it is a very delicate operation; it must regain a certain amount of elasticity and then be pressed between two sheets of glass to be photographed.

Any discussion of investigation techniques can only be very approximate. A detective's course of action must include both foreseeing and following up every means to which a criminal can resort in order to avoid being identified and condemned. His activities include following people, telephone bugging, long-range photographs, surveillance and links of informers on which the outcome of an investigation often depends. Just as in the days of Sherlock Holmes, a detective must also be able to deal with secret codes and invisible ink. In order to ensure that they are not understood, criminals often prepare coded messages whose content appears harmless but which have a hidden meaning.

New investigation techniques can, in some cases, be compared to spying techniques. Thanks to special, sophisticated and miniaturized equipment, it is possible to check telephones, hide microphones in the most unlikely places, listen and take photographs at a distance and "trail" a car with a radio spy.

Eyewitnesses

What happens if the criminal was seen by a witness? It has often been said that evidence given by eyewitnesses must not always be considered as final proof and that frequently, and even in good faith, such witnesses are unsure and can be influenced.

If there is more than one witness, the

information they give can even be contradictory. Over the last few years, there has been much talk of the identikit. This is a method by which a suspect's face can be "reconstructed" on the basis of generic information. Witnesses may say that the criminal's face was "wide with a square jaw", the eyes "protruding", the nose "pointed and hooked", the mouth "small". A drawing is made corresponding to each of these descriptions and when the drawings are put together they should approximately reconstruct the suspect's face. The pages of newspapers often show one of these strange portraits, or identikits, which represent criminals' faces and it appears unlikely that the police will ever succeed in finding them with such confusing and unreal drawings. However, the method often seems to work.

In the past, too, details of the differences in the measurements of a person's body made it possible to catalogue individuals and therefore recognize criminals more quickly. In other words, standard identification data and distinguishing marks are not sufficient to identify a person and other information on his build, weight, the shape of his head and of his limbs is necessary in addition to a detailed description of his features, such as his forehead, eyes, nose, mouth and ears. Until recently it was often said that

"it is always the same persons who commit crimes", so giving a particular style to each criminal and determining a specific way of committing unlawful acts. This is no longer true, for too many robberies, kidnappings, thefts and other crimes are committed by people with no criminal records. However, the files which the police keep on persons who have been arrested prove to be of great help. Criminals can still be "old friends", in the same way as they are in thrillers. Investigations cannot always be based on experience and must progress with the times. The true detective can no longer be compared to Hercule Poirot, the famous detective created by Agatha Christie. Nowadays he belongs to a team who work together to discover the truth and, if possible, arrest whoever is responsible.

Modern investigation methods are based on the rapidity with which signals and information are obtained and examined. Electronic equipment, such as teleprinters and computers like those in the above photograph, has proved to be of great help. Fingerprints and other information on wanted persons can be transmitted from one police station to another by telephotocopier and teleprinters (left).

Private detectives do not work alone either. When a person is caught, scientific techniques take over, but the detective's human qualities are always necessary to avoid making a mistake. By working logically, or more simply by using common sense, errors must be eliminated to come to a definite conclusion with no loose ends.

An incredible crowd at Sao Paulo's stadium (Brazil).

Population
4,000 million people

The word "population" means any group of persons living in the same place, whether a country, city, village or the whole world. Nowadays it is possible to know what the population of an area is because of registry offices, which record births and deaths on a special register. Since ancient times, men have always wanted to know the number of persons living in the area to which they belonged, but the only means of finding out in those days was a census, that is a count of all persons that make up the population.

In fact, the desire for this knowledge did not arise from mere curiosity. The census was developed as a result of other problems. The administrators needed answers to such questions as "How many people can pay taxes?" or "How many men are there who are old enough to do their military service?" The problems are clearly practical. By counting the population, a sovereign was able to establish not only the number of subjects, but also their age, sex, financial situation and job. The word "census" derives from the Latin *censere* which means "to assess", so both the number of the population and the financial and physical conditions could be assessed.

Servius Tullius' censors

Even though it is not known when the first census was carried out, we can assume that it must have been at the same time as, or immediately after, the public organization of a country. Censuses are said to have been introduced in ancient Rome around 555 BC under Servius Tullius, the sixth King of Rome, who entrusted reliable people, known as "censors", with the task of counting and assessing the population. This exercise had to be repeated every five years. The most famous census of ancient times was that

95

World population increase: 1750 to 2000

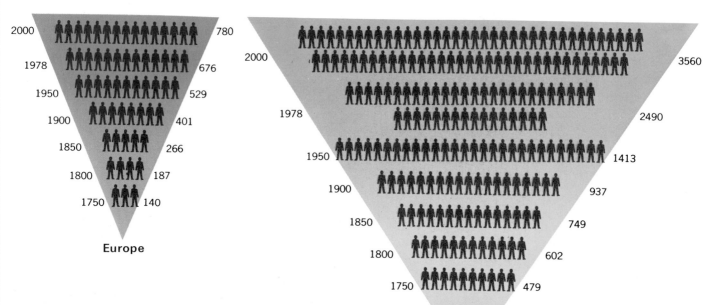

Europe

Year	Millions
2000	780
1978	676
1950	529
1900	401
1850	266
1800	187
1750	140

Asia

Year	Millions
2000	3560
1978	2490
1950	1413
1900	937
1850	749
1800	602
1750	479

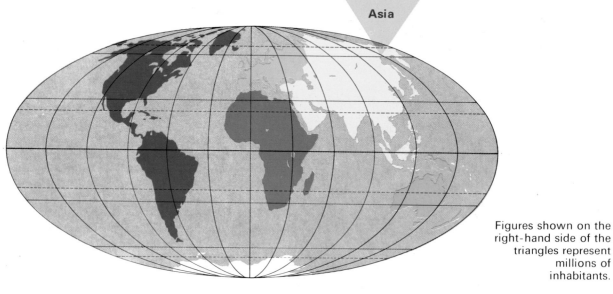

Figures shown on the right-hand side of the triangles represent millions of inhabitants.

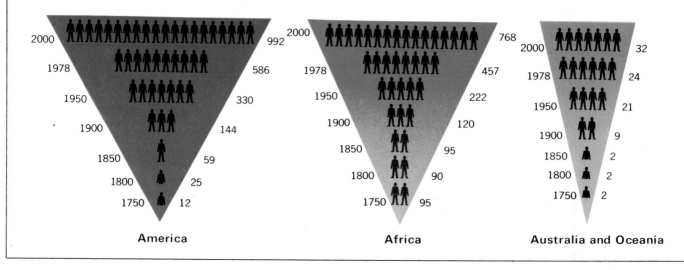

America

Year	Millions
2000	992
1978	586
1950	330
1900	144
1850	59
1800	25
1750	12

Africa

Year	Millions
2000	768
1978	457
1950	222
1900	120
1850	95
1800	90
1750	95

Australia and Oceania

Year	Millions
2000	32
1978	24
1950	21
1900	9
1850	2
1800	2
1750	2

ordered by Augustus in all Roman provinces. This led to people travelling from the country to the cities, so that the censors could count them. We all know the story of how Jesus was born while Joseph and Mary were on this journey.

During the confused and tormented years of the Middle Ages the efficient Roman organization was forgotten. Censuses were carried out haphazardly and depended on good will. Thousands of people were born and died without being officially registered. This happened everywhere; so much so, that the census completed in England under William the Conquerer at the beginning of the year 1086 is still nowadays considered to be an extremely important historical and social undertaking. As was the case with earlier censuses, the famous Domesday Book was ordered by William so that he could be sure he was collecting taxes from everyone possible.

It was only at the end of the eighteenth century that a census similar to our present one took place. In 1790, each federal state in America had to ensure that the number of deputies was proportional to the number of residents. This would have proved very difficult if the population in the area at that specific moment had not been counted. Therefore it became necessary to carry out a census at regular intervals. A census could indicate both any movement of the population and such personal characteristics as status, job, nationality, religion, etc. The first census in Great Britain was taken in 1801 and there has been one at ten-year intervals ever since, although it was not until 1920 that a law was passed to say this must be done.

Movements of population

The population must be considered not only from the social point of view, that is as part of an administrative and political system, but also from the geographical point of view. In fact, the study of geography would be meaningless if the presence of mankind on earth and the technical problems to which he gives rise were not taken into account. Geographical studies of land or sea have always helped man to make plans necessary for his survival. In fact, the

In South America (top left, the crowd in a city in Ecuador) the average density is generally low except in large cities where the number of inhabitants is very high. The same applies to Africa, where the population is mainly concentrated in coastal areas and along the Nile (top right, a market day on the Ivory Coast). On the next page another picture of a crowd, but in India this time. Asia has always been the most populated area on earth.

population is not a statistical entity, but a continuous movement; and not only, as we shall see, because of numerical changes over time, but also because of the tendency to migrate. For thousands of years, men have travelled from one country to another, hoping to find somewhere a heaven with fertile areas or land near the sea or rivers, full of fish.

These movements of population took place sometimes peacefully, or sometimes violently, with wars, invasions or massacres of previously established populations. In fact, rural migrations (those in search of lands providing ample fruit, fish and game) have always been accompanied by migrations forced on people by aggression and war. The continuous increase in the number of invasions in the Middle Ages meant that country people, isolated on their land, were continuously exposed to the risk of death. As a result, many peasants left their fields for inaccessible highlands. Here harvests were poor but the people were less vulnerable to attack and were sometimes under the protection of a powerful lord who had many weapons and other means of defence. This explains why some towns are situated in pleasant areas and others seem to have been "absurdly" created in inaccessible places, lacking agricultural wealth and often isolated. To these two reasons for population movement (search for fertile land and for a safer area), a third must be added: the search for work, this being the most important nowadays. With the beginning of the industrial age and the consequent wealth of large cities, many country people preferred to leave their fields and move to places where subsistence no longer depended upon the favours of seasons and the land. They sought a fixed wage and a well-organized economic and social system, capable of offering a better future to their children. This movement away from the land brought with it ever-increasing problems for agriculture, as well as a greater mixing of cultures and religions. The latter result can be seen very clearly in the United States, where the population consists of emigrants of a great many races, with only a small percentage of natives.

Population increase

Over the centuries, the world population has consistently increased, particularly during these last years, which have witnessed increases of 80 million people per year. This could lead to a world population of almost 7,000 million by the year 2000 and would have immense consequences for the world's food problems.

However, if we look back, we can see that even when the world population was much smaller, there were still food shortages. We can also see that men were constantly discovering new resources for human survival. In the past, not only were many areas still undiscovered, but the existing environment had not been suitably developed. It has been calculated that a thousand years ago there were only 340 million people on earth, but the amount of space they had around them did not, in any way, guarantee an easy life.

That population has now grown to over 4,000 million people. This constant increase, which was particularly rapid during some periods, is known as population increase. Demography is the science which studies the population and its numerical change over time, using statistical methods.

Why is our own period characterized by such a rapid population increase? The reason is simply the lengthening of man's life as a result of progress achieved in the fields of medicine and hygiene. Centuries ago people died at an age which is now considered young. At thirty, one was already old. As there were no vaccines or antibiotics, epidemics wiped out entire populations. The equilibrium between births and deaths depended on nature and not on the medical and hygienic measures which exist nowadays. Babies that are born now have a greater chance of survival. In the past (and by that we mean a few years ago) it was considered normal for a woman to give birth to ten or so children, but to see only two or three grow up, these being the strongest ones, those capable of resisting adverse environmental conditions and shortage of food. Still today, a healthy and well-fed population in the rich areas confronts 450 million people who suffer hunger in the poorer countries. Moreover, it is the poorest who have an unconscious desire to resist decimation by hunger, who are the most prolific, or in other words, who increase in number the most rapidly.

Surgery
Cutting to cure

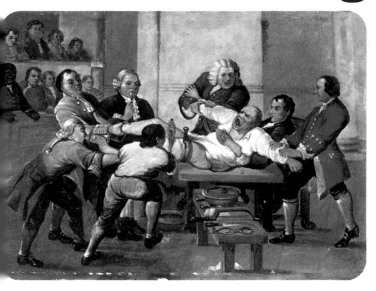

Trepanning or trephining is the oldest operation of which there is any trace. A hole was made in the patient's skull so that the demon causing the disease could escape. Trepanned skulls dating from prehistoric times have been found in Britain, France and other parts of Europe and Peru. But the origin of surgery is older. Even if we assume that trephination aimed to kill rather than cure the patient, it still required some degree of skill and ability which must have come from long-standing experience and tradition.

It was the discovery of metals that led to the first modern type of surgical instruments such as knives, scissors, forceps, hooks, needles, spatulas, scalpels and so on. These instruments were used by Assyrian, Babylonian, Phoenician, Egyptian, Indian and Jewish doctors. Surgery progressed at the same speed as anatomy and physiology, the sciences which deal with the structure of the human body on the one hand and with its functioning when healthy or ill on the other hand.

Four centuries before Christ, the medical students of the great Hippocrates in ancient Greece, already knew how to carry out perfect sutures (they could sew up wounds with great dexterity) and how quickly and safely to amputate an arm or a leg seriously injured during a fight. They also had a great deal of experience in plastic surgery (for example they re-built perfect noses for unlucky thieves who had them chopped off as punishment) and were not deterred by more complex operations such as eye operations (for

example, in the case of cataracts which obscured the eye's crystalline lens and could cause blindness). There were also, of course, the very common dental operations.

Street surgery

Ancient Romans learned about surgery from the Greeks and perfected their art, particularly in the field of surgical instruments. During the Middle Ages, much surgery was unfortunately in the hands of quacks and barbers who could manipulate razors with great skill and were therefore called upon to carry out bleedings (extraction of blood by incision of a vein in the arm), to remove abscesses as well as pull out teeth and so on. Doctors did not want to undertake such tasks for fear of "soiling their hands" as they considered surgery a craftman's job and not a science worthy of them. Quacks operated from town squares on market days and bank holidays, found a strategic point where they could draw the public's attention, assembled their stall and there carried out any type of "operation" amid the noise of trumpets, trombones and drums produced by their "assistants". These operations generally did more harm than good but were nevertheless highly paid.

It was centuries before surgery was again considered as a medical science. The Renaissance period, which saw the rebirth of art and literature, marked the triumph of science and, consequently, also that of medicine on a scientific basis.

Before anaesthetics were discovered, a great deal of courage was necessary to undergo an operation. All the patient had was a little alcohol to dull his senses and a strong team of nurses to hold him still (illustration on left). The dentist in the picture above was even less ceremonious and stood on the stomach of the unfortunate patient.

Later things improved. The picture below shows an operation during the First World War. There is little in common with today's operating theatres even though the nurses at least wore sterilized white gowns and rubber gloves.

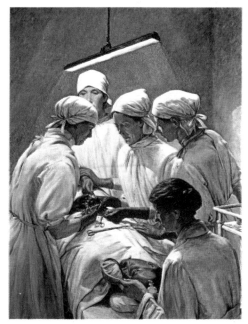

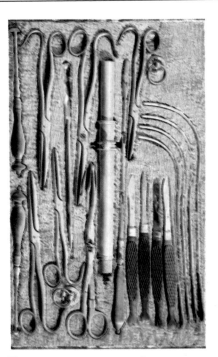

From razors to electro-surgical needles

At the end of the Middle Ages, the study of surgery was not regarded very highly. Barbers usually carried out operations which often took place in the open air. Surgery was re-established only in the eighteenth century and in 1800 the Corporation of Surgeons became the Royal College of Surgeons: medicine and surgery had at last been brought together.

Techniques and instruments have since progressed considerably. The picture above shows a surgical instrument box of the nineteenth century. Nowadays, instead of a barber's razor, surgeons use electro-surgical needles.

This new type of medicine included surgery, which was said to "depend on medicine's failures". For example, if a tumour could not be cured with drops, tablets, powder and syrups, it had to be removed. In this way, surgery, closely dependent on advanced medicine, was accepted as part of medical practice.

However, to guarantee a successful future for surgery, two basic achievements were necessary: on the one hand, elimination of pain and on the other, control of infection. When a patient undergoes an operation nowadays he knows that his pain will be controlled. In the old days, a patient needed great courage and willpower: first he was given an alcoholic drink, then forcibly held

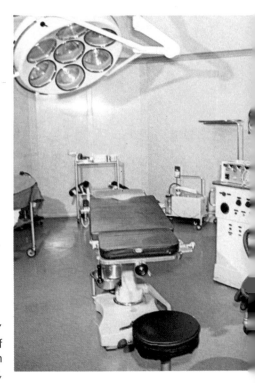

Right, a modern operating theatre. All the instruments are arranged for prompt and easy use. The air is sterile (it contains no bacteria) because special air filters prevent particles of more than one thousandth of a millimetre in diameter from getting through. All staff must wear sterilized clothes. The picture on the next page shows the clothes worn by a surgeon: first, a white coat and linen trousers and then a waterproof apron. He also wears a white cap, rubber boots and a gauze over his mouth and nose. Finally, he puts on a green overall and a pair of rubber gloves.

down by nurses and literally "tortured" while fully conscious. He was aware of everything that occurred and often screamed in the most excruciating way, making it extremely difficult for the surgeon to operate. The pain did not end with the operation and often lasted for weeks or months, made even worse by primitive medicines.

Controlling pain

Finally, anaesthetics to reduce and eliminate pain were discovered. Over one hundred years ago, an American dentist used ether for the first time when extracting a tooth on 30 September 1846. His name was William Morton and he should be remembered as one of the greatest benefactors of mankind, although he never benefited financially from his discovery and died in poverty. Ether is an anaesthetic and is capable of eliminating any feeling of pain in the same way as such substances as chloroform, barbituric acid and opiate (which derives from opium).

Nowadays a patient does not suffer during an operation because he is unconscious and so feels no pain. Moreover, his muscles are perfectly relaxed and this allows the surgeon to operate freely. Modern anaesthetics is a complex branch of medicine: it does not only induce unconsciousness and so remove suffering, but it also ensures that the vital functions of the body remain in perfect equilibrium both during and after the operation. In other words, anaesthetics are of the greatest assistance to the surgeon because they enable him to carry out longer and more complex operations such as organ transplants or delicate operations on the brain or heart, with a much higher degree of safety and confidence.

Infection

In spite of the success of anaesthetics there was still another enemy to overcome before surgery could be completely satisfactory. This was infection. The most skilled surgeons were often thwarted because wounds festered. In a few days, successful operation could be turned into a disaster by the wound becoming infected with pus and the septic condition spreading to the whole body. More than half of the patients died in this way and those who did survive under such conditions could consider it a miracle.

The reason why pus starts to form became obvious with the discovery of the first "miracle fighters". Infectious germs entered surgical wounds and poisoned them. To ensure that wounds stayed clean and healthy, all the germs causing the pus had to be destroyed. This is when the British surgeon, Joseph Lister, who had read of the research carried out by Louis Pasteur and many other contemporary bacteriologists, thought of antisepsis that is the control of sepsis or an infection and, even more, the cause of the infection. Microbes pollute the air in an operating theatre just as they do in any other room even if it is carefully cleaned. Immediately before an operation, Lister prepared a number of sprays. He filled them with disinfectant solution containing carbolic acid and told the nurses to spray the room with this during the entire course of the operation. The result was marvellous. After that, few wounds became infected and the death rate of post-operative patients dropped significantly.

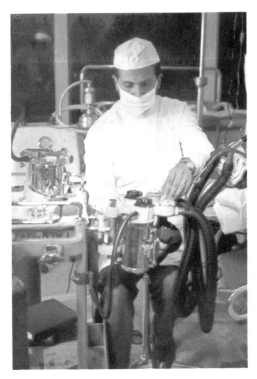

An important part in surgical operations is played by the anaesthetist (left) who must watch the patient throughout the operation.

Asepsis, that is the absence of septic matter in wounds, was achieved at a later date. This meant that the whole operating theatre, surgical instruments, doctors' and nurses' clothes and all other equipment were free from germs not only during but also before operations. Nowadays, the steam produced by special apparatus called autoclaves can sterilize all materials required during an operation. Very strong disinfectants are used to sterilize any part of the patient's skin which will be touched by the surgeon's hands and instruments.

More recently, antibiotics and chemo-therapeutics have been successfully used to achieve complete asepsis. In fact, microbes are not only attacked and destroyed outside the patient's body but also within his organism, blood, tissues and cells. Antibiotics and chemothe-apeutics (administered before, during and after an operation) therefore protect the patient in the safest and most thorough way.

Once the problems arising from the lack of anaesthetics and asepsis had been dealt with, surgeons were free to devote themselves to technically difficult tasks and tackle the most intricate operations. Until a few years ago, surgery meant actual surgical operations, that is the removal of a particular part of the patient's body. Today that is not always the case. By using new, sophisticated and const-ntly improving techniques, the surgeon uts, removes and operates on vital rgans that may be difficult to reach. He lso re-builds, re-moulds and transplants arts of the body that have become extensively damaged either by disease or during an accident.

"Repair" surgeons

Transplants include skin grafts, bone splinters, sections of blood vessels and complete organs like kidneys, hearts and lungs. The use of "inert" or artificial materials in "repair surgery" is becoming more and more widespread. Metal alloys and acrylic resins are used to replace unhealthy heart valves and to rebuild hip joints crippled as a result of a fracture or a degenerative disease such as arthritis. Synthetic fibre tubes are used to replace sections of arteries that have become worn out or are clogged up with blood clots (thrombi). These substances are generally well tolerated by the body and are not "rejected" as complete organs, such as the heart or kidney, may be. Organs must be carefully chosen in accordance with very strict biological criteria before they are transplanted.

This is why, looking to the future, many surgeons favour the replacement of unhealthy organs with artificial ones. Without discussing the personal opinions of individual surgeons, there is no doubt that surgery, in common with other modern sciences, can take advantage of discoveries and knowledge acquired in the most varied fields of technology and biology.

Instruments used by surgeons now interfere less and less with the body's vital functions and even prevent compli-cations that an operation can cause. It is now possible to operate with little risk on any part of the human body in an attempt to cure the most varied types of diseases. Therefore, there are no longer "medical" and "surgical" illnesses as there were previously. Nobody would say today that "surgery depends on medicine's failures". The two aspects are closely linked and complement and integrate with each other.

The concept of surgery was originally based on a classical idea that was purely mechanical, technical and manual. Now it is on the same level as biology and its scope is much wider than that of a simple "adjunct" to medicine. While this change was taking place, new horizons were also opening up to surgery. One of these is cryosurgery which means "surgery by freezing". Low temperatures in the body's tissues cause significant changes which can (depending on the period of application and temperature) destroy the tissues, having first destroyed the cells of which they consist. Instead of removing an unhealthy part of the body (such as a tumour) with a surgical incision, it is sufficient to apply special cryosurgical instruments or probes which freeze and destroy it by using substances that can reach particularly low temperatures. Carbon dioxide, for example, can fall to a temperature of $-78°C$ and liquid nitrogen to $-196°C$. In place of a cutting blade, cryosurgical probes have tubular "ter-minals" of different sizes which are applied to the area to be cold-treated. The method, which is painless and quick, can at present be used for tumours of the skin, eyes, throat, brain and intestine. Its advantages are that it is both simple and safe.

Veterinary surgery
Animal doctors

Veterinary science deals with animals from the biological and medical points of view. The term comes from the Latin word *veterinarius* which means "pertaining to beasts of burden".

About 4000 BC, Sumerians already had some basic knowledge on how to look after animals. Veterinary science existed in ancient India where treatises on the diseases of horses and elephants were written and there were hospitals for various kinds of animals. In his legal code, the Babylonian King Hammurabi (about 1800 BC) laid down the fees for "doctors of asses and oxen". The ancient Egyptians, too, were concerned about animals and the papyrus of Kahun (about 1900 BC) gave prescriptions for diseases of dogs and cattle.

From Hippocrates to "farriers"

Further progress was made in the studies and research carried on in ancient Greece where there was a class of *hippiatroi*, or horse-doctors. Veterinary science was stimulated by developments in medicine and philosophy. The physician and writer, Hippocrates, took a particular interest in animals, as did another writer, Xenophon, and the philosopher Aristotle who not only described many of their diseases in his books but was also the first to study in detail the stomach of ruminants.

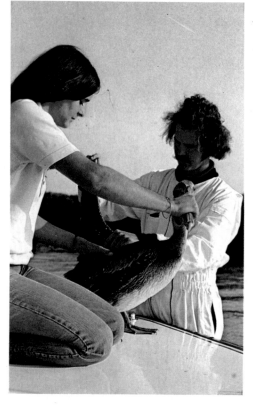

In Roman days the practical aspect of veterinary medicine was particularly important, to ensure that horses were fit for battles and that breeding animals were healthy. Hospitals for sick and wounded

horses were set up and each emperor had his *medicus veterinarius*. Several writers including Cato, Varro and Columella gave descriptions of animal disease and treatment and the Greek physician, Galen (who lived in Rome in the second century AD) wrote on animal physiology.

The writings of the Greek veterinarian Apsyrtus, during the fourth century gained him the title of "the father" of veterinary medicine. About a hundred years later, the *Artis Veterinariae* by the Roman, Vegetius, set out important principles of hygiene and preventive medicine for animals.

In Roman times, the job of the farrier was to shoe the horses, but from the Middle Ages until modern times, farriers were attached to the cavalry of most countries to treat sick and wounded horses.

Few advances were made in veterinary knowledge from Roman times until the eighteenth century. One book, however, written in 1598, is often considered as the first treatise on modern veterinary science. It was Carlo Ruini's *Anatomy of the Horse* which included a section on diseases.

Two centuries elapsed before special veterinary schools were set up. The first was founded in Lyons in France in 176_ and the second at Maison-Alfort, suburb of Paris, in 1765. By the beginning

Left, a splendid painting of the fifteenth century depicting hunters looking after their dogs. In those days there were no proper veterinary surgeons. The first school of veterinary medicine was founded in Lyons in France in the eighteenth century.

In addition to looking after pets and breeding animals, veterinary surgeons also treat wild animals. Below, a veterinary surgeon and his assistant rescuing an injured sea bird.

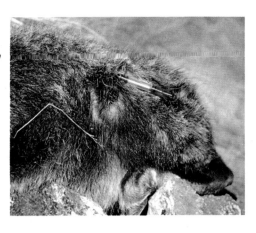

When treating wild animals, veterinary surgeons often make use of narcotics which are injected from some distance away by using special syringe-guns.

Veterinary medicine uses vaccinations in order to prevent outbreaks and infections. One disease that animals can transmit to man is rabies which is passed on by the bite of a rabid dog. Anthrax is a disease of cattle, horses, goats, sheep and sometimes pigs, and is transmitted between animals. Louis Pasteur, a French microbiologist and chemist, discovered the vaccine for these two diseases at the end of the nineteenth century (the picture above shows Pasteur vaccinating an animal).

of the nineteenth century, schools had been established in Berlin, Copenhagen and London and more followed later in nearly every important European city. Veterinary schools in other parts of the world were set up some time afterwards.

The qualifications and titles of people trained in veterinary science vary from one country to another. In the United States, for example, they are known as veterinarians, while in Britain they are called veterinary surgeons.

A veterinary surgeon's duties

What does a veterinary surgeon in fact do? He can work in various different branches of his profession. The most usual consists of looking after animals kept in the home, that is as pets. Some veterinary surgeons deal with breeding; others concentrate on farm animals and the maintenance of herd or flock health; others work for zoos looking after the animals kept there; and others study the behaviour and life of wild animals. Another branch of the work today, is the consideration of the problems of animal diseases in the underdeveloped parts of the world, so that the health of livestock can be improved and more food produced.

Veterinary surgeons also deal with vaccinations. Some animal diseases can be transmitted to man, for example tuberculosis through infected milk from cows and rabies following a bite by a rabid dog. By vaccinating animals the transmission of diseases can be prevented. Before allowing animals to enter (and in particular dogs because of rabies) some countries require that they are put into quarantine, that is undergo a period of isolation to determine whether they have any symptoms of diseases.

Finally, veterinary science has significantly contributed to the development of space research. In fact, animals were launched into orbit around the earth before men. The first was a dog called Laika, put into space by the Russians in November 1957. By checking their vital reactions (such as heart beat and breathing rhythm) and carefully examining them on their return to earth, new and extremely useful information on how human beings can survive has been obtained.

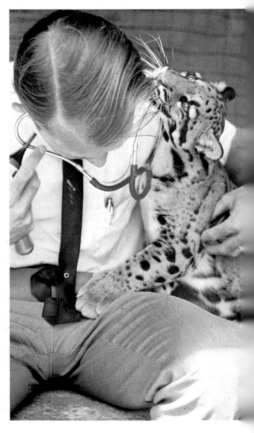

The care that a vet gives his patients is no less diverse than a doctor gives to his human patients. The difference is that the animals cannot describe their sickness, and diagnosis is a matter of experience and observation.

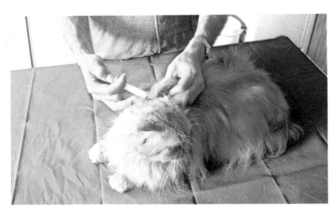

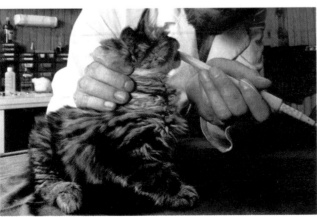

The Past
in the Present

Buddhism
The religion of the four truths

Nearly six hundred years before Christ in a village at the foot of the Himalayan mountains in north-east India, a son called Siddhartha was born to King Suddhodana and Queen Maya. He married, fathered a son and lived in wealth until the age of twenty-nine. Then he abandoned everything, studied under learned monks, retired into meditation and finally travelled from village to village preaching, in the company of pupils and friends. After much prayer and meditation, he came in time to be revered as a buddha, that is an "enlightened one". Thereafter he was known to everyone as Buddha, or more fully Buddha Gautama, since Gautama was his family name.

That Buddha of long ago lived to about eighty and died in a mysterious way, poisoned by tainted food in a little wood. At the end of the eighteenth century, it was believed he had never existed: he was thought to be someone invented by popular imagination, a legendary hero. Then, between 1896 and 1898, some European archaeologists discovered in Nepal (Asia) a very ancient column dedicated to him and an urn containing his mortal remains: he was not an imaginary god but a man of flesh and blood, who had spent his life praying and preaching.

He founded orders of monks and friars and from him Buddhism was born. Naturally, during the course of so many centuries, some strange beliefs have arisen: it is said that the mother of Buddha was a virgin; that as soon as he was born, he set off to walk towards the east to show that he would become master of the eastern world; that he would teach his teachers; and that he worked unbelievable prodigies, healing the sick and raising the dead to life. Some of these things may be true; others were attributed to him later, copied from other religions. As is so often the case with famous men, it is not always easy to distinguish history from legend.

How to become a buddha

Like all religions, Buddhism is based on precise principles. It has ten instructions (not to kill, not to bear false witness, not to steal and so on) and a catalogue of six virtues (charity, moral goodness, industry, patience, generosity and love for one's neighbours). These rules and virtues contribute to the "four noble truths" (the existence of pain, the cause of pain, the purpose of pain and the means to overcome pain) which are fundamental to this religion. By knowing the four truths and accepting the principles, it is possible for any man to become a buddha, an enlightened or holy one. When he becomes a buddha, he no longer has fear of pain, but moves, as it were, outside this world into a state of being called "Nirvana". We can all become buddhas, holy people, and enter into Nirvana, and so be freed from further suffering and from the necessity of passing from one life to another. This is a curious, but very interesting idea: Buddhists believe, in

Above right and below right, two statues of Buddha: one Japanese, the other Tibetan. Below, a strange sculpture which shows the twelve heads of Avalokiteśvara, worshipped by the Tibetan Buddhists.

108

fact, that if men are good, they pass to a better life; if they are wicked, to a worse. This theory is called "metempsychosis". By becoming a buddha one eliminates the metempsychoses and is eligible for Nirvana.

The order founded by Buddha Gautama removed all restrictions of caste, placed on all members the same requirements, denounced extreme ascetic practices, and emphasized moral principles. A monk had simple equipment, such as an alms bowl, clothes, razor and toothpick. His activities consisted of daily recitations, making rounds for alms, fasting after the noonday meal, meditation and listening to religious discourses by senior monks. He also had to give instructions to junior monks and to preach to laymen.

The religions of Asia

Buddhism spread through much of Asia while other religions like Confucianism and Taoism were also developing. Confucianism takes its name from Confucius, who lived 500 years before Christ. Confucianism believed in heaven and worshipped ancestors; it has had a great influence on Chinese thought and culture. While Confucianism emphasizes social order and an active life, Taoism concentrates on individual life and tranquillity. It was founded by the philosopher Lao-tzu, a librarian and curator of historical documents, who lived during the sixth century BC.

In Japan Buddhism encountered Shintoism (which revered its dead, famous men and the forces of nature). For a long time, these two religions coexisted. The

The religious celebrations are very emotional experiences for Buddhists who meet together several times a day in the pagodas. Special cult-objects are the relics, the sacred heads and above all the figures of Buddha, to which flowers, robes and even short passages of music are offered. Above, young Thai bonzes in a Bangkok temple: below, the interior of a pagoda at Rangoon in Burma.

Japanese Buddhist monks are known as "bonzes" and wear yellow robes. Zen philosophy, which means "meditation", sprang from Buddhism and is also known in the West.

In India Buddhism was surrounded by other religious beliefs and practices. One of the oldest and most important was Brahmanism, whose priests are called "brahmins".

How widespread is Buddhism? This is impossible to calculate accurately because in parts of Asia, where the religion is strongest, it has merged with other religions, giving rise to different rites and cults. Some Far Eastern countries such as Tibet, Laos and Cambodia have been recognized as Buddhist though in recent years statistics have not been available. However, we know that Buddhists are present in Burma (about 90 per cent of the population), Thailand (about 89 per cent), Sri Lanka (about 60 per cent), Japan (about 60 per cent), China (about 17 per cent), and in smaller numbers in India, Pakistan, the Philippines and Indonesia. There are also a number of Buddhists in the Soviet Union, the United States and South America, and a relatively small group in Europe. There is a tendency among young European Buddhists to abandon their work and studies and visit the area of Buddha's birth to assimilate the ancient message of Buddhism.

Christianity
The Son of God
born in a stable

Christianity or the Christian religion, takes its name from Christ, a word which in Hebrew signifies "Messiah", that is the "anointed" or, more generally, "the man anointed by the Lord". By the word "Christ", the Hebrews meant the king of Israel, since it was those who had authority and thereby belonged to God who were anointed. In the New Testament, on the other hand, the term "Christ" is used only for Jesus, the son of Mary, who was the wife of a carpenter named Joseph. Jesus was born at Bethlehem and lived at Nazareth, a village in Galilee, in the north of Palestine. Palestine lay almost exactly where the Hebrew state of Israel is today; its capital was Jerusalem. Jesus is sometimes called "the Nazarene" and also "the Galilean", after the places where he lived.

The birth of Jesus Christ is very important for modern man in many ways; it signalled a fundamental change in the history of mankind, and the religion which Jesus preached is followed today directly by more than one thousand million people. In addition, because it is concerned with basic values it has a substantial influence on the whole of mankind.

Even the practical aspects of life, if we look carefully, are marked every day by the memory of Jesus Christ. A single example illustrates this: in nearly every country the calendar is now based on the date of his birth. In history books we find written "before Christ", or, for short, BC to indicate the time before his birth, and "after Christ", abbreviated to AD, to indicate the years after his birth. If neither of these is written, AD is always meant. In fact, when one says 1982 one means 1,982 years since the birth of Christ. However, some scholars maintain that Jesus may have been born four years before the hitherto agreed date; thus 1982 should in reality be 1986, 1983 should become 1987 and so forth. Naturally, to avoid confusion the calendar stays as it is.

Old and New Testament

Christians claim that Jesus, the Messiah, was the man awaited by the Hebrew people of whom the Bible (a word which, in Greek, means "books") speaks. The Bible, called also Holy Scripture, is divided into the Old Testament and the New Testament. In the Old Testament, written in Hebrew and Aramaic, are collected three types of book: histories, poetry and prophecies. In these is summarized the history of the Hebrews or people of Israel, with the chronicles of the ancient tribes of Palestine, their battles, the persecutions they suffered, the natural disasters, the heroes, the priests and the warriors. The meaning of the name Israel is uncertain, but it is usually taken to mean "he who strives against God", and is the tribal name given to Jacob who had fought with the angel sent to him by the Lord.

In the New Testament (the word "testament" means also "covenant" or "agreement"), that is to say the "new agreement" between God and man, are collected the Gospels of Matthew, Mark, Luke and John, which contain accounts of Jesus' life and teaching. After the Gospels in the New Testament, are found writings of the early Church: the Acts of the Apostles, the Letters of St. Paul, St James, St. John and St. Jude (not to be confused with Judas Iscariot; the writer of

On the page opposite, a Roman Catholic Easter rite and, on this page, Dr. Runcie, the Archbishop of Canterbury, officiating at the wedding of His Royal Highness Prince Charles with the Lady Diana Spencer. The Archbishop of Canterbury is the senior clergyman in the Church of England.

the epistle was, in fact, Judas Thaddaeus) and also the Book of Revelation, in which St. John foresees the end of the world and the universal judgement.

The Jews maintain that the Messiah has not yet arrived and thus accept only the Old Testament. Their Bible consists therefore of a limited number of ancient books. Christians believe in the whole Bible, but differences exist between Catholics and Protestants as to the authority and value of some books. In Greek, the word "Gospel" means "good news".

The life of Jesus

The Gospels state that Jesus lived for about thirty years with Mary and Joseph; then he left Nazareth and in the last three years of his life devoted himself to preaching. To Christians, he is the son of God, that is to say God made man, who came to suffer in the world to save men from sin (he baptized men) and to tell of the coming of the Kingdom of God on earth.

In the Gospels it is written that Jesus worked miracles, and that he spoke to the ever-larger crowds which followed him and his disciples in such a way as to arouse the envy and fear of the traditional religious leaders. What frightened them most of all, was that he would be the herald of a new kingdom and that

consequently would wish to have himself proclaimed king. For this reason, some of the Jews denounced him to the Romans who ruled Palestine at that time. The Roman procurator, Pontius Pilate, condemned him to crucifixion – the torment of death on the cross, which was placed on a hill, called Golgotha in Aramaic and Calvary in Latin, that is the "place of a skull". When he was taken to Calvary, a crown of thorns was placed on Jesus' head in mockery, and on the cross was written "Jesus of Nazareth King of the Jews", which translated into Latin reads "Iesus Nazarenus Rex Iudaeorum", and which in the abbreviated form becomes INRI. According to Holy Scripture, Jesus rose again three days after the death, he ascended into heaven, and later showed himself to the disciples to whom he sent the Holy Spirit (third member of the Trinity with the Father and the Son). The festival of Pentecost commemorates this. The Holy Spirit represents the love which Christ left with us to unite us in fellowship.

The first Christians

Jesus left no writings of his own. His deeds and his words are recorded in the Gospels, where it is said that he appointed the apostle Simon, a fisherman, to be the "rock" because his recognition and confession of Jesus as the Christ was the rock upon which he would build his

church. This is why Simon was given the extra name of Peter, derived from *Petrus*, a Latin word for "rock". Peter traditionally became the first Bishop of Rome and therefore the first Pope. After the descent of the Holy Spirit, the apostles separated to devote themselves to preaching to the four quarters of the earth, spreading the faith taught by their Master. They reached Greece, Italy, northern Africa and the regions of the East. In Rome, at first, they were treated like other Jews, but their stern moral standard and their fear of being affected by the pagan practices carried on around them, led them to stand apart from the rest of the community. The Roman state doubted their loyalty, and the Christians came to be persecuted and were compelled to meet in the caves called "catacombs". If discovered, they were tortured or killed or fed to the lions during the bloody public spectacles at the Colosseum.

The most notorious persecution is that by the Roman Emperor Nero, which took place in 64 AD. The Emperor was believed, wrongly, to have set fire to Rome, and he tried to shift the blame on to the Christians. At that time, among others, the apostles Peter and Paul were killed. Nearly three centuries later, the Roman Emperor Constantine built a basilica to honour the shrine of St. Peter. It is the place where today the Basilica of St. Peter stands, in the Vatican. Before the reign of Constantine, more precisely between the rule of Nero and that of Diocletian, the Christians underwent ten great persecutions (not counting the small ones), which caused thousands of deaths.

The Emperor Constantine, after winning a battle against his rival, Maxentius, declared in the famous "edict of Milan" issued at Nicomedia on 15 June 313 to grant full liberty for all religions and restitution of wrongs done to the Christians. Constantine also made lavish donations to the churches and granted immunities to the clergy. At just about this date, that of the liberation of Christianity, some historians "close" the ancient classical period, and start the medieval, and it is just in this period that the Christians began to become divided into Catholics and Orthodox following the divisions of the Roman Empire; the western part with the capital at Rome and the eastern part with the capital at Constantinople. One moves, in short, from the primitive Church and the catacombs, to a church which was open and free, diffused among people of every age and interest. Little by little Christianity replaced paganism, while the Roman Empire fell apart under the invasions of the barbarian peoples.

Saints and soldiers

By the end of the early period, Christianity occupied an important and influential position in the community. It changed the attitude to manual work (the Roman "plebs" (plebians) were despised by the nobility) and also encouraged people to learn to read, write, understand history, debate problems and important topics, and to fight for their own liberty. Much of

The first churches were below ground

The early Christians did not cremate the bodies of their dead, as was widespread among the Romans. They dug underground cemeteries, the catacombs, in which to lay the dead bodies of Christians (in the photograph we see the catacomb of St. Sebastian on the Appian Way near Rome). The increasing savagery of the persecutions, however, compelled the Christians to use these underground places also for their meetings, to pray and to hold services. Roman law forbade burials within the city walls or in residential areas. The earliest that now remain date from the second century AD and are at Calixtus, Domitilla and Priscilla. The majority of the Christian catacombs belong to the third and early part of the fourth centuries.

After 313, the year in which the Emperor Constantine issued an edict which allowed the Christians to meet freely, the catacombs were abandoned and became special places of pilgrimage. Some were lost sight of until they were rediscovered by chance in 1578. Since then, they have aroused great interest as witnesses to the first century of Christian culture.

Today, the catacombs are visited by Christians and by scholars, for whom they are an important source of primitive Christian art.

this was due to the great historical figures, many of whom the Church later sanctified: Augustine, Bishop of Hippo, Ambrose, Bishop of Milan, Benedict, abbot and founder of the Order which bears his name, Francis of Assisi and Thomas Aquinas; later there were Thomas Becket, Teresa of Avila, Joan of Arc, Sir Thomas More, Ignatius di Loyola and in our own century people such as Albert Schweitzer and Mother Theresa of Calcutta.

Naturally the history of Christianity also contains episodes and people which have aroused arguments and conflicts. The Crusaders are a classic example. From the start, the practice of making voyages of prayer or pilgrimage to Palestine, called the Holy Land because it was the birthplace of Jesus, was widespread amongst Christians. When Palestine was occupied by the Turks, considered infidels as followers of another religion (Islam), the Christian pilgrims encountered ever greater difficulties. The year 1000 was a year of great terror because the end of the world was feared, and towards the end of the eleventh century the first very large popular pilgrimage was organized, accompanied by full-scale armies, for many thousands of men. The pilgrims were easily recognized because they carried a cross on their backs or the picture of a cross on their garments. This was the first official crusade. Jerusalem was conquered but the massacres then and later were immense and certainly not in the spirit of Christianity. Jerusalem was successively lost, re-conquered, lost again and the Crusaders, who numbered soldiers and merchants among them, mingled with the pilgrims, made repeated attempts to recapture Jerusalem until the middle of the fifteenth century.

Schisms and heresies

Along with the pilgrimages was spread the missionary ideal which had begun at Pentecost, (the descent of the Holy Ghost on the Apostles). Christians set themselves to preach the Gospel of Jesus in new regions. These were turbulent centuries and Christianity reflected this: in fact, while on the one hand, Christianity became ever more widespread and studies of the faith increased, on the other, different interpretations of the "good news" announced by Jesus also increased. Various Christian communities estranged themselves from the accepted norms of pope and bishops, giving rise to what the Catholics (who were the largest of the Christian groups) called schisms or heresies, that is to say divisions. Schismatics and heretics were hunted and

punished by the Church.

In the meantime, princes and kings began to dispute amongst themselves for the favours of the popes who, often betraying the divine origin of Jesus and his words of peace, acted as war-makers and politicians, bargaining with each other, recruiting armies and conquering territory. These abuses led to bewilderment and confusion to such an extent that for forty years, between 1378 and 1417, the papacy was split between two and even three popes.

The emergence of the Protestants

One century later, on 31 October 1517, the eve of All Saints' day, the German Augustinian monk, Martin Luther, fixed to the door of the cathedral at Wittenberg, where he was then preaching, ninety-five theses against the sale of indulgences and in support of the true forgiveness of sins.

The list of abuses published by Luther led to a series of ever-more violent disputes. Eventually, the monk was excommunicated. Following the Lutheran movement, other protestant movements were born: all, however, whatever their differences, consider themselves Christians.

Doctrine and Commandments

Christianity is the religion of brotherhood and love. It is one faith; we cannot understand the mystery of Jesus "very God and very man" so we must accept by an act of faith. Likewise an act of faith is the acceptance of God as "one and three" (Father, Son and Holy Spirit), one eternal God, omniscient, omnipresent and omnipotent (that is all-knowing, all-present and all-powerful) distinct in three persons. In Christianity all men, without distinction, may have eternal salvation. They are able to take part in the Mass, or Holy Communion service, which Jesus instituted during the last supper.

Christianity is rooted in Holy Scripture in the tradition of the Church and in the guidance of the Holy Spirit's speaking to the conscience of individuals and communities. Different communions within the Church lay different emphases on these – Roman Catholics emphasize the authority of the Church, Protestants that of the Bible and some Free Churches that of Conscience. But all Christians would accept the two Principles laid down by Jesus Christ as a summary of the Law. "Thou shalt love the Lord thy God with all thy heart and with all thy soul and with all thy mind. This is the first and great commandment. And the second is like unto it, Thou shalt love thy neighbour as thyself."

Christmas
The great Christian festival

Christmas Day is the most beautiful and popular of all the feast-days celebrated in the Christian religion, because on this day every year we remember the birth of Christ. His birth is commemorated by all branches of the Christian Church, Protestant, Roman Catholic and Greek Orthodox.

Although 25 December is Christmas Day, it is almost certainly not the day on which Christ was born. It was the date of a pagan festival in Rome, which was chosen by the Emperor Aurelian in AD 274 as the birthday of the unconquered sun,

which at the winter solstice begins once more to show an increase of light. By AD 336, the Church at Rome had established the commemoration of Christ's birthday on the same date.

During the same period (between 17 and 24 December) the Romans celebrated their Saturnalia in honour of Saturn, the god of seeds and farming, who was believed to have the power to bestow happiness and plenty on all. It was a time for merrymaking and the exchanging of presents and during these few days the distinctions between freemen and slaves

were set aside; all manner of licentiousness was allowed and there was even elected a mock king who had absolute power for one month and who was probably intended to represent Saturn himself.

Although it is not possible to be absolutely sure, it seems very probable that Christmas festivities were influenced by certain aspects of these older pagan practices. The fact that Christmas was celebrated on the birthday of the unconquered sun, connected the season with the Roman New Year (1 January) when houses were decorated with greenery and lights and presents were given to children and the poor.

The practice of exchanging gifts on Christmas Day makes it a particularly happy and exciting time for children. It is especially to children that the days between Christmas Eve and Epiphany belong. Epiphany (6 January) is, of course, the day when we celebrate the arrival in Bethlehem of the three kings, bringing to Jesus gifts of gold, frankincense and myrrh.

Many of the customs celebrating Christmas and Epiphany vary from country to country. In Italy, for example, Epiphany is also popularly called the day of Befana. A traditional story tells how on that day a kind old witch may come down riding on a broomstick, carrying a sack laden with presents. During the night, while everybody is asleep, she lets herself down from the chimney top and fills the waiting stockings with gifts for the good children and lumps of coal for the naughty ones. We know very little about the origins of Befana but one tradition relates that she was too busy to see the three wise men as they passed on their journey to visit the Christ Child, saying that she would see them on their return. They went back another way and Befana has to look for them for ever.

The manger and the tree

Among the Christmas decorations, we often find a nativity crib or a Christmas tree.

In many churches, the crib has become part of our Christmas services. The practice seems to go back to 1223, the year in which St. Francis of Assisi set up a shrine recalling the birth of Jesus, at Greccio, a small town on the Rieti hills in

The birth of Christ, which Christians remember every Christmas, has inspired many artists. Left, we see a nativity scene by the Venetian Bartolomeo Vivarini, who lived in the fifteenth century. As tradition requires, next to the baby Jesus there are Mary, Joseph, the ox and the ass. Someone who creates an immediate atmosphere of festivity is Father Christmas (above), the famous old man with the long white beard and the red clothes. The transformation of St. Nicholas into Father Christmas took place first in Germany and from there spread to other countries.

Italy. By reconstructing the manger in which Christ was born and surrounding it with figures in plaster, wood or stone, we make that moment come alive every year.

Many examples of old cribs remain in museums and churches. Some that are especially remarkable for their detail and the rich background scenery are found in the Naples area of Italy.

Evergreens have a long association with Christmas festivities. They may date from the eighth century when St. Boniface was spreading Christianity in Germany and dedicated the fir tree to the baby Jesus to replace the sacred oak of Odin. There is a tradition that the German monk Martin Luther, who lived in the sixteenth century, first decorated the tree. As he was passing through a wood by moonlight, he was enchanted by the sight of the icicles sparkling on the trees and decided to reproduce the spectacle by adorning a fir tree in his garden with candles. The tradition has been handed down for centuries and reached England in the nineteenth century, soon after Queen Victoria's marriage to the German Prince Albert. We still decorate Christmas trees today, making them sparkle with lights, tinsel and coloured glass balls. Holly, too, is used in Christmas decorations. It is called "Christ's thorn" in Germany and Scandinavia because it is used in church decorations and also because its berries appear at about Christmas time.

In some countries, it is believed that the lighted Christmas tree attracts the attention of Father Christmas so that he will leave his presents beneath it. Father Christmas is by now a world-wide phenomenon He is always depicted as cheerful and generous, with a long white beard and a red cloak; he travels on a sleigh with his bottomless sack of presents. His popularity has spread to communist countries, in particular the Soviet Union (where he has taken the name of Father Frost).

It is not difficult to understand that this old man, burdened with years, as well as snow and gifts, symbolizes the old year which is passing away. He embodies the desire to celebrate, so as to give thanks to the old year for everything which it has given us, just as presents are exchanged as tokens in the hope that the coming year will be "good".

In some countries of northern Europe, the presents are not distributed during Christmas night, but on the night of 5 December: this is the feast of St. Nicholas (who is called Sinter Claes in the Low Countries and Sankt Nikolaus in Germany). It is a typical sight to see the bishop St. Nicholas and his stable-boy black Peter, travelling through the town and villages surrounded by a happy shouting crowd waiting for the sweet and fruit which will be thrown out handfuls. The festivities end in a magic night during which gifts are distribute

Hinduism
A belief in
re-incarnation

"Hinduism" is a western term: it is the name which the people of the West used to describe the main religion of India. Indians call it the *sanatana dharma*, the eternal faith.

Hinduism is not a single religion, but a mixture, a fusion (the exact term is 'syncretism') of other doctrines and cult forms. The central idea comes, however, from the ancient Vedic religion, so called because it is based on the "Veda", sacred writings which go back to the tenth century before Christ.

The Vedic religion was polytheistic, worshipping numerous gods rather than just one. A profound crisis occurred around the sixth century BC: as a result of the development of other important sacred texts (the "Brahmanas" and the "Upanishads"), man acquired an ever-growing importance in the religion. He became the centre of the universe, so that he no longer needed to be in touch with the gods, but found it sufficient to search within himself, (within his *atman* as the Indians call it) for the real world of the spirit and all essential truth. The ideal of the religious life thus became meditation and ascetism, rather than religious observance or worship.

It was from this crisis of the Vedic religion and the emergence of other religions, like Buddhism and Jainism, that the doctrines and spiritual practices which we call Hinduism arose.

Brahma, Vishnu and Shiva

Notwithstanding the central position given to man in their beliefs, the Hindus still worshipped a group of gods: pre-eminent was Brahma, the "Iśvara" (that is the lord of the universe), with whom were associated two other important divinities, Vishnu and Shiva, together with a number of minor figures venerated as manifestations of the lord of the universe or, if female, as his wives.

Today Hinduism is divided into various sects: the main ones are Vishnuism, Shivaism and Shaktism.

The Vishnuites worship Vishnu, the ancient Vedic god who has become for them the one Lord. Vishnu is incarnate in various guises to do his work as preserver and protector of the world. Some of these "manifestations" are worshipped as true divinities in their own right: for example, Rama, the ideal ruler and warrior who fights against devils and overthrows them, and Krishna, the god of salvation.

The Shivaites worship Shiva, who has the power to create and destroy, the lord of life and death. Shakti is a wife of Shiva and is the central figure of the cult of the Shaktas. She is the mother goddess and is sometimes known as Parvati, Uma or Annapurna (the tender mother who bestows blessings) and sometimes as Durga or Kali (when she becomes a terrible, cruel giantess).

As well as the three great gods, there are many others who are worshipped on special occasions. The best known of these is Ganesha, the elephant-headed son of Shiva, who is petitioned for success before all the most important undertakings.

The laws of *karma*

In Hinduism, a fundamental role or principle is given shape and substance by what the individual does and by his meditation: a person's actions during his life will decide his future.

All Hindus believe in the "laws of *karma*", that is in the law of cause and effect by which the soul passes through a series of reincarnations. This step-by-step exaltation from an inferior position towards the final goal is regulated by *dharma*, a system of conduct, obligations that have to be fulfilled.

Many ways to self-improvement exist: there is the simple cult of the gods and there is, on a higher plane, meditation and asceticism; there is the religious master (the so-called *guru*), but there is also the person who acquires merit by looking after the *guru*'s needs and serving him with complete self-sacrifice. Everything depends on the level which a member of the faithful has reached, and on the path he has followed in his earlier lives.

There is a ritual ceremony for practically every circumstance of life, but they are connected especially with the significant times of birth, puberty, marriage and death. The bodies of the dead are not buried, but are cremated and the ashes sprinkled in the river Ganges, to mingle with its holy waters. Another practice is to travel on foot as a pilgrim, as far as Benares, the holy city.

What is "yoga"?

Yoga is a widespread ascetic practice which aims to achieve the absolute mastery of one's self, both of mind and body. In Europe particularly, yoga has become popular and is practised also as a form of healthful exercise.

It is not easy to become a yogin. First of all, one has to study and meditate on the "Veda", follow special diets and observe a series of practical devotions; then, one is admitted to the various stages which lead to the achievement of salvation. These stages are: to obey the five commandments (non-violence, truthfulness, honesty, chastity and poverty); to follow the five observances (purity, sobriety, the so-called "ascetic heat", reciting of sacred texts and worship of the Lord of the universe); to learn the positions of the body which lead to concentration and to the control of breathing; to learn to divert one's attention from objects; concentration; meditation and, lastly, the perfect union of one's self with the cosmos.

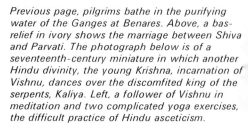

Previous page, pilgrims bathe in the purifying water of the Ganges at Benares. Above, a bas-relief in ivory shows the marriage between Shiva and Parvati. The photograph below is of a seventeenth-century miniature in which another Hindu divinity, the young Krishna, incarnation of Vishnu, dances over the discomfited king of the serpents, Kaliya. Left, a follower of Vishnu in meditation and two complicated yoga exercises, the difficult practice of Hindu asceticism.

The heart of Islam's "holy city", Mecca, destination of the pilgrims. A colonnade around the square containing the Ka'-ba, the holy black stone, enclosed by a cubic structure.

Islam
The religion
of Mohammed

Islam, that is the Moslem faith, is the world's second religion, with more than 700 million faithful. Christians number about 1,200 million. In third place, still in terms of number of adherents, are the Hindus, with Confucianists and Buddhists coming fourth and fifth. The followers of Islam are also called Mussulmans or Mohammedans. The Arabic word "islam", from which the name of the religion comes, means "to surrender oneself to the will of God". From "islam" comes the word "muslim" which, in the most correct and literal translation, means "obedient to islam". Lastly, Mohammedan comes from Mohammed, the founder of Islam (as Christian comes from Christ). The religion, in its different rites (Sunnis, Shiites, Kharijites, Ismailis,

Zaidites etc.), is professed mainly in Asia and Africa. The principal countries where the great majority of the population is Mohammedan are Indonesia, Bangladesh, Pakistan, Afghanistan, Syria, Iraq, Iran, Jordan, Turkey, Saudi Arabia, the Yemen, all the African states which border the Mediterranean and also the Sudan, Senegal, Chad, the Gambia, Guinea, Mali, Mauritania and Niger. It is also recorded that about 60 million Indians are Mohammedans, as are 50 million Chinese. There are also large Islamic communities in the Soviet Union, in Albania, in Jugoslavia and in Lebanon.

This long list of countries gives us a basic idea of how fragmented and complex the Islamic world is and helps us, perhaps, to understand the international

problems which it can cause. As we shall see, Islam is the "youngest" of the great religions, and particularly on account of its special nature, still exercises a profound influence on culture, civil life and both internal politics and the relations between the different states. It is necessary to remember, moreover, that in the not-too-distant past, about 1000 years ago, Islam was also a powerful empire, at one time perhaps larger than the Roman Empire.

The life of Mohammed

The "prophet" of the Moslems is thought to have been born in about AD 570 (the exact date is not known) at Mecca, a densely populated centre in the Arabian peninsula, not far from the Red Sea, in the territory which today forms part of Saudi Arabia. Mecca is famous as the holy city of Islam, but even then, when Mohammed was still a boy, it already possessed an outstanding religious importance. It was there that the Arabs worshipped their numerous idols and it was a place of

117

pilgrimage for the furthest-flung nomadic tribes of the desert (the Bedouins). At the same time, it was an important commercial centre, the meeting-point of the caravans of dromedaries which came there from the Persian Gulf, from the traders' landing-places on the Indian Ocean and on the Red Sea, bringing from the Far East and Africa gold, ivory, precious stones, spices, amber, cloth, hides and slaves.

Commerce with the territories to the north, and in particular with Constantinople, was then at its height. In that century, while in the West the remnants of the Roman Empire were under the heel of the nordic barbarians, the Byzantines (eastern Roman Empire), under the leadership of the Emperor Justinian, were going through a period of great wealth and ostentation.

Mecca was governed by powerful and rich tribes of the Quraish to which the clan and family of Mohammed belonged. Mohammed was very soon orphaned and had a difficult childhood. He spent his early years in poverty as a shepherd boy, living among the nomads in the mountainous regions near Mecca. Later, he accompanied some of the caravans and entered the service of a family led by a woman (a most exceptional occurrence in that type of society), the widow Khadija. Eventually Khadija and Mohammed married and until the age of about forty,

Mohammed lived a peaceful and prosperous life.

The later periods in Mohammed's life are fairly obscure. Nevertheless, it is known that both at Mecca and at other places to which the caravan routes extended, it was his practice to observe and compare the various primitive tribal religions, based as they were on the most extreme idolatry, with the great monotheistic religions (those acknowledging a single god): the Christian religion and especially the Jewish, which was represented in Arabia by several communities.

When he was around forty years of age, after a period of personal crisis and solitary meditation, Mohammed began to preach and to make known the revelations of Allah (the Arabic word meaning God). It is these revelations which, faithfully reported by Mohammed, were to make up the Koran. The Koran is the sacred book of Islam, which contains the revelations made by Allah directly to Mohammed. It became for Moslems what the Gospel is for Christians.

An increasing train of followers soon formed around the prophet, but great hostility was shown by the leading representatives of the Mecca aristocracy in this period. About the year 619, this hostility compelled Mohammed and his followers to leave the city. This event was decisive: it is known as the Hegira, the emigration or exile (622), the period to which can be traced the real founding of Islam and on which the Moslem calendar is based. The Moslem year 1 therefore corresponds to 622 of the Christian era (and so when Christians celebrate the year 2000 it will only be 1378 in Moslem countries: that is 2000 minus 622).

In this year, Mohammed entered Medina, a city of the interior (about 300 kilometres north-east of Mecca) where the situation was quite different, either because the power of the old idols was less strongly felt there or because the people had realized that it was necessary to remove the conflicts between the two rival tribes which governed the area. A further important point was that at Medina there was a numerous and authoritative Jewish community whose faith did not then seem very different from that preached by the Arab prophet. Mohammed, whose fame by then had reached every corner of the Arabian peninsula and who was followed by a conspicuous nucleus of believers, among whom were some eminent people, was received and recognized as religious head and absolute governor of the city. In this way, the first great Moslem community came officially into being. With it was

founded the first centre of Islamic power which soon was to be transformed into a military force, giving to Islam the outer appearance of a truly authoritarian state, with the right to make laws and regulate every aspect of the life of its subjects.

There followed a period of bloody conflict between the Moslems and warriors from the Quraish tribe, at the same time as the Koranic laws were being developed. Mohammed defined the unique nature of Islam more clearly and, though recognizing both Abraham and Christ as great prophets, in practice he decreed that the Arab "holy city" should outrank the city of the Jews and Christians. Thus, while at the beginning Moslems had preached revolt against Jerusalem, from that moment they turned their faces towards Mecca.

This change in Mohammedan doctrine reveals, among other things, the desire to exalt the essentially Arab character of Islam and also to establish links with adjoining traditions and cultures: Mecca was the most simple and vital expression of this and was to be honoured for ever as the birthplace of the prophet.

The Jews were soon driven out of Medina and Mohammed signed a truce with the Meccans. However, the Meccans broke this pact of neutrality and in 630, year 8 in the Islamic calendar Mohammed advanced on Mecca. The city capitulated almost without a blow and Mohammed entered his holy city in triumph. He destroyed all the idols (at least 300 it is said) with the exception of one, the black stone (the "Ka'-ba"), to which he wished to attach a religious significance, in acknowledgement of his respect for the old traditions of its people.

Very soon the majority of the Arab tribes were converted to Islam and made their submission to Mohammed: the Islamic state was born and extended to cover almost the whole peninsula. This was the base from which the new faith and its ideology could expand beyond the confines of the peninsula. And so it came about. Immediately after the death of the prophet (this happened in Medina in 632, the tenth year of the Islamic calendar) and in the centuries which followed, hordes of war-like Moslem conquerors brought Islam to the whole of northern Africa, the Near East and into the heart of Asia as far as India. Islam became a very powerful empire which even penetrated the Christian world (in southern Italy and in Spain, but this was occupation without conversion) and attacking France. When the impetus of Arab pressure slackened, it was replaced in part by the fierce expansionism of the Turks, a nomadic people converted

evidence, many bonds which go beyond a common belief in Allah, such as the official language, and the spirit of Islamic nationalism which sees all Moslem peoples as "brothers", especially when confronted by non-Moslems.

The laws of the Koran

The Islamic faith is based on five fundamental duties: the affirmation that "there is no god but God and Mohammed is his prophet" together with the obligations of prayer, almsgiving, fasting and pilgrimage to Mecca.

In the Koran, ninety-nine attributes of Allah are given (which Moslems, in their prayers, recite using a rosary which has exactly ninety-nine beads). No picture of the divine being exists to which the faithful can turn. The places where the rites are observed, the mosques, can be very rich indeed in decorations, but they never have paintings or statues representing Allah; there is only a small niche which points in the direction of Mecca towards which believers must direct their prayers.

These, for someone who wishes to honour the Koran strictly (the Koran does, however, allow for extemporary and individual prayer), have to be repeated five times per day: before sunrise, just after noon, in the late afternoon, immediately after sunset, and the last one about two hours later. All the prayers are public and collective and must be said in "a state of personal cleanliness and in a clean place". This state of cleanliness, or purity, is obtained by sprinkling water on the head and washing the face, hands, arms up to the elbow and feet in water.

For Moslems, a greater obligation than prayer is the absolute requirement of fasting for one month in the year (Ramadan), every day, from sunrise to sunset. Abstension from food and drink, from smoking and the use of scent and from every "physical indulgence" is important. Only the old, children, pregnant women, the sick and travellers who may find themselves in certain circumstances are excused.

Quite apart from the fast of Ramadan, Moslems are always forbidden to drink alcohol, to eat pig meat and to gamble. The Islamic feast day is Friday, but this is a recent development. At first, it was only a day of prayer and did not imply the complete cessation of work.

As far as the pilgrimage to Mecca is concerned, this is an obligation which every Moslem who can must discharge at least once. Lastly, Moslems believe in the immortality of the soul, in the day of universal judgement, in the existence of heaven and hell, in angels and in the jinns.

Above, the sanctuary in memory of Fatima (the daughter of Mohammed) in the city of Qom (Iran). It is the object of great pilgrimages: Qom is, in fact, the holy city of the Shiites, those Moslems who consider as true heirs of Mohammed only those who are descended from Ali (Mohammed's first cousin who married Fatima). The Shiites are divided into many sects and are numerous, especially in Iran. In the photograph below, some Moslem faithful praying in a small mosque on the island of Mauritius.

Islam, who were finally to dominate a large part of the Moslem territories until the beginning of the present century.

Meanwhile Islam had undergone remarkable transformations, though maintaining a strict regard for the fundamental laws of the Koran. The dismemberment of the empire into various states, often in conflict with each other, had finally meant that it was the religious aspects of Mohammed's system which prevailed. Yet there remained, and remain today more-than-ever alive and much in

Judaism
The Hebrews, the Bible's people

Hebrew means "one from the other side (of the river)". This name was given to a small group of people of Semitic extraction, originating from Mesopotamia, where they established themselves on the western side of the river Jordan in Palestine about 1800 years before the birth of Christ. They preferred, however, to be called Israelites in memory of their patriarch Jacob, also known as Israel. They were also later called Judeans from the name of one of their main tribes, Judea.

The history of these people from their origin to the Roman conquest is narrated in the most famous sacred book in the world, the Bible. It is a fascinating story, full of adventures and miracles and it occupies most of the Old Testament (this is the first part of the Bible). It seems surprising that the history of a people should have become the subject of a sacred book, but the story of the Jews is accompanied by a feeling of deep devotion and worship. Of all the ancient populations, they are the only one who has passed on from father to son the faith of a single, invisible and almighty God. Other peoples worshipped a large number of gods, often the personifications of natural forces (such as the sun, fire, wind) or divine animals such as the Egyptians' famous bull, Hapi, or even heroes promoted to the rank of immortals such as Romulus, the founder of Rome, who became a god and was given the name of Quirinus.

The Hebrews proclaimed that there was only one God and that he was a pure spirit. Their religion is their pride and strength. They speak of themselves as the Chosen People, loved especially by God and destined to see the rise of the Messiah, the anointed one, who will defeat evil and deliver his people from bondage.

Patriarchs, judges and kings

The Hebrews have been waiting for a Messiah since ancient times when they were nomad shepherds moving with their herds, tents and a few basic belongings. These were the days of the patriarchs, when each family nucleus obeyed its leader who had absolute authority over all who lived with him, wives (there could be more than one), children, nephews, slaves. Later, the Jews moved to Egypt, probably because of a shortage of food. They stayed in Egypt for many years but the Pharaoh's hostility and concern about their increasing numbers, eventually led them to leave the country altogether, guided by their leader Moses. The Egyptians tried in vain to stop them. The Bible relates the story of the crossing of the Red Sea, when the waters divided to let Moses and his followers through and then closed back over their pursuers who were all engulfed by the waters.

After numerous struggles, the Hebrews settled in Canaan, between the Jordan and the Mediterranean. They abandoned their nomadic life and became farmers. There were twelve tribes which took their names from the twelve sons of the patriarch Jacob and lived autonomously. It was only when there was danger, in the form of a threat from neighbouring states, that the Hebrews united under one leader, known as a judge. The Bible mentions the exploits of twelve of them including Gideon, Samson and Deborah, whose victory is commemorated in the so-called "Song of Deborah", one of the oldest surviving pieces of Hebrew literature.

The rule of the judges lasted about two centuries, from the time of the Israelite conquest of Canaan to just before the crowning of King Saul, roughly 1200 to 1050 BC. Then the Hebrew people decided to have a more compact integral organization and established a monarchy. The most famous of the kings was David. He was already well-known when he succeeded to the throne because, whilst still young, he had killed the Philistine giant, Goliath, and established unity and power in the country. He is also remembered for having conquered the fortress of Zion, the Hebrews' political and religious centre which became Jerusalem. Here Solomon, David's son and successor, had a huge temple built to preserve the Ark of the Covenant which contained the tablets of the law given to Moses by God. Seven years were necessary to complete this superb building and a further six to build the royal palace next to it.

However, the Hebrew monarchy quickly declined. At Solomon's death in 922 BC, the kingdom was split in two with Israel with Sichem as capital, and Judea with Jerusalem as capital. In spite of the preaching of the prophets, the hostility that grew between the two kingdoms caused the political collapse of the country. First Israel and then Judea fell under the dominion of the Assyrians during the eighth century BC and both were later invaded by Nebuchadnezzar, king of Babylon, who destroyed the fortresses and the temple of Jerusalem and deported its inhabitants. The return of the exiles to their fatherland took place fifty years later when Cyrus, king of Persia, attacked and conquered the Babylonian empire (539 BC) and the next year allowed the Hebrews to go back to Palestine.

The survivors' first task was to rebuild the temple which symbolized national and religious unity. The monarchy was not re-established. The "high priest" became responsible for civil power and the country remained under the supreme control of the Persians. Their ancient supremacy no longer existed. In 332 BC Alexander the Great, conqueror of the Persian empire, annexed Palestine. Later, when Macedonia's power came to an end

120

with the death of its great conqueror, the Hebrews were first dominated by Egyptians and then Syrians. Finally, after a short period of independence, they fell under the control of Rome in 63 BC.

A Hebrew called Jesus

Jesus was born in Bethlehem in Judea during Roman domination. Only a few Hebrews saw in Jesus the arrival of their Messiah (Christ, which is the name given to him, is a Greek translation of the Hebrew word). After Jesus, the preaching and death of these few Hebrews spread the word of love and fraternity throughout the world, giving rise to a new religion, Christianity, which started in Jerusalem and quickly found many followers amongst pagans.

Most Hebrews continued to believe in their fathers' faith and to dream of a warlike Messiah who would put an end to Roman dominion and bring back their ancient supremacy. This led to a widespread rebellion against Rome in AD 6 which was energetically opposed by Flavius Vespasian. It was finally ended by his son Titus who destroyed Jerusalem in

the year 70, setting fire to the temple and unmercifully punishing all rebels. Some Hebrews were sold as slaves whilst others became scattered throughout the emperor's land. They had no homeland for twenty centuries and during this period a phenomenon known as "Diaspora", a Greek word meaning dispersion, took place. However, in the same way as during their exile in Egypt and deportation to Babylonia, they succeeded in maintaining a religious unity and identity and avoided mixing with other people among whom they lived.

Persecution

They constantly refused to become part of other nations and this frequently caused them to be treated as an unpopular and often oppressed minority. From the fall of Jerusalem onwards, the story of the Jews is filled with persecutions. In many countries, they were refused admission to certain professions, had to live in separate areas (ghettos) which were locked up at night like a prison and often had to wear identification marks on their clothes. Throughout the centuries, this hostility often developed into real massacres, such as in Spain at the end of the Middle Ages and in Eastern Europe between the nineteenth and twentieth centuries. Strong anti-Hebrew feelings were even noted in France.

The most bloody persecution occurred during the Second World War when about six million Jews were barbarously killed in extermination camps organized by Germans obeying Adolf Hitler's ferocious campaign against "international Judaism". These terrible massacres

Two pictures of the "Wailing Wall" in Jerusalem which is visited by many Jews on Saturdays and during celebrations in accordance with a custom that goes back to the first century AD.

made the few surviving Jews determined to rebuild their national home. The Zionist movement which started at the end of the nineteenth century with the aim of creating a national centre in Palestine, was intensified. From this, the state of Israel was finally established in 1948, in the very area which witnessed the events related in the Bible.

Jewish festivals

The Jews observe five principal annual festivals. Three, Passover (Pesach), historically connected with the exodus from Egypt under Moses, Shabuoth (Feast of Weeks, or Pentecost), celebrating the harvests of barley, wheat, etc., and Sukkoth (Feast of Tabernacles or of the Ingathering) marking the ingathering of all fruits at the season's end as well as the Israelites' dwelling in tents in their wilderness wanderings to the Promised Land, last several days. Rosh Hashana, the New Year, and Yom Kippur, the Day of Atonement, are one-day festivals, the former taking place about mid-September, the latter ten days later.

121

Discoveries
Man's great adventures

What is a discovery? What is the difference between discovering and inventing? The dictionary answers the first question: discovery is learning about facts, phenomena, things and places which were previously unknown, and finding what had not been known before. In this definition, there is an element of chance (that is, accident plays a part) which partly answers the second question, which is more complicated. In the majority of cases, the inventor knows what he is aiming at and strives to reach a certain result by experiments and research. The discoverer, however, is often assisted by luck. In everyday language, nevertheless, "invention" and "discovery" often coincide. The two words are used synonymously most of the time.

The history of man is also the history of his discoveries and his progress towards an ever-higher level of civilization. History can be divided into three periods: the period of the unknown inventors (which lasted for thousands of years); the period of the great inventors (which coincided at one time with that of the great explorers, that is the discoverers of new lands); and lastly the third period, the one we are in now, which depends above all upon the work of teams and relies heavily on the technical, economic and industrial resources of a country.

It is difficult to say which of these periods is most fascinating. For its aura of mystery, the first period could not fail to stimulate the imagination and admiration of man today. There is no doubt that even at that time invention and discovery were, in practice, the same thing. Fire, for example, was discovered, in the sense that it was probably the result of lightning striking a dried tree trunk, and bursting into flame. It was then up to man to transform what at first appeared as a threat into a valuable asset. In fact, man used fire to improve his living standards, to defend himself from wild animals, to manufacture instruments for work and war, to cook (cooked food was an important step forward in human development), and to exploit the other elements offered by the natural environment.

The pictures on this page show that the Egyptians understood the use of the plough, travelled in boats with oars and sails and knew how to smelt metals.

Even before he discovered fire, man may already have begun to use his intelligence to modify his living conditions. Who was the first man to make a weapon and a hammer at the same time by continually striking one stone with another? Every object which is a normal part of our everyday lives owes its origin to man's amazing ability to "see" beyond appearances. Let us imagine, for example, the moment when, observing a slender bone, a cave-dweller suddenly realized that he could make from it the perfect instrument for sewing together the skins that protected him from the cold.

From accident to design

The history of discoveries is too confused and complicated to be told in an orderly manner. We must proceed in steps, jumping from one century to another. Once someone asked Albert Einstein, "How do you discover something?" The famous scientist replied, with irritation, that if he had known that, he would have been able to manufacture anything, even gold.

As time passed, history was able to name the discoverers, observation began to be supported by study and research, individual ability, genius and determination. The second period was dominated by the great inventors and the great scholars: from Archimedes to Galileo, from Leonardo to Newton, from Lavoisier to Maxwell and Einstein. It was a period of over two thousand years (from the Greeks to the beginning of this century) during which the highest peaks of the arts, exploration and the mysteries of the spiritual world were reached.

Curiosity was linked with enthusiasm and determination in research. This was the new direction; man already had the knowledge of the past on which he could work and apply his intelligence.

During this second period, geographical discoveries were also made, first by accident and then, with increasing frequency, by individual inititiative. Many were the result of military expeditions but others were due to the curiosity of an individual voyager. Only since man began to plan his discoveries, of whatever kind – scientific, artistic, practical or geographical – has it been possible to give names and accurate dates.

To explore and to discover are words that often mean "to conquer", since the discovery can give power and wealth to the man who made it, or rather to the man who exploits it. When America was discovered in 1492, no one could have estimated the immense riches that Europe would derive from that continent. Yet Christopher Columbus, who had found it

Right, a fourteenth-century miniature showing a page from the Treatise on Automata, *attributed to the Arab al-Ghazzali. This work, which dates back to the twelfth century, described ancient mechanical devices and actual automata which could perform various movements with the aid of levers and wires.*

by accident while looking for a westward route to India, immediately realized that this mysterious new land promised important acquisitions and economic benefits.

We often see pictures of Columbus on board one of his three galleys, scanning the horizon with a telescope. This is a mistake. At the time of Columbus, the telescope had not yet been invented.

The discovery of potatoes

As we have said, a discovery does not always refer to a new land or to a mechanical or practical instrument designed by a scientist; often it is something much more simple. Let us jump the centuries and consider one of our most common foods: the potato. To us, it seems that the potato has always been part of our daily meals. In fact this is not so, for like many other foods, the potato was unknown in Europe until a few centuries ago. It is said to have been an unknown priest, a follower of Francisco Pizarro (one of the great colonizers of South America) who discovered the merits of this vegetable and introduced it into Spain in the sixteenth century. It spread to other countries, but it was not until the middle of the following century that the potato was cultivated throughout Europe. Its acceptance was delayed by the mistrust of some clergy who, since the potato was not named in the Bible, feared that it was a food prohibited for Christians.

Let us turn to the year 1000 and try as far as possible to proceed in an orderly fashion. Very little had been discovered since the end of the Greek and Roman civilizations. Even the needle, discovered by cave-dwellers, had made little progress and it was to be several centuries before the emergence of the steel needle we use today. In the year 1000, however, the Italians discovered the fork: it was used for the first time in Venice, at the table of the doge Orseolo, who had married a Byzantine woman. She introduced the use of good table manners and persuaded her husband not to eat with his fingers. The practice was slow to spread, however. By the Renaissance, forks were used for eating throughout Italy, but the habit was not generally accepted in England until the seventeenth century.

By the year 1000 (the dates are uncertain) gun powder had also probably been discovered by the Chinese. It is difficult at this time to plot the course of discoveries. During these centuries, discoveries were passed from one European country to another. The attitude of the Church and the authorities was often suspicious of anything new and man was taught to be contented with what he had.

The great navigators were perhaps the only people to feel the need to look beyond the domestic horizons. Slowly, however, every man grew into a new historical and social dimension. The craftsmen studied ancient experience and developed new methods of working: a

discovery can even arise from daily routine work.

The solitary geniuses

What great inventors do we hear about in the beginning? Certainly they existed. We often read the names of inventors and accept them without going any deeper. Yet the true story is always longer and more complicated. Even the telescope, universally attributed to Galileo, was actually based on previous discoveries by others. These were discoveries in the true sense of the word, since in the case of the telescope, it was a boy who put to his eye a cardboard tube with two lenses in it and noticed that with it he could see people and objects in the distance. To sum up, the history of discoveries seems to show that the "solitary genius" rarely if ever existed.

Nevertheless, Leonardo da Vinci is often seen as an example of this type of genius. There is little that his fertile mind did not consider, from the aeroplane to the submarine, from the steam engine to the cinematograph. He even drew detailed plans and designs of his ideas. It is difficult, however, even without the usual confusion of terms, to number Leonardo among the discoverers: he was first and foremost an inventor, a man who by detailed study and close observation was able to foresee the life and the instruments of the future.

After Leonardo, the solitary genius became even rarer, just as the probability of discovering new lands became less. Today explorers have covered nearly all of the earth's surface, have penetrated the jungles, braved the polar regions and desert expanses and, having photographed the earth from space, know that there can be little left to discover. Now man has turned towards space where he knows there are no limits. He has already reached the moon (Neil Armstrong was the first man to set foot on our satellite on the 21 July 1969), in the future, someone could walk on Mars. Apart from this, man knows there are many things left to discover, if not on the earth, then within it. What do we know, in fact, about the inside of the earth? Oil, one of the most important discoveries for the modern world, comes from the sub-soil. Who can say what is in

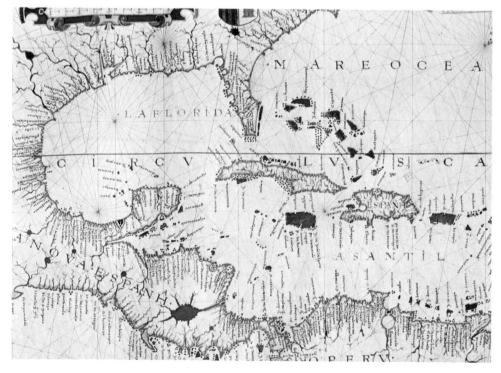

Important discoveries in every field took place during the Renaissance. The geographical expeditions of this period, which led to the discovery of America, caused a revolution in the way the world and creation were viewed. Above left, a painting of Christopher Columbus on the bridge of the flag ship. Left, a map of Central America, made in 1571.

124

store in the subterranean world that has already given man carbon, precious stones, gold and other metals? Underwater exploration may also bring extraordinary discoveries which will greatly affect the future.

In this necessarily disjointed story, where the discovery of a continent is equated to that of the potato or the fork, we should not undervalue man's aggressive instincts. Many of his inventions were and are born not from a desire for progress, but from a desire to conquer and subdue. Inventions such as, for example, the plough, money, the sewing machine, medicines and the telephone arose from the hope of improving the quality of life. Inventions such as gun powder, the cannon and the atomic bomb, however, were born (as was the first sharpened stone of the cave-dweller) from the exigencies of war.

The warlike discoveries did not always result from man's latent violence. Scientists such as Albert Einstein and Enrico Fermi, who were held responsible for the

most terrible weapon of all time, did not make their discoveries for homicidal purposes. The use to which their studies of atoms was put was beyond their control. The force of the explosion of the first atomic bomb on 16 July 1945 in New Mexico, caused the scientists to try to dissuade the American president from using such weapons. Their appeal was not heeded and on 6 August 1945 an atomic bomb was dropped on the city of Hiroshima.

Between the two opposing forces (one for creation and the other for destruction) the world nevertheless progresses and even research to produce terrible devices like the nuclear bombs can have peaceful applications.

Today, for example, nuclear power stations are being constructed as alternative sources of energy, for the time when oil will no longer be available in sufficient quantity. Discussions on this subject naturally become heated because opinions are so sharply divided concerning the possible risks involved.

During the eighteenth century, the English navigator James Cook explored the Pacific Ocean, discovering many islands. He eventually died in the Hawaiian islands, as shown in the painting above. His voyages brought a great deal of valuable knowledge to the western world.

In the seventeenth century, academies of learning flourished in Europe. The two engravings above show the Accademia del Cimento at Florence (left) and the Académie Française (right). Below, a table inspired by the studies of the great anatomist, Marcello Malpighi.

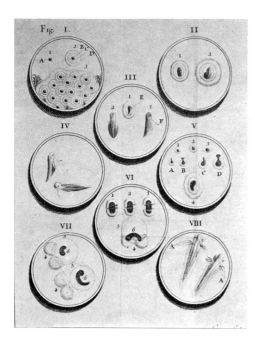

The third period

The present century, it is said, has seen the greatest discoveries. In the twentieth century, antibiotics, radar, the laser, nuclear energy, plastics were discovered together with all those achievements which were the result of research started in the preceding century (as in the case of the aeroplane). Today we arrive at a definite result by working in teams, pooling labour, knowledge, experiments and resources. We live in what we defined at the beginning as the third period. The desire to know the name of inventors is decreasing, that is the heroes and personalities that in the past were often identified in legend. It is impossible to know whether this is a good or a bad thing. History will no longer be enlivened with anecdotes, but today there is no longer any need for legends and myths to add to the value of the discovery. Imagine, for example, the triumph of Pierre and Marie Curie when, after study and research in the laboratory, they discovered radium at the end of the nineteenth century, or the emotion of Guglielmo Marconi when for the first time, on 12 December 1901, he heard a telegraphic message across the Atlantic Ocean. It is this type of joy which unites the great and humble discoverers: for example, from Luigi Galvani, who studied electrical phenomena, to the unknown inventor of the soap pad for polishing saucepans and kettles.

It would be interesting to make continuous comparisons between geographical and scientific discoveries, but that is not possible. The skill and curiosity of man do not always move on parallel lines. For example, at the time of Christopher Columbus, Ferdinand Magellan and Sebastian Cabot, people died from various infectious diseases for which there was no remedy except hope. The new civilization that emerged from the Middle Ages was full of vigour, but its efforts were not accompanied by sufficient scientific investigation. What mattered was to understand the world, to see what already existed and to take home what could be useful. Only when mankind tired of this quest did he begin to think of himself, his standard of living and his health. Inventions then followed one after another. Before inventing the cinema, television, the quartz clock or the vacuum cleaner, man had to satisfy his need for survival. Luxuries were discovered after necessities.

We could conclude at this point that discovery is always a reflection of a collective interest (geographical, technical or scientific), but this is not so. Discovery can be personal. We all discover what we do not know. A baby, in his early development, continually "discovers" things, people, situations, words. He invents nothing, but his day brings even more surprises than that of an explorer who learns about new lands and peoples for the first time.

It is not necessary to be a genius to know the excitement of discovery and intuition. We can all experience it. Self-discovery, learning more about oneself, can lead also to far-reaching consequences for others. Consider the importance of psychoanalysis. Sigmund Freud could not have influenced medicine (and psychiatry in particular) if he had not first of all discovered within himself, in his consciousness, the truth and explanations of certain human behaviour. To sum up, discoveries will continue to be made as long as man exists.

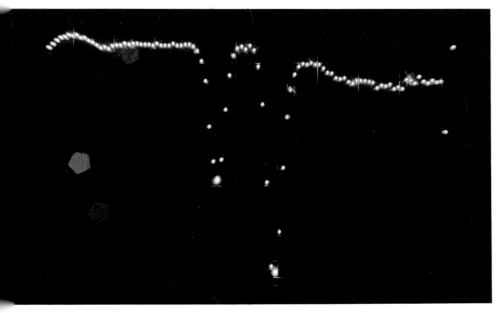

Top, the laboratory where Marie Curie, while studying the rays emitted by uranium salts, discovered radioactivity. She and her husband Pierre also discovered radium (1898). Above, the eighteenth-century laboratory of Leopold II of Lorena, Grand Duke of Tuscany. Left, the emission curve of a radio-active element, caesium, shown on the screen of a modern computer.

127

Explorations
In search of mysterious lands

E MESTA PLANA
esta ho Reino de scosia ho Reino di mglaterra
a vn derlanda ho colado de framdes ho Reino
devormadia bretanha de liao de tula framsa bis
caya esturias galiza portugal ho algarue am
dalusia ho Reino de granada de vulensa ytalia
toda secilia ho Reino de tunes dargel de salis de tu
tiuo de fes de mafogos sardenha Corsega ma
lyorca a conxonia todo gine ho Reino de benim ha
mala geta a mina has Jlhas decabo Sule hasta
as de canaria as Jlhas dos açores

The history of explorations is long and complicated. It tells how one civilization or previously isolated place comes into contact with another for the first time. Discovery and exploration have often gone together; the discovery may be the result of an exploration and the exploration the consequence of a discovery.

In the beginning, it was chance and necessity which drove man towards the unknown: the nomadic life was the first unconscious attempt at exploration. Later, there were other incentives: the lure of riches, the simple desire for adventure, missionary fervour and military expeditions. The first navigators, were also explorers: Cretans, Phoenicians, Greeks and all the peoples of the ancient Mediterranean world, travelled to escape from the confines of their own lands and search for greener pastures elsewhere, woods with more birds and animals for hunting and more fertile countryside. We know, for example, that about 600 BC an Egyptian pharaoh ordered some ships to circumnavigate Africa and that a similar Carthaginian enterprise set out in the fifth century BC under Hanno to whom 30,000 men were entrusted for the mission.

True or legendary descriptions

Explorers also have to describe what they see. It is as an explorer as well as a historian that we should see the Greek Herodotus, who in the fifth century before Christ journeyed to various countries with the precise intention of writing down what he heard. "I am giving", he wrote "the results of my enquiries, so that the memory of what men have done shall not perish from the world nor their achievements . . . go unsung." The conquests of Alexander the Great are today considered as expeditions of exploration: the desire to know and understand the countries and people they conquer has always been part of military expeditions.

That was the attitude of the Romans. They were untiring travellers and courageous explorers of the countries they conquered, providing the government at home with very detailed descriptions of all they saw. With this evidence

An atlas compiled in 1563 by the Portuguese Lazaro Luis shows us Europe and West Africa as they were then known and the explorations made to them at that time.

he geographers of ancient times were
ble to draw the first reliable maps of the
hen known world.

At this time, people travelled from
ecessity or military obligation rather than
or love of knowledge. Strange legends
vere born. The new maps of the earth
vere no longer drawn to provide
nformation for the learned, but to feed the
uperstitions of fools: unknown lands
vere thought to be populated by
monsters and fantastic creatures. Nonetheless, in the same period, one northern
ce felt the lure of adventure: they were
he Vikings, who made long voyages in
heir graceful and seaworthy longships. It
not known exactly how far they went
n their daring journeys. From their
omes in Scandinavia, they raided the
oasts of Iceland, Germany, France,
ritain, North Africa and Italy. They
ttled in Greenland in around AD 980
d in about the year 1000 landed on the
ast of North America, 500 years before
olumbus reached it. Over two hundred
ars later, a Franciscan monk, Giovanni
Pian del Carpine, was sent by Pope
nocent IV as Ambassador in Asia to the
eat Khan; we still have his *Historia*
ongolorum, in which the habits and
stumes of the people he met are
igently recorded. Just as interesting is
e tale of another medieval explorer, the
emish monk, William of Rubruck, sent
ong the Tartars by the King of France.

The adventures of Marco Polo

The great Venetian traveller, Marco Polo,
wrote about his journey across the world
from Venice to China and back and his
adventures in the lands of the Mongol
Emperor Kublai. Marco Polo was seventeen years old when in 1271 he left his
native Venice with his father and uncle to
visit the court of Kublai Khan. The journey
to China took nearly three years. The
Polos spent seventeen years with the
Great Khan but at last they set out for
home and after a long journey, eventually
arrived in Venice after an absence of
twenty-five years. Their relations did not
recognize them.

War had broken out between Venice
and Genoa and Marco Polo was taken
prisoner during a battle. While he was
imprisoned, he dictated his memoirs to a
fellow prisoner. This book, entitled *The
Book of Marco Polo, Citizen of Venice,
Called Million, wherein is Recounted the
Wonders of the World,* became known
later as *The Million.* From it the West was
able to understand more about Asia, its
peoples, its products and its geographical
and social characteristics. By arousing
interest in the countries of the East, the
work also helped to inspire later explorations. For two hundred years at least
Europeans dreamed of going to the
distant East to make their fortunes and to
discover new marvels. In time, the

*Marco Polo at the court of the Great Khan. He
recorded his experiences in* The Million, *the work
which, besides making Chinese civilization
known to the West, gave great encouragement to
further exploration.*

development of commerce effectively
reduced the distances and contributed to
the rebirth of study and related activities.

Meanwhile the Arab countries had
carefully preserved the Greek and Roman
discoveries by continuing to visit China,
India and West Africa and in so doing had
enriched their cultural basis which for
those days was already well-founded.
Contacts between the Arab and Christian
worlds were limited to battles and
religious rivalries. The Arabs had a sound
geographical knowledge of the world, but
little of the results they obtained in their
explorations reached Europe where progress was entrusted for the most part to
individual initiative, ambition and
curiosity.

A school of seamanship at the castle

From the fifteenth century onwards,
explorations and discoveries are more
difficult to trace. The son of a Portuguese
king, Henry entered history with the
nickname of "the Navigator" because he
transformed his castle into a school for the
nautical arts where men received a
thorough training which turned them into

129

fully fledged sailors. The plan to send ships to explore the African coast was Henry's idea, but it was not until after his death that Portuguese caravels entered the Gulf of Guinea. The dream of circumnavigating Africa was taken up again by Bartolomeu Dias, who managed to cross the Tropic of Capricorn and to get as far as the southernmost tip of the continent. On the return voyage to Portugal, he erected a pillar at the Cape of Good Hope, which one tradition says he named "the cape of storms". It was finally Vasco da Gama who, sailing round the entire coast of the continent, arrived in India and opened the way not only to explorations and to commerce but also to European domination and to new rivalries and wars amongst the leading powers for the capture of those rich markets.

Columbus and Magellan

How does Christopher Columbus fit into the picture at this time? He reached America in 1492, convinced that he had arrived in Asia, basing his belief on the descriptions by Marco Polo. In his objectives, he was an explorer and he died without realizing how important his geographical discovery was, still believing that he had done no more than show his contemporaries a better sea route to the Indies. After him, however, the exploration of the New World became more organized. The reports made by Amerigo Vespucci on his successive expeditions finally demonstrated that that continent was not in fact Asia, but a "New World". In honour of Vespucci, a German geographer proposed to name the new continent "Land of Amerigo": America, in other words.

Columbus' discovery and the certainty of a sea route to India encouraged other navigators to attempt voyages of exploration beyond the oceans. The Portuguese, Ferdinand Magellan, obtained from King Carlos V of Spain both ships and men (denied him in his own country) to circumnavigate the globe by sailing along the Atlantic coast of South America and then thrusting out into the unknown Pacific Ocean until at last he reached the Philippines. He sailed from Spain on 20 September 1519, and had to contend with storms, mutinies by his crews, scurvy, hunger, massacres and cannibals.

Of the 265 men who left with him, only eighteen returned to Spain, "weaker than men have ever been before". He himself was killed in an ambush by the natives of the island of Mactan on 27 April 1521. Amongst the survivors of that disastrous voyage was an Italian, Antonio Pigafetta, and it is to him that we are indebted for the chronicle of that astounding voyage.

The sixteenth century: the century of voyages

Other routes were explored. While Spaniards and Portuguese established the sea routes to the south, the English and the Dutch sought the hazardous routes of the north. At the end of the fifteenth century and for the whole of the sixteenth, several people tried to reach China by crossing the northern seas, but all were pushed back inexorably by the barrier of ice.

One of the most famous explorers of the fifteenth century was John Cabot, who was born in Genoa but settled in England, from where he set out on his expeditions. During one of these voyages, in June 1497, he landed in Newfoundland, or Labrador, which was never definitely established. On his return he obtained authorization from King Henry VII for a second expedition. Later he died in mysterious circumstances. His son Sebastian carried out a thorough investigation of North America and afterwards explored the coasts of South America.

The great explorers of the Elizabethan age in England continued the search for new lands. Their main objective was to find a westward route to the Far East. The best-known explorers of the period were John Hawkins, Walter Raleigh and, especially, Francis Drake who in 1577–80 became the first Englishman to sail round the world.

Towards the end of the sixteenth century the Dutch navigator, Willem Barents on his third journey north in 1596, became trapped in the ice off the coast of Novaya Zemlya. He abandoned his ship and together with the rest of his crew built a large wooden hut in which they all lived for seven months struggling against the icy cold, the storm-force winds and hunger. As soon as they had built two sloops as replacements for the lost ship, they resumed their voyage: Barents, by now at the end of his powers, died during the voyage. For a long time after that there was no further exploration of the northern seas.

The "conquistadores"

The years following saw a great deal of violence. Exploration often brings conquest, plunder and tyranny. The vanguard of colonization in South America, were men like Hernán Cortés and Francisco Pizarro, calling themselves conquistadores (conquerors), a name which often implied pillagers, to whom is due the fall of ancient and noble civilizations like that of the Aztecs in Mexico and the Incas in Peru.

In North America, too, it was greed

which drew the new explorers. Their main motivations were the search for riches and the exploitation of the land. The old native populations were decimated. The Indians were the legitimate inhabitants of those lands which the Europeans took from them. Adventurers from every part of the world arrived in the new continent to make a new life for themselves, to found colonies and to exploit the immense resources of a still unknown paradise.

For many Europeans, the Americas became a land of promise, a still unconquered continent. At the same time, the Far East was attracting merchants and missionaries who entered peacefully but led the way to later colonization.

The fever for exploration did not diminish in the eighteenth century. The ships were stouter and more seaworthy, the equipment greatly improved, and so long voyages became less dangerous. In 1728, the Dane, Vitus Bering, undertook several expeditions on behalf of the Czar of Russia towards the ice-fields of the north. His main task was to determine whether Asia and America were connected by land. He decided that the two continents were not joined and the strait which separates the two today bears his name.

The great explorer Cook

The most famous of the explorers of the eighteenth century was an Englishman, James Cook, born in 1728, the son of a farm labourer, and a cabin-boy on a merchant ship by the time he was fifteen. He led three important expeditions. In the first (1768–1771), Cook had to take observers to Tahiti to observe the transit of Venus across the sun, and then to continue the geographical study which had already been started. Unfortunately, the astronomical observations proved uncertain. Cook then set himself to explore the island of Tahiti and small neighbouring islands and afterwards to set sail again in the direction of New Zealand and Australia. In the summer of 1771, he returned to England. The following year he left England again charged with the task of finding out whether or not there existed a continent to the south of Africa and, if there was, to explore it. After sailing along the African coast, he reached Antarctic water, crossed the Antarctic circle, but failed to find any habitable land.

He then decided to set course toward New Zealand and from there to undertake another thorough search of the southern seas to discover this mysterious land which in reality did not exist. During the long and dangerous voyage, he disembarked on Easter Island, which did n then appear on any map. In his third expedition (1776), finally, he set out once again to explore the northern Pacific, but the voyage cost him his life. But in 1779 the inhabitants of the Hawaiian (Sandwich) islands, after worshipping him like a god, killed and hacked him to pieces.

Many navigators followed the trails which Cook had blazed. The coasts of Australia were explored and people from Britain settled there, but for many years the interior remained unexplored, and some parts are still unexplored today.

Home again from their adventures, the explorers hastened to commit their experiences to writing, illustrating them with drawings. We see some of them on this page: an encounter with a "terrifying" sea-lion near the Strait of Magellan; the exotic temple of the king in the Sandwich Islands (now Hawaii); a boldly-conceived bridge of ropes across a small river in Peru.

Meanwhile other men were still going in search of fortune in the distant Americas, struggling with the most hostile country, fighting the redskins and massacring them, sailing on unknown rivers and looking for gold in the rocks and river-beds. The march of thousands of treasure-seekers towards California and the Far West intensified and the penetration was not always peaceful. Sometimes, however, the expeditions were for scientific reasons only: their purpose was to identify the most fertile regions and the places most suitable for building roads and, later, railways. The penetration of South America was equally intensive, though often hindered by mountains, jungles and swamps.

The opening up of Africa

In the nineteenth century, a great curiosity developed about the African continent, which until then had been thought of mainly as a hunting preserve for the slave-traders. European geographers and scientists dreamed of revealing the secrets of the dark continent, of discovering the sources of its rivers, mapping the boundaries of the deserts and learning about the ways of the native peoples. Some met their deaths in the course of these investigations. One of the most intriguing questions concerned the source of the Nile. Where did it rise? Nobody yet knew.

The most famous of those who followed the course of the Nile are the Englishmen, J.H. Speke, J.A. Grant, S.W. Baker and the German, G.A. Schweinfurth, but it was above all David Livingstone and Henry Stanley who were the heroes of African exploration in the last century. Livingstone was a Scottish doctor and missionary. He had no need of elaborate support for his plan to penetrate to the very heart of the continent, once he had left Cape Town and was on his way northwards. His method was simple: he walked from one village to the next like a pilgrim, and his weapons were a Bible, a doctor's bag and a supply of medicines. He preached the gospel and cured the sick: the natives always welcomed him with open arms. In this way, Livingstone was the first white man to set foot in the interior of Southern Africa, to admire the magnificent falls of the river Zambesi and to cross Lakes Nyasa, Mweru and Bangweulu. Contact with him was lost when he reached Lake Tanganyika, the whole of whose shore-line he explored. He was found again by the journalist Stanley, who had been sent out by an American newspaper, with the bare instruction, "Find Livingstone". He died soon after of dysentery without ever

David Livingstone and Henry Stanley: two names indissolubly linked with the exploration of Africa. Livingstone, who was a doctor, crossed the "dark continent" from village to village (on the right we see him being received by the natives), until eventually all trace of him was lost. Stanley, an American journalist, set out to find him: we see Stanley, below right, in typical explorers' clothes while shooting the rapids of a river.

An old print records the meeting in 1818 of English explorer Sir John Ross with the natives of Prince Regent Inlet on his voyage to Baffin Bay.

returning to his homeland. Stanley continued the exploration work of Livingstone and covered the whole of that part of the African continent known as the Congo (roughly the modern state of Zaire).

In the same period, Asia regained the same fascination which it had in the time of Marco Polo. During the nineteenth century, two French missionaries crossed Tibet and penetrated as far as the forbidden city of Lhasa, seat of the Dalai Lama, leader of the Buddhist faithful. A Russian, Przhevalsky, explored central Asia, discovered Lake Lop Nor, the sources of the Blue and Yellow rivers and for fifteen years overcame every type of obstacle, accurately describing what he saw. The Swede, Sven Hedin, and other Europeans followed up his explorations. The Himalayas, in particular, attracted many expeditions but it was not until May 1953 that the Englishman, Edmund Hillary, succeeded in reaching the highest summit of all, Mount Everest. The following year an Italian expedition led by Ardito Desio and including the famous climbers Lino Lacedelli and Achille Compagnoni, conquered the second highest mountain in the world, known as K2.

The conquest of the poles

The North and South Poles also aroused man's curiosity. In 1909, Robert Peary succeeded in reaching the North Pole and in 1926 another American, Richard Byrd, flew over the Pole in an aeroplane as Amundsen and Nobile were to do a little later in a dirigible. In 1958 the American atomic submarine *Nautilus* was actually able to sail beneath the ice of the North Pole.

The same Roald Amundsen on 14 December 1911, had reached the South Pole and planted the Norwegian flag, beating by only a month his friend and rival Robert Falcon Scott who perished on his return from the Pole, overcome by fatigue, hunger and cold.

The taste for exploring remains to this day. The earth still holds many secrets for man, who continues to explore by mapping the ocean depths and even going down into the craters of volcanoes. Above all, the attention of science is drawn towards space, the missions by American and Soviet astronauts and space probes into the unknown are only the beginning of a long adventure.

. . . and lastly the exploration of space

It is difficult to compare the explorers of former times with the astronauts: not only because the "worlds" they set out to discover are so different, but above all because space voyages form part of scientific research rather than explorations pure and simple. Most of the important space enterprises to date have been carried out without direct participation by human beings: the probes launched in recent years provide us with pictures and information about the other planets without the enormous expenditure and grave risks of manned missions. The conquest of the moon (from Armstrong and Aldrin in July 1969 to Cernan and Schmitt in December 1972) nonetheless remains a great historic achievement.

Inventions
The wheel and the spaceship

To invent means to have a completely new idea, to plan or make something that has not been thought of before. Today we live in a world full of inventions: cars, aeroplanes, radio, the telephone, television, calculators, missiles, robots and electronic games, but even the sewing needle and the plates from which we eat would not have existed if man had not one day invented them.

An invention may be the result of years of study, chance, or necessity. A well-known saying declares that "necessity is the mother of invention". Sometimes there is one inventor, but more often there are several. Although an invention may be attributed to one person, the hard work, curiosity and experience of many others have contributed towards it.

Even behind the most everyday inventions there are often stories of strange changes in fortune, chance occurrences, arguments and disagreements. For example, take the invention of the match. This must surely be one of the most common and least-regarded inventions. Surprisingly, the match is not a very ancient invention: it originated only in the last century. Before that people had to strike a flint against a rough surface to produce a spark.

The "modern" sulphur match came into use in the nineteenth century and there is much controversy over who actually invented it. Germans, Austrians, English, French and Italians are all contenders for the honour. However around 1830 the increasing use of "lucifers" unleashed furious arguments because they were considered dangerous. They were extremely difficult to ignite and often erupted in a shower of sparks. They had a very unpleasant smell and some English boxes carried the warning, "Persons whose lungs are delicate should by no means use lucifers".

In 1844, a Swede, Gustaf Pasch, had the idea of making matches safe by placing some of the combustion ingredients on the striking surface of the box. The next year, red phosphorus was discovered by Anton von Schrötter. This was of great interest to matchmakers as it was nontoxic and did not burst into flames when exposed to air. Seven years later, in 1852, another Swede, J. E. Lundström, used red phosphorus and the principle of separating the combustible ingredients to manufacture a safety match. By 1856 matches of this type were being manufactured in several European countries.

The history of invention is the history of the world: in the beginning of man's existence, he lacked any of the possessions which we now take for granted. Today man's environment is what he himself, over the centuries, has been able to create, both for good and evil, in the discoveries of peace and the inventions of war. The creativity of man works in two different directions: prehistoric man invented both the arms necessary for defence and attack and also the tool needed for a peace-time existence.

The invention of the boat, like many others, is lost in antiquity. The earliest record goes back to the development of the ship between 6000 and 3500 BC and is attributed to the Egyptians, but even before this man had discovered the possibility of making water transport for himself. Above, two boats on Lake Titicaca (on the Peru-Bolivia border): their shape and the way in which they are built remind us of their Egyptian predecessors.

Left, a solid wheel from the Bronze Age; below, a spoked wheel from the Iron Age. The spokes were a great step forward: it became possible to build lighter and faster carts.

A seal of the fourth millennium before Christ, recovered from a royal tomb at Ur in Mesopotamia, bears the oldest known picture of a plough. On the left is an Etruscan plough.

Ancient inventions

Many objects which are familiar today have remote origins. We may wonder, for example, who invented cloth. The first clothes were made out of animal skins, and then woven materials were made, perhaps as a by-product of another invention – fishing nets. It is in this way that one invention sets off another. Who thought of the plough? Probably it was those first men who, hurriedly scratching furrows in the ground with a stick, found that it would make the sowing of the seed easier. And who invented boats? The first man who, seeing a tree trunk floating on a river, jumped on to it and was carried down by the current. There was also that other man who dug the trunk out, and the one who, realizing how strongly the wind blew, thought of using it to push the boat into motion. He fastened a large piece of cloth to a vertical pole and so invented the sail. Civilization is especially indebted to the man who invented the wheel, and so set in motion a series of other inventions which today allow us to travel almost anywhere. The earliest wheels came from funerary wagons or hearses and were found in graves at Kish in Mesopotamia and date from 3000 BC. Pictures of carts have also been found on clay tablets from Mesopotamia.

The discovery of metals stimulated man's imagination and inventive powers. The desire to find uses for new materials encourages the research which leads to more inventions. Man also wanted to produce beautiful objects as well as useful ones. The production of glass helped him to gratify his aesthetic sense. The earliest wholly glass objects from Egypt are beads dating from soon after 2500 BC. About a thousand years later, small glass vessels were being made there. They were of opaque blue glass and were decorated with coiled threads of yellow, white, green or red glass.

The intelligent and creative man became vain and ambitious and these feelings also furthered research. A poor community is satisfied with mere essentials, but a rich and sophisticated society demands far more. A humble man is content to own a house, while a rich man wants that house to be beautiful and well equipped. The idea of what was useful, therefore, expanded, adapting itself to what individuals and society as a whole wanted and were able to achieve.

This presented the inventor with another challenge: to create machines which would allow men to work better and with less fatigue. Hands alone are not enough. We need extra power to do complicated work, to dig out mountains, to bridge gaps, to communicate at great distances, to construct ever taller buildings and to go at ever increasing speeds. But man wants even more: he wishes to create new substances, to transform natural resources and adapt them to his own expanding needs. Take plastic, for example: until a few decades ago it did not exist, but today it plays a large part in our lives and has in many cases replaced metals, wood and cloth.

It is impossible to decide what are the most important inventions for mankind. No scale of merit can exist and it is only in recent times that history has recorded the names of inventors and described what they have done. Of course, the ancient past also has its great men, such as Archimedes of Syracuse, who lived in the

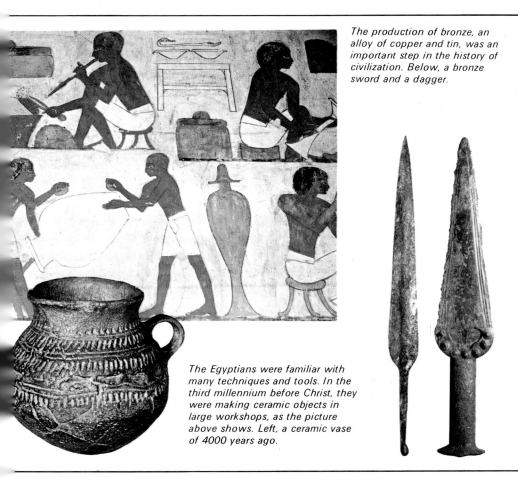

The Egyptians were familiar with many techniques and tools. In the third millennium before Christ, they were making ceramic objects in large workshops, as the picture above shows. Left, a ceramic vase of 4000 years ago.

The production of bronze, an alloy of copper and tin, was an important step in the history of civilization. Below, a bronze sword and a dagger.

This statuette which depicts a warrior with sword and bow is also of bronze. It comes from the nuraghi culture, named after the nuraghi or stone towers built in Sardinia about 3000 years ago.

third century before Christ and invented the pulley and at least forty different machines. However, we need to let many centuries elapse before being certain that legend is not contaminating truth. For example, the Chinese, the Arabs, the Greeks, the Etruscans, the Finns and the Italians have all been claimed as the inventors of the compass. The earliest authentic information concerning its use comes from China in about AD 1100, but the compass may well have been used long before it was written about. It is still impossible to be certain where it was first invented and whether knowledge of it was passed from one country to another or whether it was discovered independently in different places.

It seems most probable that women were responsible for all the important early household inventions, from the basin to the needle. Their names rarely occur among those of the early inventors, but there did emerge, probably soon after the first century AD, the name of Mary the Jewess as the inventor of stills, that is receiving vessels suitable for the production of perfumes, medicine and liquors. Tradition attributes to her the invention of the method of cooking food over boiling hot steam, and even today, many centuries later, we speak of "cooking with a *bain-Marie*". This *bain-Marie* was really a part of the equipment for distilling.

The credit for the great inventions, which made a significant change, for better or for worse, in the human condition, is often divided not only between various individuals but also between different races and civilizations. For example, who invented gunpowder? It was probably the Chinese who used it around the year 1000 to fire rockets. Nevertheless, before this, incendary materials were often used in war. Many ancient writers mention the use of flaming arrows, fire pots and substances such as pitch, sulphur and charcoal. The Greeks used "liquid fire" against the Saracen ships in AD 673. The composition of the mixture was a closely guarded secret and has remained a mystery ever since. Scholars still argue about whether the Arabs brought gunpowder from China to Europe or whether the Europeans developed it. Certainly by the thirteenth century Europeans knew about gunpowder and by 1326 began manufacturing firearms.

The genius of Leonardo da Vinci

There is also confusion when one speaks of Leonardo da Vinci, the inventor *par excellence*, who was curious, intelligent, with many different resources and interests, an artist and scientist at the same

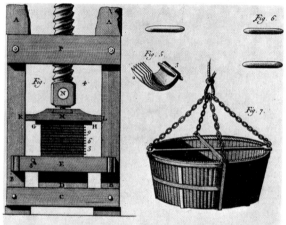
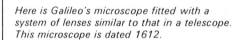

The invention of printing by movable characters is generally attributed to Johann Gutenberg (above is a page of the Bible, the first book printed by him in 1455), but it seems that the Chinese had already had the idea centuries before. Connected with printing is the invention of paper, and this, too, is attributed to the Chinese. Left, the manufacture of paper from the Encyclopédie *of Diderot.*

Here is Galileo's microscope fitted with a system of lenses similar to that in a telescope. This microscope is dated 1612.

Above, a curious thermometer with a spiral tube made by the Accademia del Cimento, a centre of learning founded in 1657 by the Grand Duke Leopold II of Tuscany de'Medici.

The print above shows sixteenth-century pumps for extracting water from the river and raising it to the reservoir of the aqueduct; these pumps were worked by a water-wheel.

A valuable watch of the eighteenth century. The first spring-driven clocks date back to the end of the fifteenth century.

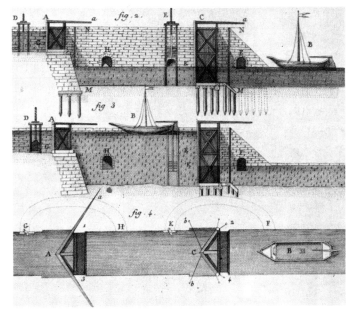

The building of canals can also be considered as an invention. The print on the right shows a navigable canal with many locks and lock-gates.

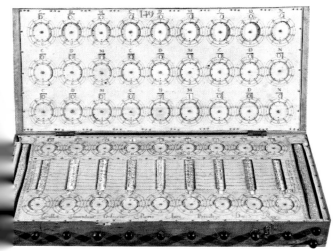

This complicated arithmetical machine dates from 1678, but the first true mechanical calculator was devised by the Frenchman, Blaise Pascal, at least thirty years before.

time. His plans and drawings anticipated many modern inventions from the helicopter to the parachute, from the aeroplane to the car, from military equipment to hydraulic mechanisms, from the diving suit to the armoured car. But the great variety of Leonardo's interests limited his achievement in any one of them. He would have had to live ten lives to achieve, as an inventor, the fame which he earned throughout the world as a painter. In most cases it was others who put into effect what had been to him a new, intuitive idea.

There is confusion over many inventions. Galileo, for example, is said to have invented the telescope, but he would not have been able to do this without the scientists and technicians who lived before him. In fact the telescope started in Holland in about 1608 and there are several stories about who first discovered it. One is that the young son of a Dutch oculist, Pieter Jansen, placed two lenses taken from his father's shop in a cardboard tube and found that when he looked through it he could clearly see people and objects a long way away.

This episode is useful to illustrate the difference between "discovery" and "invention". The young Pieter "discovered" the telescope by chance and deserves no real credit. Galileo "invented" it, rigorously applying the principles of geometrical optics and the results of his own studies. He devoted much of his time to improving the telescope, overcoming the difficulties of grinding and polishing the lenses, and soon succeeded in producing telescopes of greatly increased power. His telescope, which saw objects magnified, "almost a thousand times larger and more than thirty times closer than with the naked eye" and allowed him to see the sky and the stars. "It is intriguing to see the Moon as if it were very close," wrote Galileo. He then turned his attention to the microscope. He made several improvements to the compound microscope which had just been developed, and called his instrument a spyglass. "The flea is horrible in the extreme," he wrote, still intrigued after examining the insect with his new instrument. On the other hand, "the mosquito and the weevil are very beautiful".

Time passes over inventors, but the inventions remain, and one of these is the instrument which measures time. Long ago the shadows of trees were enough to regulate the daily activities of men and alarm-clocks to wake people up in the morning were not needed. The sun dials used by the ancient Egyptians, Greeks and Romans had the defect of working

137

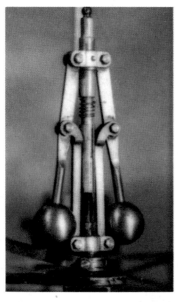

Left, the Leiden jar, the first electric condenser. The Dutchman Pieter van Musschenbroek discovered its properties in 1746.

The rapid development of industry, starting in the eighteenth century, led to great progress in the field of metallurgy. Right, the interior of a French foundry in 1850.

An early example of automation (above): an idea of James Watt to regulate the working of a steam engine which he had invented in 1769.

Below, another example of automation: a weaving loom of 1725 controlled by a perforated belt.

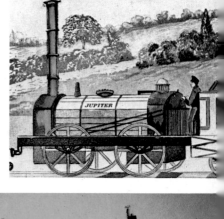

The introduction of steam was another fundamental step in the history of inventions. It served industry, agriculture (top right) and began the era of transport. Cugnot's engine of 1769 (above), one of the first locomotives and (below) one of the first ships without sails.

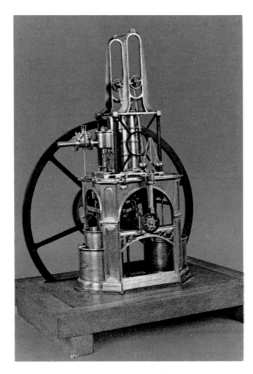

Machines from the nineteenth century. Above, the planing machine made in 1836 by the Englishman James Nasmyth. Right, the hydraulic lift by Augusto Stigler from Milan in Italy; below, a powerful steam engine, perfect in every detail, devised by Henry Maudslay in about 1815.

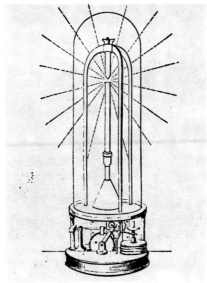

One of the greatest discoveries of the nineteenth century was electric light. The diagram on the right shows one of the pioneers, the voltaic arc-light made in 1847 by W.E. Staite. The incandescent lamp was invented by Thomas Alva Edison in 1879.

only by day. There were also water clocks, known as clepsydras, and sand glasses. The clock as we know it appeared towards the end of the thirteenth century and there are references to public striking clocks in Europe from about 1290 onwards. The first domestic clocks were smaller versions of these large public clocks. Spring-driven and pendulum clocks were developed during the fifteenth and sixteenth centuries, and clocks have continued to change and develop to the present day.

The history of inventions proceeds like a zigzag, forwards and backwards. The aeroplane is an example of this. We have to go back to mythological times, to the legend of Icarus and his wings of feathers and wax, which the sun melted with its heat. Man has always wanted to imitate the flight of birds and this desire has sown the seed of invention. Leonardo da Vinci designed flying machines, but in the end his machines remained merely as drawings. The possibility of flight interested many people over the centuries, but it was the Montgolfier brothers, who invented the balloon which made the first manned flight in 1783. The balloon became known as the Montgolfier in their honour. The history of the development of the aeroplane is long and complicated, but it was the American brothers, Wilbur and Orville Wright who, following a series of experiments, succeeded at last in lifting themselves into the air in 1903, in their first powered machine. This was the first successful mechanical flight.

From the eighteenth century to today

The closer one comes to modern times, the more inventions multiply. This is not because man has become more intelligent but because he has more detailed experience to draw on and better means at his disposal. There are successes in every field of human activity. In the eighteenth century, automation interested many scientists and small automata, or robots, were even built which, although only toys, contributed to the later development of more practical mechanisms. Also in the eighteenth century, Luigi Galvani discovered a new type of energy, electric energy, by observing the results of some of his experiments on frogs, but it was Alessandro Volta who later put these deductions on electrical phenomena to good use when he invented the battery. The importance of this invention was lost on its creator who wondered in what way his ''little toys'' could prove interesting. ''I believe'' he wrote, ''that in all this there

A great innovation in the field of typography was the steam-powered rotary printing press. Above is the one constructed by Richard Hoe between 1849 and 1851 for the daily newspaper, the New York Sun.

Right, detail of a model of the turbine motor made by the Englishman Lester Allen Pelton in 1889.

Below, the enormous antenna installed by Guglielmo Marconi at Cape Cod (USA) for the first transatlantic telegraph transmissions at the beginning of the twentieth century.

Above, the first sewing-machine made by Isaac Merritt Singer in 1851. Many of the attachments are still used in present-day models.

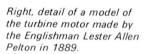

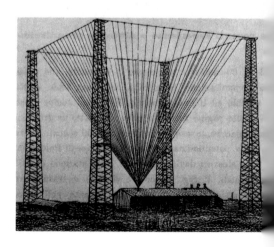

Right, the Olivetti Typewriter M20 was made in 1920 and was an improved version of an earlier model.

An old Swedish telephone of 1895, with a handle for establishing communication with the exchange.

In our century inventions have multiplied, especially in the field of communications. Above is the tele-stereograph of Édouard Belin (1907). Even at that time it was able to transmit photographs and drawings.

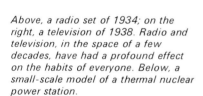

Above, a radio set of 1934; on the right, a television of 1938. Radio and television, in the space of a few decades, have had a profound effect on the habits of everyone. Below, a small-scale model of a thermal nuclear power station.

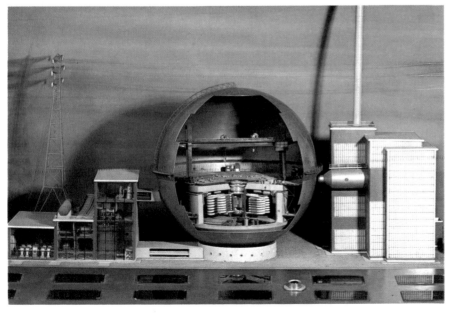

may be nothing more than the furore that goes with fashionable ideas. I have found nothing new or important.

The Great Age

The nineteenth century was rich in inventions. Discoveries in the field of electricity profoundly affected the behaviour of society, as so many activities were no longer restricted to the hours of daylight. The advances in mechanization had far-reaching consequences for the world of work, for while mechanization enabled production to increase, it also impelled men towards the contradictions of the industrial era. The improvements which James Watt had made to the steam engine in 1769, led to other inventions such as the locomotive, the steam-ship and industrial machines like the steam-powered rotary machine which revolutionized printing.

It is difficult to keep pace with all these inventions and often we do not know exactly when they came about. When was the submarine, for example, invented? The credit for building the first submarine is usually given to a Dutchman, Cornelius van Drebel, who carried out trials in the Thames between 1620 and 1624. It was not until the nineteenth century that submarines worthy of the name began to be built. The same process occurred in the fields of metallurgy, arms, the preservation of food, agriculture and industry, electricity, building and transport.

In 1837, the American Samuel Morse invented the telegraph or, more accurately, he constructed the first electromagnetic writing telegraph machine. In 1830 a French tailor, Barthélemy Thimmonier, built a rudimentary sewing machine and in the early part of the same century the honour of inventing photography goes equally to Joseph Nicéphore Niepce and Louis Jacques Daguerre. The nineteenth century also saw the birth of the typewriter (the first working model was made by the American Christopher Latham Sholes in 1867) and of the first incandescent lamp. This was invented in 1879 by Thomas Edison who also developed an electricity generating station in the centre of New York to light the streets.

Further inventions of the nineteenth century were the gramophone, the bicycle (even though the first four-wheeled velocipede was earlier), the telephone, the machine-gun, the railway, the internal combustion engine, the wireless telegraph and, at the end of the century, the cinema and the automobile.

Architecture
Functional beauty

Eight centuries separate these two buildings: the collegiate church (the church of a religious order), built in the Middle Ages in Romanesque style, at Santillana, in Spain, and the ultra-modern skyscraper of General Motors, in the centre of New York, with its prominent characteristic of straight lines.

A city bristling with skyscrapers: that is the picture that comes to mind when we think of modern architecture. The world seems to have shrunk through the speed of modern communications; for this reason, similar ways of life and identical styles of architecture can be found in very different parts of the world, in New York or Cape Town, Tokyo or Hong Kong.

When journeys from one continent to another were rare, contacts between widely-separated civilizations were almost impossible.

In those times, the architecture in distant countries looked different from that at home. Nevertheless, startling resemblances did occur between buildings in civilizations far apart in time and space. In Mexico the Aztec cities, discovered by the Spanish conquerors at the beginning of the sixteenth century, remind us in a surprising way of ancient Egypt (particularly by the presence of pyramids) and of the buildings of the Assyrians and Babylonians. It is a matter for discovery as to why this should be so.

Greeks and Romans

Apart from recent techniques and materials such as reinforced concrete, steel, aluminium, glass and plastics, the ancient craftsmen had already invented almost everything they needed. The Greeks, who loved beauty and harmony, and the more practical Romans, established basic rules, drawn from the best of their architectural work: they were rules concerning balance in buildings, and proportion between volumes and dimensions, in addition to arithmetic calculations and constructional techniques.

The architecture of any race can tell us a great deal about the people: how they live and sometimes even how they think. A Greek temple reveals clearly how the Greeks practised their beliefs. The temple enclosed by a colonnade was designed to be seen from afar. The statue of a god enclosed in an inner room remained hidden from public view. Greek religion seemed rather externalized, without that intimate relationship between man and God of the Christian religion.

In a Roman city, the public buildings including temples, palaces, baths and theatres were set apart from private buildings. The houses turned inwards on themselves: the rooms did not look onto the street, except in the houses of the poor, but onto an inner courtyard. This urban layout shows that the Romans regarded public and private life as quite separate. These rules of town-planning reveal the principle of order, which underlies the principle of authority.

The first churches

Christianity was accepted by the Roman Emperor Constantine in the year 313, and in 330 he moved the imperial capital to Byzantium, which was renamed Constantinople. It was at this time that architects turned to the problem of building churches. They solved it by modelling them on basilicas which originally were royal palaces and which for the Romans became the covered places used for tribunals and markets. The Christian basilica or cathedral, however,

erved a different purpose – to house both the worshippers and the altar. The altar was positioned at the back of the oblong building in a semi-circular recess called an apse. The rectangular space was divided by lines of columns into areas of differing importance. The one in the centre was the ship" (hence "nave" in English from Latin *navis*, ship) of the followers of Christ and Peter (from the gospel language which likens the Church to a ship); joined to the nave, which was reserved for the clergy, there were aisles at the sides for the faithful, one reserved for men, the other for women.

A variant of this structure, is the church in the shape of a Latin cross, in which a transverse nave, called the transept crosses between the apse and the central nave.

The second type of church which developed at the same time as the basilica, consisted of a round or octagonal space surrounded by an ampulatory, that is a semi-circular or many-sided aisle. Later these churches were sometimes in the form of a Greek cross (in which the arms of the cross are all the same length). This design with its central cupola or dome (a system of beams is sufficient for churches with a rectangular nave), occurred frequently in the Byzantine world. Byzantium took the culture of Rome and

elaborated it in its own terms (but influenced by the artistic forms of oriental civilizations), producing architectural results of great strength.

In the early days of Christianity, the building of a church involved the whole community. No secular buildings have come down to us from the dark ages (the period from the fall of the Roman Empire to the year 1000) but examples of church architecture remain.

Influence of the Arabs

The Arabs invaded Europe around the eighth century, disrupting the established order, but also bringing with them a great civilization and an architecture based on complex calculations (the Arabs were good mathematicians) and characterized by cupolas and boldly constructed minarets. Islam spread rapidly throughout the Middle East and into Europe, producing a wide range of national architectural variations. The luxury and ostentation of the mosques of Baghdad were copied in Spain, especially in the Great Mosque of Córdoba, begun in about 787, which shows a blend of European and Islamic architectural traditions. Its sanctuary contains more than 850 classical columns, ornamented with coloured marbles and supporting open Moorish arches. Not until the eleventh

century with the Norman style in England (and the Romanesque on the Continent) did an architecture flourish which was worthy of the tradition of ancient Rome. Everything, however, became more massive and severe, with square corners, not only in fortifications and castles, but in churches, too. Church building greatly increased and Christian influence was present everywhere. The stone-masons built solid roofs for their cathedrals, reinforced the walls, built powerful pilasters in place of columns, created roof-vaults with ribbing and sometimes added external buttresses to support the thick walls of the side naves.

From Romanesque to Gothic

At the same time, cities surrounded by a defensive wall come into their own again. The medieval city developed upwards in the enclosed space within the walls, multi-storey houses and towers vying in height with the bell-towers or campaniles. The streets, seldom straight, opened

(continued on page 146)

CLASSICAL PERIOD
Seventh century BC to fifth century AD

The Parthenon, Athens (Greece),
Fifth century BC, Doric Temple.

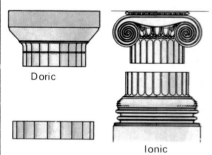

Doric

Ionic

Capitals of Greek columns:

Corinthian

The Arch of Titus at Rome, first century AD
The Romans utilized the arch which
was unknown to the Greeks.

ROMANESQUE
Eleventh to twelfth century AD

Basilica of St. Ambrose at Milan.

Interior of St. Ambrose's basilica. Column
-pilasters, ribbed vaulting and rounded arches
evident also in the windows.

GOTHIC
Twelfth to sixteenth century

The cathedral of Ulm, in Germany
(as it was before completion).

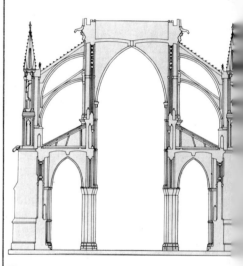

Flying arches, buttresses and pointed arches
which can also be seen in the windows.

RENAISSANCE
Fifteenth to sixteenth century

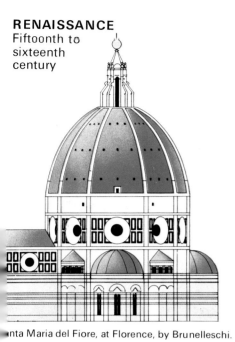

Santa Maria del Fiore, at Florence, by Brunelleschi.

Courtyard of the Palazzo Riccardi at Florence.

A façade with the stones squared off and jutting out.

BAROQUE
Seventeenth to eighteenth century

Oratory of the Filippini at Rome by Borromini.

Canopy of St. Peter at Rome by Bernini.

The sense of movement of the Baroque style is visible even in the frieze above the window.

MODERN
Nineteenth to twentieth century

Neo-classical: end of the eighteenth century to the beginning of the nineteenth.

The church of La Madeleine in Paris (France).

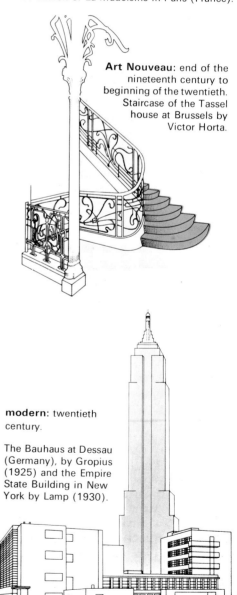

Art Nouveau: end of the nineteenth century to beginning of the twentieth. Staircase of the Tassel house at Brussels by Victor Horta.

modern: twentieth century.

The Bauhaus at Dessau (Germany), by Gropius (1925) and the Empire State Building in New York by Lamp (1930).

145

(continued from page 143)

on to squares large and small. Private and public life were closely linked because man, abandoning the countryside and the feudal life, discovered that he was a town-dweller and so more towns grew up. Man played an active part in the problems of the town: the work of skilled artisans flourished, commerce as we know it was born and craft guilds came into existence. As the towns became more prosperous, they wanted their own churches which could also be symbols of civic power. The clergy as the only educated people, directed operations and attempted to divert men from concern for material prosperity to a greater spirituality by preaching and building cathedrals.

From Romanesque, there emerged in France, in the second half of the twelfth century, the Gothic style which precisely reflected this new spirituality in architecture. The buildings began to soar and become more graceful, decorated with pinnacles and statues. Ribbed vaults and pointed arches were adopted and seemed to stretch upwards and increase the height of the building. Gothic architecture reflects man's striving to build vertically.

External supports were indispensable to hold together the upper structure of these Gothic cathedrals. Buttresses were built for the aisles and flying arches to support the central nave. From France the style spread to England, Spain, Germany and Italy, in both churches and secular buildings such as castles, palaces, manor houses, colleges, bridges and the gates of walled cities.

The Italian Renaissance

While the Gothic style spread and became more richly ornamented throughout the rest of Europe, fifteenth-century Italy saw the emergence of the Renaissance style. The term refers to a "rebirth", a rediscovery of old values re-created in a new spirit. For the first time, the leading

Above left, the interior of the Gothic cathedral at Bourges (France) and, above, of the Baroque cathedral at St. Gall (Switzerland). The difference between the two styles comes principally from the shape of the arches, columns and the decorations.

Below, the façade of the Banqueting House in London. During the Renaissance, as well as building for religious purposes, there was a great expansion of civil architecture, with well-proportioned palaces with austere facades.

Above top, the Ca' d'Oro, in Venice, built on the Grand Canal by the architects Bon and Raverti between 1421 and 1440. It is a typical example of florid Gothic, a style fairly common in the palaces and churches of Venice. Above, the famous villa La Rotonda by Andrea Palladio, at Vicenza. Built around 1550, it is the prime example of a civic building suggesting the structure of Greek temples

Left, the elegant small villa Ruggeri, at Pesaro, built with great skill in Art Nouveau style in 1908 as part of an architectural project by Giuseppe Brega. This style, also called "floral" or "liberty", became established in Italy especially after the great Turin Exhibition of 1902 and was particularly popular for furniture, decorations and wrought iron.

architects were deliberately creating a personal style. Brunelleschi's works in Florence began the whole movement. He planned the cupola of the cathedral and also chapels, churches and palaces after careful study of the principles of the architecture of the ancient world: he utilized classical Greek and Roman forms such as columns and arches, in buildings with classical proportions but with a new sense of the space and spirit which animated them. As well as the works of Brunelleschi, the masterpieces of Alberti, Bramante, Michelangelo, Palladio and many others were springing up.

The fame of the Italian Renaissance spread throughout Europe and during this and the following century kings, nobles and bishops were asking for palaces and churches built in this style. In England, the style reached its peak in the work of Inigo Jones (1573–1652). In many European countries, the Gothic style was so well entrenched that the architects continued to erect Gothic buildings camouflaged with rounded arches and columns, just to satisfy their patrons' demands.

In fact this Italian style had relatively little impact. The Baroque style which followed it in seventeenth-century Italy had a much more far-reaching effect. The word "baroque" originally meant irregular or misshapen and came from an old Portuguese word used to describe ill-formed or worthless pearls. It was applied to European architecture of the seventeenth and eighteenth centuries which art historians condemned as being contrary to classical principles. The name has stuck, although it is no longer used as a criticism.

The Baroque style developed in Rome between 1620 and 1660. It expressed the spirit of the Roman Catholic revival which was taking place after the reforms of the previous century. The architects who created the style in Rome were Gianlorenzo Bernini (1598–1680), Francesco Borromini (1599–1667) and Pietra da Cortona (1596–1669). They used new methods to express their ideas. Their buildings were on a vast scale and used curved shapes which produced an effect of movement. This gave the impression of having been subjected to twists and waves while being built, and a further impression of movement was conferred by scrolls, curves and those types of decoration characterized by what may best be described as "suspended animation". All this accentuated the sense of movement and allowed the architects to use new types of ground plan. They liked complexity and rich colours rather than simplicity and used dramatic lighting effects.

The triumph of the Baroque

Although the Baroque style was invented in Rome, by the end of the seventeenth century it had spread to other parts of Italy. It also began to reach other countries. In France, the Sun King (Louis XIV) built a monumental royal palace of extraordinary scenic effect at Versailles. This served as a model for the great palaces of Spain, Austria and Germany. From there, the Baroque spread east to Hungary and Poland, and even as far as Russia.

The Baroque had less effect in the Protestant countries of northern Europe. In England, however, the architects Sir Christopher Wren, Sir John Vanbrugh, Nicholas Hawksmoor and James Gibbs were influenced by the style. In the eighteenth century, English country houses in Palladian style came into fashion (Palladio was a sixteenth-century Italian architect who built palaces and houses with classical proportions but of original conception). In France and Italy, too, the serene virtues of the fields were rediscovered and the massively heavy shapes of the Baroque were replaced by the smaller and lighter forms of a new style, the Rococo. This grew up to meet a taste for elegance and convenience rather than grandeur. It spread across Europe and remained in vogue until the end of the eighteenth century.

The Neo-classical style

The French revolution shook the states of Europe to their foundations, and inspired a radical change in architecture. People set out to re-create the democratic life of Athens and so architecture turned to the classical forms, and the Neo-classical style was born. It tried to repeat, but in a simpler way, the advanced style of Brunelleschi and Palladio. However, it did not last for long, or exhibit the same vigour and force as Baroque. In that period, the architects learnt to use the various styles without affectation, to suit their own taste and the purpose of the buildings.

Steel and cement

In the nineteenth century, major changes occurred. The Industrial Revolution, which had begun in Britain at the end of the eighteenth century and spread during the nineteenth to Europe and America, introduced new materials and techniques and a demand for new types of building to meet new social needs. Towns were expanded and new cities sprang up. Many of the new buildings, such as viaducts, railway stations and textile mills, were the work of engineers who used an ancient material in a new way: iron, or more accurately, steel. Steel (together

Various examples of modern architecture. On the page opposite: above, the palace of Congresses (Brasilia, 1960), work of the Brazilian, Oscar Niemeyer; below, the distinctive shape of the Guggenheim Museum (New York, 1950) by Frank Lloyd Wright, in which the study of curved and spiral structures is evident, typical of the last period of this great American architect.

On this page: above, the Carré house at Bazoches-sur-Guyonne (France, 1956) by the Finn Alvar Aalto, an exponent of the form of architecture which emphasizes the importance of the natural environment; right, the "dwelling unit" (Marseilles, 1945) by Le Corbusier, who provoked much adverse criticism with his idea of a house as a "machine for living"; below, the Catholic cathedral (Tokyo, 1962–9) by the Japanese Kenzo Tange which recalls, as with so many modern architects, the concepts of Le Corbusier.

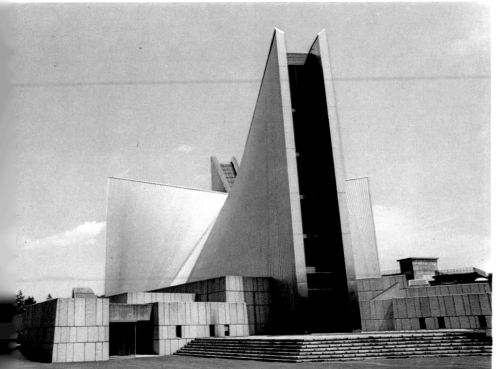

with glass) became the most suitable material for many of the new architectural forms.

At the same time, there was a renewed interest in past styles of architecture. The Gothic revival was especially popular in Britain where churches, law-courts, hospitals and hotels were built in the Gothic style. Architects also extracted particular features from former styles and incorporated them as they wished.

Towards the end of the century Art Nouveau (new art) emerged. It moved away from imitation of the past and covered a wide range of styles, including floral motifs and Chinese and Japanese stylizations. During its peak, from 1890 to 1906, it was recognized mainly by the names of individual designers, such as Charles Rennis Mackintosh in Scotland and, later, Antoni Gaudi in Spain. However, with the introduction of reinforced concrete the traditional styles and even Art Nouveau suddenly seemed outmoded and useless. The new materials (reinforced concrete, steel and glass) allowed many very varied structures to be built.

The demand grew up for functional buildings which were practical, economic and could be built swiftly. Japanese domestic architecture had achieved centuries ago a very modern simplicity in which every element had its own function. For example, in the imperial villa of Katsura (built at about the same time as the imposing Baroque palace at Versailles, near Paris), the interior was simply divided by movable screens mounted on frames.

Since the first decades of the twentieth century, several architects have tried to mould a functional and thus rational architecture. Until the 1930s, Germany was the centre of the new architecture, mainly because of the Bauhaus at Weimar, a school of architecture founded by Walter Gropius in 1919. The school moved to Dessau in 1925 and occupied a series of steel, glass and concrete buildings designed by the international staff and students.

The most famous American architect of this century was Frank Lloyd Wright who set out to reconcile the structural requirements of the building itself with the necessities of those who live there and the outside environment. The same scale, appropriate to the needs of man, manifested in the detailed calculation of proportions, was always present in the work of the famous Swiss architect, Le Corbusier, who lived and worked in France. He was, perhaps, the most brilliant and influential of all the architects of the twentieth century.

Clocks and Watches
The time-machines

How did orators, addressing a public tribunal, measure the length of their speeches before they had timepieces? We all know that time cannot be gauged simply by our own feelings and in general this is even more true when the estimate is based on the opinion of the person making the speech or listening to it. The ancient Romans, to resolve the problem, decided to rely on clepsydras or water-clocks, which had already been used in Egypt and Greece. These were glass globes with a neck closed by a stopper and at the bottom a series of small holes. The globe was filled with water which then trickled out slowly through the holes. Each orator was permitted to speak so long as there was still water in the water-clock and in this way the addresses could all be made the same length.

The system was progressively improved. The water which ran out through the holes was collected in a graduated container with a pointer floating inside. By reading off the mark on the graduated scale which was level with the pointer, the time which had elapsed could be deduced. With this apparatus one could measure short periods accurately.

Using sand, oil and the sun

Many of us have sand-glasses at home, in the kitchen or as toys. In former times, they were used mainly on ships. They consist of two pear-shaped glass bulbs con-

nected by a very narrow tube, also of glass. The bulbs contain a quantity of sand and when the sand-glass is turned upside-down, the sand runs from the upper bulb to the lower through the small opening. The size of the connecting tube is so proportioned that the sand will completely run through from one bulb to the other in the time it is desired to measure, usually an hour or a minute.

In the Middle Ages, and earlier in some places, there were oil clocks: they were lamps which burned a certain amount of oil in a certain time. Time was also measured by making marks on wax candles.

These systems, and others used in ancient times and in the Middle Ages, measured only time intervals and had no bearing on the actual time of day.

Egyptians, Assyrians and Babylonians, on the other hand, used a vertical stick or pillar called a gnomon. The length of the shadow which it cast gave an indication of the time of day. On a smaller scale, our solar clocks (sun-dials), use the same principle. The time of day is shown by the direction of the shadow of a pole or stick against a circular or semi-circular graduated scale. Sun-dials were very popular, especially in very sunny countries, and until only a few centuries ago were often built into the façades of palaces. There were also small portable sun-dials. Timepieces of this type are obviously of no use at night or on cloudy days and, in any case, the time measured depends on the length of the day and this varies from season to season.

The first, rudimentary mechanisms

For centuries Europe made no progress in telling the time and sun-dials continued to be used, as did also the other systems for measuring time intervals we have

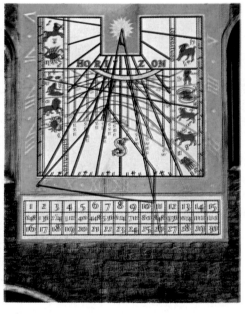

Top centre, a splendid astronomical clock of the fourteenth century, preserved in the Cathedral at Lund (Sweden). Left, two sun-dials, one of the column type (far left) and one on a wall, richly decorated, from Cambridge. Above, an Egyptian clepsydra, over 3,000 years old.

Above, a painting dedicated to Christiaan Huygens who was the first to use the pendulum in clock-making. Above right and immediately below, pocket watches (1600 and 1700). Right, a table clock of the eighteenth century and (far right) one of the earliest ones from the twentieth century.

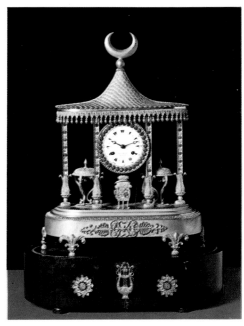

mentioned. However, advances were being made in the neighbouring Islamic countries. At the beginning of the ninth century, Caliph Harun al-Rashid presented Charlemagne with a clock which caused quite a stir. It is not known how it was made, but certainly the movement was provided by a falling weight and it even seems that the hours might have been indicated by metal balls falling noisily into a bronze basin.

In the fourteenth century, many towers and belfries in Europe had large striking clocks. They were simple and makeshift mechanisms, moved by a weight hanging by a rope wound round a drum. The weight, pulled down by gravity, unwound the rope and turned the drum, which was linked to a system of geared cogs. In this way, the movement was transmitted to the hands of the clock. Smaller versions of these large public clocks appeared late in the fourteenth century as the first domestic clocks.

By the middle of the fifteenth century, alarm-clocks had been introduced into the courts of Europe. These were the forerunners of the devices which now wake us up so noisily in the morning.

A little afterwards, there was another great innovation, the first truly portable clocks or early watches. They were sometimes called "Nuremberg ovals", because they were oval in shape and came from that town. They were made of precious metals and were highly decorated. They were worn round the neck or in a pocket but could not be relied upon to measure time accurately. In fact, some of them probably lacked minute hands, thus showing only the hours, and they tended to go more quickly just after being wound up than later.

The manufacture of even the most primitive clocks is a complicated task, which demands great specialization. In those centuries, groups of clock-makers were formed and by the second half of the sixteenth century, Italian, French and Flemish craftsmen had founded a clock-making industry in Geneva which grew rapidly and soon made Switzerland famous throughout the world for the high quality of its products.

Pendulum and balance-wheel

In the seventeenth century, as a result of the studies by Galileo and Huygens of the pendulum, it finally became possible to make a timepiece with a regular movement. The system, seen through present-day eyes, seems fairly simple, but in those days it was certainly not easy to construct a mechanism to translate the alternating movement of the pendulum into the rotary movement of the gearing.

The way it was done is as follows: from one side the cog is made to turn by the motive force of the weight or spring, while

The weight and the pendulum

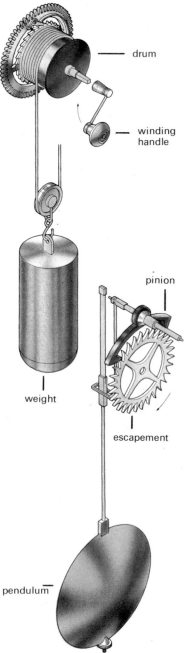

drum

winding handle

pinion

weight

escapement

pendulum

The principal parts of a pendulum clock with power supplied by a weight. As it descends, the weight unwinds the cable and rotates the drum. This motion is transmitted through geared cogs to the hands. The accuracy of the movement is achieved by the pendulum and the anchor on the escapement; the motion of the toothed wheel is regulated by a small rocking lever, very like an anchor in shape.

A spring-driven clock

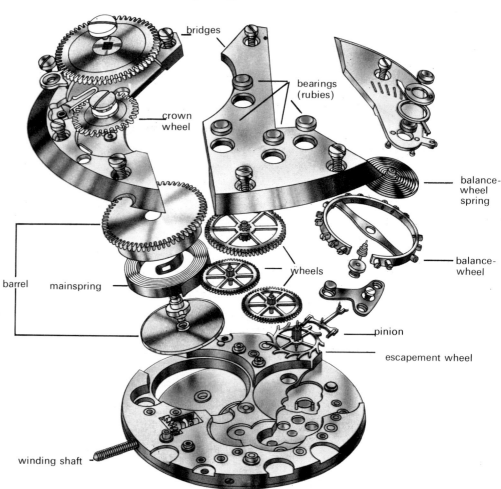

bridges

crown wheel

bearings (rubies)

balance-wheel spring

balance-wheel

wheels

pinion

escapement wheel

barrel

mainspring

winding shaft

A spring clock "exploded" to show all its parts. The bearings on which all the pivots turn are made of rubies, which are very resistant to wear. The accuracy of the movement is assured by the balance-wheel (invented by the Englishman Robert Hooke, in 1675). With the aid of a small spring, this oscillates to and fro on a pivot, allowing a very delicate device called the "anchored escapement" to make small, controlled jumps.

One tooth at a time

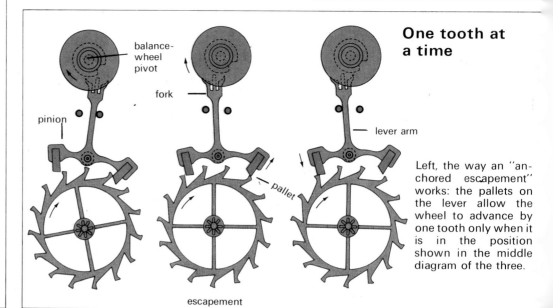

balance-wheel pivot

fork

pinion

lever arm

pallet

escapement

Left, the way an "anchored escapement" works: the pallets on the lever allow the wheel to advance by one tooth only when it is in the position shown in the middle diagram of the three.

on the other side it is braked by an anchored stop or pallet.

The pallet is connected to the pendulum and releases one tooth of the cog, which immediately turns as far as it can since it is pulled by the "motor", but only when the pendulum reaches its maximum amplitude. In this way, the wheel makes small jerky movements, at regular intervals.

The same system is found in watches. In this case, however, the movement is regulated by a balance-wheel. Naturally the mechanism is constructed so that the interval of time between one movement and the next corresponds to a fixed unit of time.

Days are divided into twenty-four hours, each consisting of sixty minutes, each sub-divided into sixty seconds. This method of dividing time intervals, however, is not really "natural": there is no reason why the day should not be divided, for example, into twenty hours and the hours into a hundred minutes and so on. It is a matter of choice, a convention to which all the countries of the world have decided to conform. This goes for all other units of measure (length, weight, etc.).

Electric, electronic and atomic. In later centuries, mechanical clocks were perfected (by new methods of metal-working and the introduction of high-precision instruments) and became much more complex: they often have three hands, one to show the hours, one the minutes and one the seconds, and the rotary motion of these hands is co-ordinated by a system of cogs.

There are also electrical clocks where the source of power comes not from a falling weight or a spring, but from electric currents. Battery-powered clocks, too, have become popular for domestic use. Some spring-powered clocks no longer have a winding-key, because they are wound automatically. Inside they have a metal cylinder filled with a gas which expands or contracts with the slightest change in temperature, operating a piston connected to the mainspring. Another system of automatic winding, used in wrist-watches, is to have, as part of the timepiece, a fly-wheel which responds to the slightest movements of the wearer's arm.

Nowadays it seems that mechanical timepieces are destined to disappear gradually, as they are supplanted by more accurate and cheaper electronic devices. These have been developed from electronic control instruments, such as those used to measure frequencies. They consist wholly of electronic components and entirely lack moving mechanical parts. Accuracy in time-measurement is

Right, the opposing internal faces of an electromagnetic timepiece of the oscillator type. It is based on the uniform frequency of the vibrations of a small oscillator. These oscillations are induced by two coils powered from a special battery.

Above, two watches: the quartz watch (left) beside the "old-fashioned" spring-driven pocket-watch. Left, a quartz digital alarm-clock, using the same display system as electronic calculators.

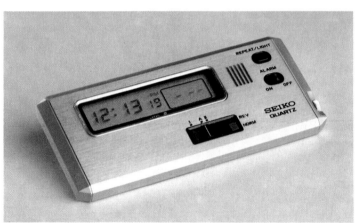

provided by a small quartz crystal which, when excited electrically, gives out millions of impulses per second, and these are detected by an electronic circuit. This circuit, as soon as it has received a certain number of impulses, displays the figures which show the time on the small screen. Small portable clocks can be made accurate to about one fiftieth of a second per day.

An even more accurate instrument for measuring time is the atomic clock, which uses the high-frequency vibrations of certain types of atom. An atomic clock can have a range of error as small as one second in 30,000 years. Of course, such a high degree of accuracy is not necessary in everyday life, but is essential in some laboratory experiments.

The Wheel The great invention

According to legend, a Chinese mandarin, fascinated by the grace and speed of a flower head that the wind was rolling along the road, had the bright idea that led him to invent the wheel. It is only a legend, however, because, unlike many other things, the wheel was not a Chinese invention. All the experts agree, in fact, that it was invented by the Sumerians in Mesopotamia, during the fourth millenium before the birth of Christ and that it then spread to the rest of the ancient world. The wheel probably reached China from Persia; a little later, it spread through Egypt and from there through the Cretan civilization to Greece and the rest of Europe.

Nearly all the inventions of the distant past, such as the use of fire or the art of smelting metals, were attributed to the gods or heroes of mythology. It is curious to note, therefore, that there is no myth that mentions the wheel as a gift of the gods, just as it is surprising that great civilizations such as the Mayas and Aztecs of America never knew the wheel, even though many of their symbols included something very similar in shape to the simple or the cogged wheel. It is precisely because of this, that some experts believe

that the wheel was not inspired by watching a natural phenomenon, but that it really was the brain wave of one of our distant ancestors.

The oldest picture of a cart with wheels appears on some clay tablets from Mesopotamia, dating from 3500 BC. The Royal Standard of Ur (2500 BC) in which there appears a war chariot on wheels, pulled by a pair of oxen, was discovered amongst the ruins of this splendid Sumerian city. The wheel was made of solid wood and formed of two "half moons" and a central section joined by two cross pieces; it is thought that the outside edge was covered by strips of leather.

The relative sophistication of the Ur wheel suggests that it evolved from another, older and more rudimentary wheel. Many experts believe, in fact, that the first application of this more modern instrument was not on vehicles but in pottery. The potter's wheel rotates horizontally on a vertical pivot at the base of which is another wheel which the potter works with his feet. This allows the clay to be modelled evenly by keeping the hands still and making the clay go round instead.

From wood to metal

The first wheels were solid and attached to the axle (which means that the rod joining them went round with the wheels); then the fixed axle was invented and the wheels were loose, that is they could move independently of one another. The need to make wheels lighter led to attempts to make them with openings in them, and from there it was a simple step to the next stage, the construction of a big ring with spokes.

By the fifteenth century BC, spoked wheels were used on chariots, in Syria, Egypt and the western Mediterranean and by 1300 BC they were also used in China. A four-spoked wheel is shown on a chariot carved on a chieftain's grave at Kivi in Sweden in about 1000 BC, and from then on they became common in northern and western Europe. During this time solid wheels were used for agricultural purposes.

In Roman times, the Celts were the most advanced in the field of wheel construction. Some of the finest surviving wheels have been found in Roman sites in Celtic areas and in southern Gaul. The Celts were the first to use a wooden wheel with

Opposite, these two bas-reliefs date from the second millenium BC. They show two ways in which the Assyrians made use of the wheel. Opposite below, a Roman ox-cart used for the transportation of wine. Right, a model of a nineteenth century carriage.

an outer ring of protective metal mounted hot and which, while cooling, contracted and fixed itself firmly onto the ring of wood. To avoid wearing away the hubs, the Romans lined them at both sides with bronze rings, but the Celts made grooves in the hub and inserted small wooden cylindrical blocks between the hub and axle. These are the ancestors of our ball bearings.

With the fall of the Roman Empire and the consequent decline of the great communication routes, the development of the carriage and cart was slower. At the end of the Middle Ages, it was a simple wooden rectangle with front and rear axles. The first form of suspension reached England from Hungary at the end of the sixteenth century, when the body of the carriage was suspended on leather straps from a wooden chassis. It was only in the seventeenth century with the introduction of metal springs that carriages became properly efficient.

When the first mechanical means of propulsion came into being (first the bicycle, then the motor-car and the motor-cycle), the wheel improved further. Hubs, spokes and outer rings were made in metal rather than wood, and from then on it made rapid progress.

In 1868, the famous French pioneer of aviation, Clément Ader, patented a solid cylindrical rubber covering to put on the wheel to make it run more smoothly. This was improved still further when ball bearings were added to the hub. Finally, with the introduction of the pneumatic tyre by John Boyd Dunlop in 1888, the wheel reached its present degree of efficiency. Nowadays, some wheels are moulded in one piece in light alloy: the most common are alluminium and magnesium alloys.

All kinds of mechanical devices

The whole of our civilization, all of our technical progress, is based on the wheel, not only because it is an essential item in land transport, but also because from it, through the primitive wooden cogged wheels, all kinds of mechanical devices are derived.

Another important development was the water wheel which was used as a source of power in industry before it was replaced by the steam engine, the electric and the internal combustion engines and, more recently, by the turbine. An example of the use of the water wheel are the mills that were built on the banks of rivers during the nineteenth century.

The paddle wheel was an important mechanical device for propelling ships. In 1803, the American Robert Fulton carried out experiments on the Seine in Paris with a boat fitted with a steam engine which turned two paddle wheels on the sides of the vessel. The experiment was not followed up and it was only in 1807 that Fulton, making the 300-kilometre journey from New York to Albany in his paddle ship, *The North River Steamboat of Clermont*, laid the foundations of river travel by paddle boat.

From the first pottery wheel, the invention of an unknown Sumerian genius has carried us a long way along the path of technology and civilization.

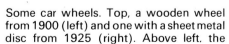

Some car wheels. Top, a wooden wheel from 1900 (left) and one with a sheet metal disc from 1925 (right). Above left, the spoked wheel of Rudge Whitworth (1930 to 1960) and, right, a modern one with a circle in light alloy.

Houses
A roof over your head

From cave to skyscraper, from a rude hut to a country cottage or a large house with a swimming-pool, from the tiny houses crammed together higgledy-piggledy in a medieval burgh to the barrack-like dwellings laid out in rows on the edges of present-day cities: the history of dwelling-houses is, in many respects, the history of civilization, human progress, social life and family relationships. From the house and its more or less indispensable fittings such as stairs, sink units, cookers and central heating, we can easily trace technological progress.

What is the most significant characteristic of a modern house? Perhaps it is that everywhere they are much the same, in the East and in the West, in Norway or in South Africa. New houses have come to resemble each other more and more, just as styles of dressing and patterns of living have done, even where there are profound differences in attitudes of thought. Unlike the past, it is now difficult to find any "essential" difference between a block of flats in Japan, Germany or Britain, much as there is by now no fundamental difference between the modern house of a manager and that of a worker: both are built of bricks, both have plaster on the walls, and both have glazed windows, electric light, running water, sanitation, a kitchen and bedrooms.

The difference between luxury and wretchedness is determined by other factors together with considerations of personal tastes, the type of furnishing, local traditions and the varying climatic and geographical conditions. Even without considering those who still live in

These three types of house, so different in other respects, have one thing in common: they are camouflaged in their surroundings and use materials provided by nature. The Mali village (above) has the same colours as the ground on which it is built; the ancient Turks did even better: they dug their houses out of the rock (below left); lastly, in Lapland, the realm of the birch, the cabins are built solely from the branches of this tree (below right).

In the newer parts of the towns, buildings are now much the same right across the world, but in many places, particularly those which have remained untouched by progress, the houses still retain the ancient characteristics. Here are some examples in different and distant countries which all use straw and reeds as a building material: a Berber hut in the Algerian desert (top left); peasants' houses in Nepal (left centre); a large Indonesian hut on stilts with its elegant lines (above left); a cluster of pile-dwellings in Burma (at top); a typical thatched cottage in Cornwall (above). In the photograph at bottom left, we see in contrast the most unusual houses in the Italian tradition: the famous "follies", found especially in the Alberobello area, are built wholly of stone, with conical roofs.

A boat as a home, with a river as a street

Man has not always felt the need to have "his feet on terra firma": indeed he has often chosen to build his house on the water, as in the ancient pile-dwellings, which are still in use in some countries. These are not, however, the only example of "water dwellings": even boats, suitably modified, can serve as houses. Many people live on these "floating houses" either by tradition and culture, as in Holland (below), or even by necessity, as in Asia (above), where the size of the population has compelled thousands of people to live permanently on the water, often on craft knocked together for the purpose and in an unsound condition: for example, on a decrepit boat covered at best by a roof of cloth or straw.

There are also people who, though they have a house on dry land, wish to live on the water. This desire has given rise to the luxury yacht or the simpler house-boat.

primitive conditions, lacking the basic essentials, the type of ordinary dwelling has changed little since prehistoric times. In fact there are still people who live in huts on piles, in mud hovels or even in caves, and on the edges of many large towns whole families exist in miserable slums.

In a civilized society, everyone should have a healthy, clean and comfortable home, but this alone does not guarantee happiness. Of course, it would be pleasant if we could all choose our own house, a spacious, sunny building with an attractive garden. Many people, however, are compelled to live in small flats in city blocks and not everyone has even the moderate good fortune to have, if not an actual garden, then at least a balcony or patio. Nevertheless we should be content with what we have. A house is comforting and welcoming when the people who live in it look after it and each other honestly and kindly.

If, on the other hand, a house is considered mainly as a luxury possession to show off or, worse, some sort of island in a hostile sea, a place in which to protect oneself from the outside world, people become a slave to it or prisoners inside it, and the furniture around them becomes symbols of wealth instead of objects to be used.

Houses of wood, stone and snow

In ancient times, there were two ways of living. The nomad, moving from place to place and living off the land, learned to build temporary dwellings: a cabin made of tree-trunks, a tent of animal skins, the hiding-place dug out under ground or even a type of windbreak of leaves and bark fixed to the ground. The man who settled down in one place, attracted by the good climate and the proximity of water, tried to build a permanent house which could be improved and enlarged. Naturally he used the local materials, so he built huts of wood and interwoven reeds or else of wood and stone. Man even learnt to make a shelter out of snow, and today there are still some Eskimos who live comfortably inside igloos. Later man discovered that clay soil became solid when it was baked. He invented bricks and with them was able to build houses to a more standardized pattern.

Little by little, houses were transformed, improved and embellished. The taste for decoration has, over the years, been a major stimulus to comfort: as archaeological excavations show, conceit is an ancient human vice. The humble hovels where poor people lived in ancient

days have disappeared for ever, but the remains of palaces, large and small, bear witness to extravagant luxury, ostentation and power. If we were to reconstruct, for example, the palace of Minos, at Knossos, we should lose ourselves in a labyrinth of rooms and be amazed at the splendour of the statues, the decorations, the thrones, the staircases and the columns, in other words by everything that was beautiful and ornamental. The history of man's dwelling-places is also the history of his ambitions. Perhaps this is why we strive now for the basic right of a roof over our heads: for many centuries, too much attention was given to building to satisfy the vanity of the few rather than the needs of the many.

The house was a token of privilege even in the very refined civilization of ancient Rome, where it was called *domus*, meaning the commodious house of the rich. There was also the *insula*, the tenement-block structure of many storeys, resembling a foul-smelling human anthill. In these buildings, the space available was fully exploited: the individual apartments were little more than cells and the sanitary arrangements reduced to a bucket at the foot of the stairs. Altogether this was a historical case of speculative building, detrimental both to the poor and to the public good: a "building scandal", as it would be called today.

In spite of all this, during the same period, the practice grew up of having a second house. The ancient Romans of ample means built country or seaside houses in which to spend their holidays or just their week-ends.

Castles and palaces

The Middle Ages made matters worse. The poor continued to live in hovels while the nobles, concerned mainly with warfare, rated security higher than beauty, comfort and hygiene in the houses they built. The medieval castle came to be more a fortress than a dwelling-place. The walls were tall and thick for defensive purposes and the only openings in them were narrow slits, not windows. Usually built on the top of a hill, the castles were surrounded by a ditch, or moat, to make it more difficult for the enemy to approach. To enter one had to cross over the drawbridge, a wooden structure which, in times of danger, was raised by special pulleys so that the castle was isolated.

The peasants lived in the countryside round the castle, either in scattered cottages or collected together in villages. When attack by an enemy army threatened, everyone sought refuge inside the castle, taking even their cattle in with them, turning the grand courts into chaotic encampments.

In the towns, life developed inside the stout enclosing walls which, like the castle walls, were erected for defensive purposes. The streets were narrow so as to use as little space as possible and, particularly, to make defence easier should an enemy succeed in scaling the walls. As the population grew, the houses increased in height.

Craftsmen and traders lived in the towns. Many houses in the medieval citadel had the double function of dwelling-place and shop or workshop. People worked on the ground floor and ate and slept on the upper floors. Often the master craftsman and his apprentices lived and worked together in these workshop-houses: they ate at the same table, slept in the same dormitory and the place was home to a group of workers rather than to a family. The houses were often built of wood, and it was only noble families who had great houses or palaces built to last. These they adorned with pictures, sculptures, furniture and tapestries for their own enjoyment and that of their descendants.

In Tudor England, many large houses of stone or brick were built. They were symmetrical with a large number of windows. Rooms were more spacious and were often panelled with oak. Smaller houses were less elaborate and were built of brick and timber or timber and plaster-covered rubble. Furniture became more important and people began to want more comfortable homes.

The Italian Renaissance gradually spread the taste for beautiful things throughout Europe (at least amongst those who could afford it). The ruling lords of the time were often cruel and bloodthirsty men, but in their homes they surrounded themselves with objects of great beauty and refinement. As life became somewhat less dangerous, commerce expanded, more money came into circulation and more people were able to improve their living-conditions and possess a house of their own. Even the grand houses no longer resembled fortresses and the house of the middle-classes replaced the house-cum-workshop. From the concept of "community", in other words, a return was made to that of the family. The lady of the house no longer wanted workers about the place night and day: the husband took himself off to his employment or workshop and left the house to her. After as many as twelve or fourteen hours of

The streets of Stratford-on-Avon, the birthplace of Shakespeare, are recognizable at a glance by their characteristic timber-framed houses. Right, a building in Spanish style in Peru provides non-religious evidence of the former presence of the "conquistadores".

work, the workers would arrange to sleep how and where they could. Greater prosperity, then, indirectly generated greater poverty.

Residential areas and areas for the masses

In the seventeenth and eighteenth centuries, many grand houses were built in Europe. The great families discovered the attraction of the countryside and built luxurious mansions, splendidly decorated, and set in parklands laid out in the same grand and formal style as the interiors. In the larger towns, meanwhile, rich and poor were no longer living in such close proximity as previously: the so-called residential areas, with beautiful squares and gardens, came to be reserved for the rich, while the poor began to move into the less favoured areas where rents were lower.

The Industrial Revolution which started in Britain at the end of the eighteenth century and spread to Europe during the nineteenth, had an effect on housing. Alongside the first factories, groups of houses for the families of the workers grew up: new urban centres were born, that is to say, towns within towns, in locations made unhealthy by the fumes from the factory chimneys nearby. During the same period, a new phenomenon was emerging: the former, clear-cut division between the houses of the rich and poor was becoming blurred by the efforts of a

new class, those employed in clerical occupations. They devised a different way of living, with some comforts, high ambitions and careful expenditure. All this produced much that was in bad taste but it is from precisely this middle-class mediocrity that today's houses have evolved. In the early years of the twentieth century, some of the large houses, if not fallen into ruin or turned into hotels, were split up into flats. The space which had earlier been occupied by a single family and their domestic servants now housed ten or twenty families who could live there with less luxury but more comfort.

The Second World War posed the question of housing again with great urgency. Rebuilding after the bombing was often, quite understandably, hurried and often ill co-ordinated. In contrast to the skyscraper designed by the famous architect, there is the building put up cheaply and as rapidly as possible, and there is also the pre-fabricated house or prefab. Many towns grew upwards but they also grew outwards by encroaching on the surrounding countryside. On the edges of large towns, residential villages and satellite towns came into existence. New materials and new techniques of construction displaced the old. Apart from bricks, cement, iron, glass, aluminium and plastics were used. We should not be surprised that houses are tending to resemble each other more and more closely everywhere in the world, as architects attempt to provide an increasing population with adequate shelter.

A roof for every climate

Now that space is at an increasing premium and gardens are becoming smaller, many of the characteristics in building which previously led to variety in the construction of houses and flats are being lost. Naturally, some differences remain. A flat roof, for example, is seldom seen in a country with a very cold climate because it would eventually collapse under the weight of snow, so today in the more northerly countries preference is still given to building houses with pitched roofs.

The question remains of whether the kind of life we lead in our flats and small houses is satisfactory. There is no question that we live better than those who lived in the hovels of the past and certainly better than in the splendid residences of the nobility and the castles of long ago. We have water, electricity and gas. We have sanitation. Of course, we pay dearly for it all: the town encroaches on the fields, destroys trees and the air is often polluted by the fumes of car exhausts, central heating boilers and factories. Even human relations have become difficult: the house ends up being a place of isolation and of loneliness.

Parallel with this, as a result of a changing concept of the family unit, the idea of a dwelling is also changing. Because so many people choose or are compelled to live on their own, one-person flats, and bed-sitters are increasing in number. Blocks of service flats, a half-way house between the rented appartment and a hotel, are also becoming more popular. Another aspect is that general lack of space brings about large changes to the interiors of more traditional flats and houses: every small corner

Above left, the famous Paris quarter of Saint-Germain-des-Prés. In the old quarters of the great cities, the ease with which human contacts can be made, the ancient and well-tried habits of communal life, sometimes endow a "personality" and a dignity even to the meanest houses. The photograph on the left shows one of the most densely populated and crowded quarters of Singapore.

The rapid rise in population and growing urbanization (the massive displacement of people from countryside to the town) have decided in a very obvious way, during these last few decades, the lay-out of the residential areas. On the page opposite, we see another aspect of Singapore, its new "tenement blocks" which spring up round an oil depot, and (in the large photograph) a model suburb at Cholet, in France, where a spread of one-family living-units surrounds the group of buildings containing flats.

is utilized, walls are knocked down to give a more spacious feeling, the kitchen is reduced to a small niche for cooking so that the rest of the space can be added to the room, low partitions instead of walls separate "rooms" and great use is made of multi-purpose furniture, such as easy chairs and sofas that can also be used as beds.

There are people who are experimenting with new ideas of communal living. For example, several individuals or families take over a single large house and live there with certain facilities in common, organizing the shared duties on a rota system. This is the modern version of the old house-cum-workshop, but there is no one person in charge and everybody works according to his ability. Families who live in such communities often prefer to establish themselves in the countryside in the hope of being self-sufficient with the produce of the land. Up to now these experiments have met with little success, but they still suggest to architects new ideas about the kind of dwellings people may wish to occupy in the future.

Fashion Changes in taste

"It's the fashion" we often hear. The fashion may be for short skirts, a certain make of car, Swedish interior design, the colour blue, folk music or anything else which happens to affect our lives. The fashion may be for a book which enjoys ephemeral fame, or a turn of phrase, or a person. Even ideas and attitudes alter with the passing of time.

There is nothing more certain than that a sudden, widespread enthusiasm will wane, it will "go out of fashion" and return to oblivion. The objects of such interest almost always end up by being abandoned. People tire of them and they are forgotten. Tastes change rapidly.

Fashion expresses the desire for novelty and change.

The word "mode" is often applied to fashion, usually to fashions in dress. If something is *à la mode* it is fashionable. "Mode" is a French word, from the Latin *modus*, and was first used in England in the seventeenth century.

Yet the phenomenon to which it refers occurred long before the word came into use. Fashion has always existed, inspired and encouraged by man's vanity. Every season the designers (or "creators of fashion") produce new models, promoting a particular style or colour, and these gradually affect the clothes people wear.

Sooner or later, we accept the changes. Think of the changes there have been in skirts in recent years. It was "unfashionable" for a woman to wear a skirt of the "wrong" length, but today the situation is more flexible and skirt lengths vary considerably.

Fashion needs time to become accepted. It arouses curiosity, desire, imitation and even envy. Public opinion always has to overcome an initial rejection and hostile amazement. In the twenties, the first women to bob their hair were frowned on and regarded very dubiously. This may make us smile today, but think of the scandal caused by topless sunbathing

1913

1919

1921

1922

1926

1932

1934

on some Mediterranean beaches, which is only a fashion. Before it was generally accepted, as it is now, the other great bathing scandal was the bikini, which is bound to be with us for a very long time.

There are occasions when by the time the last people have accepted a fashion, those who were enthusiastic at the beginning have already tired of it and are turning to something else. The time required for this to happen has varied through history and used to be very much longer than it is now. Styles of clothing, jewellery, furniture and houses, for example, lasted for decades or even centuries: think how long the Roman toga remained in fashion.

In the past, fashion was only the concern of the aristocracy and the rich; it never affected the poorer people who for generations continued to wear the same kind of old rags and were content with the same poor objects. Usually some eminent personage was indirectly responsible for instigating a major change, using a great

ball, an evening at the theatre or some other society function to display a new style. It was enough for the king to forget to do up the bottom button of his waistcoat or for the Prince of Wales's manservant to turn up the bottoms of his master's trousers because they were too long, for these details to be copied immediately by everyone in society.

Today fashions change more quickly, accompanied by reports and comments from the press, television, radio and, of course, by advertising. We can open any newspaper and see dozens of new suggestions and ideas which are seized on by the trade. Suppose one season there is a fashion for blue and yellow stripes. The shops and stores are immediately supplied with clothing in stripes of these colours, to suit all tastes and requirements, in varying quality and at a variety of prices.

There are two opposing aspects of fashion: on the one hand, there is the desire for change and on the other, the

This is a parade of high-fashion clothes, from the beginning of the twentieth century to our own time. Of the many exclusive models signed by famous designers, we can see one of the first suits (1921) or the scandalous dress accompanied by the garçonne hairstyle (1926), until we come to the miniskirt (1965) and the comfortable outfits of recent years (1980).

1953

1955

1948

1965

1937

1967

1980

The illustration on the left shows the characteristic male clothing of the beginning of the nineteenth century: the trousers became longer, shirts had high collars, and jackets reached the knee.

tendency to dress the same as everyone else.

This dual pressure is very strong and can even be observed in children. They like something, want it and then ask their parents for it, partly because it is new and different, but also because some of their friends already have one. The desire for change is linked with the desire to imitate, though it is imitation that produces boredom and weariness and so the wish to change again.

The three reasons for changes in fashion

How is a fashion born? Today it comes from the need to make money, to offer and sell one thing and then to offer and sell something else. Fashion is invented and destroyed by the logic of consumer spending. In the past, on the other hand, fashions had deeper origins; the motivation was rooted in human nature.

One of the primary causes of fashion, wherever it occurred and whatever the subject, was the desire to be noticed and to express social superiority. Clothes became rich and ostentatious. Fabrics were costly. Even the style was intricate and complicated and could not be worn or imitated by any but the rich. Think, for example, of some of the sleeves of clothes in the Middle Ages: they were very wide and often so long they touched the ground. Someone who had to work could never have worn such clothes. Every aspect of fashion expressed above all wealth and nobility.

Nowadays, any consumer can buy whatever he or she can afford. This has removed much of the discrimination of the past and fashions today appeal to the vanity of all, whatever their positions. It is even directed at the very young, by

playing on their desires. If, for example, the television and cinema spread the fashion for robots, many children feel that they want and must have at least one toy. Industry makes the most of the situation, producing both highly sophisticated and very expensive robots as well as small plastic ones costing a few pence. It means that today the need to be noticed is

rarely as important as being able to say, "I've got one, too".

Another important cause of fashion in the past, which still applies today, was the search for aesthetics, the pleasure of having something beautiful. This is why from time to time there is an interest in a particular colour, fabric or design.

The search for aesthetic qualities is clearly expressed in clothing. Women have always dressed to look more attractive, or at least more interesting. Girls who, for example, choose to dress as gipsies, with wide flowery skirts, sloppy jumpers and long, tangled hair, are also trying to put over an aesthetic message, to stand out and look flamboyant. If a number of girls adopt the style, it becomes a fashion and they conform to the new idea. People usually want to highlight a particular feature or one part of their body, and this has been reflected in styles which emphasize the bust, waist or legs.

In the twenties, a woman's body appeared as flat as a pancake. The very short skirts implied more than a current taste: they were also a sign of rebellion, a farewell to the nineteenth century and everything it stood for, the modesty and prohibitions which had characterized a severe and puritanical period. Women's

Waistcoat and long jacket with a scarf at the collar dictated the sober fashion for men at the end of the nineteenth century (as shown on the left). On the right, on the other hand, is a picture of the same date showing the characteristic female bustle holding up the skirt.

legs, which it was once a scandal to show, even an ankle, became a symbol of the freedom of the new times.

The third cause is the desire to be different from previous generations, in appearance as well as attitudes. After the last war, when Christian Dior's bell-shaped skirts and stiletto heels appeared all over Europe, the new fashion was given the auspicious and appropriate name of the "new look". The enthusiasm with which it was immediately adopted showed not only that people liked the new style, but that they were glad to abandon the clothes, shoes and hair styles which reminded them of a tragic and miserable past of suffering and deprivation.

What is true of clothing is true of other things, too, such as music, films, or literature. We say, "It's the fashion", but we could also say, "We like it, we have chosen it because it does not look at all like the things that were popular yesterday".

Imitation and looking "different"

The attempt to look a little different from the dictates of fashion is no new thing. Today it is the young who rebel, but in the past it was the aristocracy who became concerned when less wealthy people tried to imitate their style of dress. At times, measures were even taken to prevent the clothes and accessories of the nobility from being copied: in the year 808, Charlemagne published a decree governing the mode of dress of all the social classes in an attempt to curb such imitation and hence "confusion" between the classes.

When, as the centuries passed, the middle class gained greater economic importance and so became wealthier, there was no need to look to its social superiors for models of behaviour and dress. It created its own fashion, with its own standards of elegance. It did, however, continue to imitate the aristocracy for some time, even though the latter were losing their power and wealth. Above all else, the rich untitled woman wanted to "look like a real Lady". Fashion became a matter of manners, and etiquette. Elegance meant appearance. It was not enough to have beautiful clothes, one had to wear them with a certain air of distinction and breeding.

During the nineteenth and early twentieth centuries, this desire to emulate social superiors, who were often stereotyped figures, accompanied discrimination in other areas. The middle class wanted to confirm their own superiority based on the money, recreating the very differences against which the French revolution had fought. Everything was divided into classes, upper, middle, lower. The dream of equality seemed lost in ambition and was broken down into a number of fashions and types of behaviour.

In the hands of the upper middle class, who were the most powerful, fashion took on a greater social importance than it had had in the hands of the aristocracy. The rich middle classes did not have titles or crowns as signs of their importance, but they did have money and everything that money could buy. Appearances became essential to indicate social position and differentiate between one income group and another.

The feathered hat of a rich banker's wife at the beginning of the twentieth century was quite different from the small modest hat of a young schoolmistress. It was not only a question of money, but of social propriety. The novels of the nineteenth century are full of examples of this: from a description of their dress it was possible to recognize immediately a great lady,

French and Italian fashion are famous throughout the world. Above, a parade of practical and very colourful Italian quilted coats, co-ordinated with warm berets. Right, a man's suit, with a slim and elegant line; the suit has stayed much as it was, with only a few real changes.

dancer, daughter of a poor family or working woman.

Etiquette, the conventional rules of polite behaviour in society, became important and helped to raise new social barriers.

Then people started to talk about "good taste", another way of discriminating between one class and another. Good taste gradually moderated the ostentatious display of wealth, although such restraint was too much for the *nouveau riche* who immediately considered the thing that cost the most to be elegant. The misfortune was that the upper middle class, the new arbiter of fashion, found a new element of distinction in moderation itself.

In the nineteenth century and in our century up until our time, the dress of the rich was refined but simple, based on details of cut, the perfection of the accessories, the quality of the cloth, and each outfit was suited to the person who wore it. The concept of the "woman of breeding" began to come in.

This effort to be different, simple and better made the fortune of the great

Two Italian models, presented at the parades for the spring-summer 1981 season, which are practical and easy to wear: left, a sailor suit, right a comfortable showerproof jacket.

designers. It was much easier to make a "rich" outfit than an "elegant" one. All the former required was numerous jewels, kilometres of ribbons and frills and the most costly fabrics, as in the portraits of some ladies and gentlemen of past centuries. For the second, skilled cutting, architectural simplicity and indisputable originality are essential.

In the hands of its "creators", fashion inevitably became "high fashion" and the barriers were raised between the different social levels.

The popularity of market stalls

In recent years, there has again been a tendency to destroy these differences, by making fashion more generally available, and not only fashions in clothes.

The sale of second-hand clothes has become popular, even fashionable; market stalls have sprung up with both new and old clothes and are eagerly patronized. We have seen the success of ethnic clothes and jeans for people of all ages. In other fields, the fashion has developed for naïve or free and spontaneous painters and, in the literary field,

"primitive" writers, able to express themselves without paying too much attention to syntax.

All this, as with its predecessors, has been a fashion with the same values and defects as other fashions. The people who have followed it are saying, "I am different from the others, I am more intelligent than you, freer than you, more open-minded than you. And because of this I am superior to you." This message is valid until it becomes too widespread, thus losing much of its effectiveness.

Now fashion is being reborn on other discriminatory bases. As the economic crisis which is afflicting the countries of the world is making more acute the division which has always existed in society between the rich, less rich and poor, the yardstick of money remains largely what determines taste. We still have clothes shops, boutiques and departmental stores, but newspapers and magazines are again showing the high fashion which is emerging. When high fashion is again worn by the very rich, the taste of the majority will be determined by how much they can afford.

167

Furnishing
The history of comfort

Even primitive man had somewhere to live (a cave or a hut) and the first couch on which he lay and the first stone slab on which he sat were the beginnings of that branch of human endeavour devoted to promoting comfort, furnishing in other words.

History, fashion, religion, culture, geographical and climatic conditions and the materials available were and still are what determine the various styles of furniture, but man's ambition has always been the major influence: man has always wanted to feel that he was important in his own house. Even certain types of chair conceal a desire for power: the king's throne and the soldier of fortune's saddle are in fact thought to be early examples of this.

By furnishing we usually mean western furnishing. Different traditions have influenced other styles and it is difficult for us to understand, for example, why a Japanese person prefers a mat to a bed or why an Arab feels more comfortable on a carpet than on a divan. The past nomadic life of some peoples (living in tents and moving continually from place to place) has contributed to these practices but on its own is not enough to explain them. There are other historical and social reasons which have become overlaid and intermingled. Today, however, the differences are disappearing and ways of living are becoming more similar throughout the world.

By the term "furnishing", moreover, we are mainly talking about (at least as regards the past) large houses, castles and palaces, that is the dwelling-places of the rich. The houses of the poor (especially if the nation to which they belong is also poor) always resemble each other, in different places and at different times, and only fulfil the most elementary needs (sleeping, eating, protection from the cold and preservation of food and clothing).

Early furniture

In Egypt, only the rich possessed beds which look rather uncomfortable and hard, with a head-rest instead of a pillow. Like the thrones and stools, they were decorated and had legs with carved ends shaped like animal feet such as a lion's paws. Dining-tables as such did not exist, but only wooden planks or stone slabs from which the diners helped themselves. In the homes of the rich, there were also innumerable vases, urns, ceramic, wood and metal utensils.

The Greeks and above all the Romans loved comfort in their houses: they dined and received visitors lying on couches. Mattresses, cushions and pillows had woollen or linen coverings woven in intricate patterns and the couches were often draped in fine cloth. Small tables, benches and foot-stools were used. A Roman craftsman was probably the inventor of the sideboard, an improvement over an ordinary chest, as a place

Stylistic evolution in chairs

Ancient Egypt
(4000 BC)

Romanesque period
(thirteenth century)

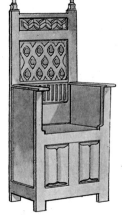

Gothic period
(fourteenth century)

Renaissance
(Italy fifteenth century)

Renaissance
(Spain sixteenth century)

Chippendale style
(England mid-eighteenth century)

Regency style
(England nineteenth century)

Hepplewhite style
(England late eighteenth century)

Empire style
(France nineteenth century)

Louis Seize style
(France end of eighteenth century)

where food could be put. For heating purposes, the Greeks had braziers, but the Romans had a central heating system with underground rooms from which heat was transmitted to the upper storeys.

There was little furniture in the Middle Ages. The most important item was the trunk or chest, which had handles making it easy to carry: if need be, it could be used as a bench, or for storing clothes or, when joined to another one, as a bed. Tables were merely planks placed across wooden supports at meal times. It was not until life grew a little more secure that items of furniture became fixed components in the scheme of furnishing and even then they remained more functional than comfortable. Fire-places with chimneys provided some sort of heating. Inside the castles it was bitterly cold and this explains why the walls were covered with wood panelling and tapestries. And sanitation? People seldom washed, and then only in a tub, and there was nowhere at all to take a bath.

During the fifteenth and sixteenth centuries, the craftsmen produced strange styles. Cupboards, beds and sideboards were carved and often painted, too, to show off the wealth of the household. Some of the most elaborate beds ever made date from about this time. The most famous of the English Elizabethan beds is the great bed of Ware which is about three and a half metres square and was one of the sights of London. Chairs, including arm-chairs, became more common and were made more comfortable, although stools were the usual form of seating, even in Elizabeth's palaces. New articles of furniture were introduced: display cabinets, bookshelves and writing-desks.

Furniture as monuments

The pretentious and ornamental style of the seventeenth century was called Baroque. It featured precious woods and carvings, gilding, inlays and decorations in ivory. Some pieces of furniture looked like monuments, particularly the large wardrobes, cupboards and cabinets which had twisted columns, broken pediments and heavy mouldings. Bed hangings became progressively more sumptuous. The great bed at Versailles had crimson velvet curtains that were so heavily embroidered with gold that the velvet scarcely showed.

During the eighteenth century, a lighter, more delicate style in furniture was preferred, partly as a reaction to the excesses of the Baroque. With the Rococo style, which arose in France, small furniture triumphed: small cabinets, side tables and low settees provided the furnishing in a new type of room, the 'boudoir', that is a small private salon for the ladies of the time. The first craftsmen to achieve international fame belong to these times: Jean Oeben in France and Thomas Chippendale in England.

Each new fashion advanced to the detriment of its predecessor and towards the middle of the eighteenth century an austere style, inspired by the Graeco-Roman world and thus called Neo-classical appeared in France in opposition to the affected Rococo style. The straight line replaced the curved and floral motifs became formalized as repetitive geometrical patterns.

In England, the architect, Robert Adam, also designed furniture which was copied and modified by cabinetmakers such as George Hepplewhite. At the end of the century, Thomas Sheraton produced furniture that was more delicate and refined.

At the beginning of the nineteenth century, the Empire style in France, called the Regency style in England, became popular. Later in the century, a continuous zigzag of new ideas took all the excitement out of furniture by modifying it to suit the practical everyday needs of the family. After the French revolution, it

Louis XII
(France sixteenth century)

Ming style
(China seventeenth century)

Lombardy Baroque
(Italy seventeenth century)

Flemish Baroque
(Flanders end of
seventeenth century)

Windsor style
(USA eighteenth century)

Louis Philippe style
(France mid-nineteenth century)

First mass-produced chair
(Germany mid-nineteenth
century)

Art Nouveau style
(France end of
nineteenth century)

Metal chair
(USA 1926)

Seat made of moulded plastic
(Italy 1974)

Bedrooms furnished in different styles. Above, a room from late Renaissance times (end of sixteenth century) with furniture in wood carved in severe lines. The decorations become richer as the seventeenth century approaches until the dominating style becomes Baroque (above, right). The rooms were adorned with frescoes, tapestry and mirrors; the furniture was very heavily gilded. In the nineteenth century, the Empire style was in the ascendant. Its shapes were heavy and the furniture mainly of mahogany. Beds of a variety of shapes were popular; "Imperial" beds (right) or even a bed in the shape of a boat (below).

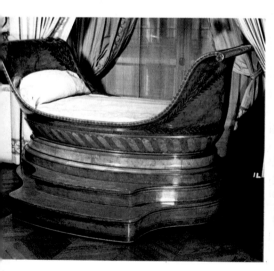

was no longer the palaces which dictated furnishing style but the houses of the bourgooio, whose owners lived not on their rents but from their work. It was not till our own century that furniture began to be mass-produced, though still in imitation of pieces from earlier times. However, new styles soon crept in, such as Art Nouveau, inspired by natural forms and by Japanese prints. This style of furniture was not as popular in England and the United States as it was on the Continent.

Space-saving tricks

In recent times, the basic necessity to employ space effectively has become more important than taste to a large extent. The population rises, flats become smaller and every square metre is vital. The interior decorator, the manufacturer and the craftsman have the same objective: to make the best use of the environment, that is to say to adapt furniture to the room where it belongs and make it functional. Pieces of folding furniture are hidden away, and it can sometimes be quite complicated to use them. Other furniture may have a dual-purpose. A bed for example, can be converted into a sofa; a table can disappear into a cupboard by means of a gadget made of springs; another table, only as deep as a book-case and flat against the wall, has drop-leaves which can be pulled out when necessary to give it a normal appearance. In practice, every furniture designer is primarily concerned with solving the space problem.

It is this need to save space which has inspired those very large pieces of furniture which sometimes cover a whole wall or even serve as a partition to divide a room in two: frequently they are used as cupboards, bookshelves, tables-cum-writing-desks, television stands and shelves and cupboards for china and cutlery, (while on the other side, quite different requirements may be met).

Paper furniture

The lines of present-day furniture are generally simple. The use of new materials, especially plastic, metal, glass and foam rubber, has given a "new look" to furniture and largely accounts for this simplicity of line (though the need for economy makes its contribution, too). Even materials which were at one time considered unsuitable produce very good solutions. Experiments have been carried out on the use of paper for tables and cupboards: this, however, seems to be more a consequence of consumerism and its arguable emphasis on making every-thing 'disposable', rather than a genuine economy measure.

It is true that industry has not yet given up imitating the older styles, but the furniture which is characteristic of our age consists of original creations, which were at first called 'avant-garde' but which cease to be so when mass-produced. These avant-garde styles still take their inspiration principally from Le Corbusier, a great French architect (though born in Switzerland) who brought both architecture and furnishing back to their true purpose: to serve the needs of people and not any passion for grandeur. Le Corbusier died in 1965 but his teaching on what a house should be is still pertinent. Apart from anything else, simple and functional furnishing is the most beautiful.

Furniture terms

At one time, all furniture and all the other items making up the furnishings had their own names, for the most part of French origin, which allowed instant identification and almost gave them a "personality". Some of these names survive. Here are some of the most used or most curious.

Abat-jour: lampshade. **Armoire:** cupboard. **Baldachin:** canopy supported by columns and placed over the bed. **Bergère:** arm-chair with an upholstered back half-surrounding the sitter. **Boiserie:** wooden wall panelling. **Buffet:** small sideboard for the dining-room. **Bureau:** writing-desk with drawers. **Chaise-longue:** sofa with a rest for the back at one end only. **Commode:** chest of drawers. **Console:** half-table against the wall beneath a mirror. **Credence:** side table or sideboard. **Etagère:** piece of furniture with shelves for ornaments. **Gueridon:** small pedestal stand for a candlestick. **Ottoman:** low couch concealing a box. **Pouffe:** low padded stool. **Teapoy:** small tripod table or stand, supported on a central pillar. **Tester:** wooden canopy, especially over a bed.

Below, the interior of a Japanese house. There is very little furniture and that is very low. There are no chairs. Traditional elements in this furnishing scheme are paper partitions, dividing panels, mats and lacquered objects. Above, an extremely modern bedroom, in which an attempt has been made to reconcile function and utility with breath-taking effect.

Clothing Why are they dressed like this?

As we can see in this photograph which is about a hundred years old, people once covered themselves up with very complicated clothes and the children looked like miniature adults. Many other things were different too, especially their way of thinking. Each age, like each culture, expresses itself in its own way, and this applies to clothes.

Everything that we wear, not only garments but also accessories such as hats, belts, scarves, gloves and shoes, is called clothing. Why do we dress? First of all, to protect ourselves especially from the cold and other effects of climate, as well as for modesty. We also dress for pleasure and to look attractive. These instincts have been deeply rooted in man since ancient times. It is probable that primitive man first dressed in animal skins from an aesthetic impulse and a desire to look better and stronger. These could be "magical" powers transferred from the skins. Having killed a wolf, bear or lion, the hunter wore its skin so he would look powerful, agile and swift like a wild animal. He then noticed that this skin, as well as making him look good, also protected him, and he began to use it for practical purposes.

Besides these basic requirements of adornment and protection, there are other reasons, some deriving from the above and some different. Man, for example, soon realized that clothes could be a sign of identity, to show other people who he was. In the case of the primitive hunter, a man who always wore the same old tattered animal skin looked weaker and less brave than someone who wore two or three skins. Vice versa, the strongest hunter, who killed many wild beasts and dressed in better skins, always acquired greater importance and could be regarded as a possible chief.

Dressing like a king

Out of this, another very different situation could arise. A cunning hunter, who wanted to be chief but was not particularly strong, might try to obtain skins without hunting for them. In this way, it would be the skins themselves and not his actual strength which made him important. This is the symbolic value of clothing; we dress differently according to the position we occupy (or would like to occupy) in society.

Someone who held power often displayed it by dressing ostentatiously. The robes of kings and emperors were covered in gold and precious stones, not only to show clearly how powerful they

172

Here are three prints dating from about two centuries ago, showing the very clear differences which existed then between the clothes of the ordinary people and the rich and between the West and the Orient. The lady getting into her carriage is wearing a bustle under her skirt at the back, which was a strange Parisian fashion adopted throughout Europe for a long time. The third print shows a pair of austere English travellers before three Indian jugglers.

were, but also to impress ordinary people and so obtain reverence and respect, and, even more important, obedience and submission.

Of course, although the powerful dressed in a certain way, others wanted to look important and tried to dress like them. This tendency was discouraged, partly so that the powerful could remain in isolated splendour, and also to limit the excessive aspirations of less important people.

It was during these historical periods when wealth was being established, that fixed rules arose for the dress of certain occupations and social positions. During the fourteenth century in some European countries, for example, the colour green was prohibited for the clothes of women of humble birth; blue was reserved for workmen, materials striped in many colours indicated servants, waiters and messengers. There were even rules for the long pointed shoes we see in many of the paintings of this age. The point was extended and very pronounced for princes; half the length for the rich middle classes who did not have any aristocratic blood, and a few centimetres or so for the ordinary people.

Later when the powerful were very ostentatious, laws were even promulgated on several occasions (called the "sumptuary laws") prohibiting excessive elegance among the middle classes who became more and more eager to hide their lack of noble birth under gold and velvet.

Big hats and collars

Today the rules of dress have become more subtle, less obvious. Those with power try not to show it too much in their clothes and other people can wear what they like. Yet clothing still has very specific symbols today. Many articles give a precise indication of a certain social status, even though this is less evident than it once was: the jacket of a great designer, the bag or belt with a particular initial, the watch by a famous jeweller and so on.

Besides revealing the condition of people, clothing also reflects the history and culture of a society. This is not so apparent; you have to know the details and characteristics of an age to see them

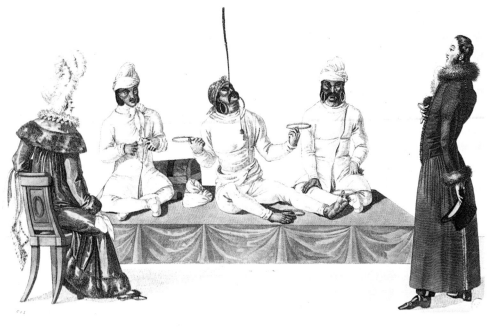

PERIOD OF HENRY VIII
(England: early 1500s)

LATE RENAISSANCE
(England: 1600)

GOTHIC PERIOD
(Germany: 1200–1300)

RENAISSANCE
(Italy: 1400)

LATE RENAISSANCE
(Spain: 1600)

reflected in the clothing. For example, the strange pointed head-dresses, which were very tall or with a double cone, which women of Northern Europe wore in the fourteenth century, reflected the Gothic influence, a type of architecture with pinnacles and pointed arches which became established in this period. In the same way, we can recognize in the frilled collars of the sixteenth and seventeenth centuries the Spanish influence, behaviour which was ostentatious yet severe at the same time, the religious feeling which flowed into baroque art. The frilled collar was large and thick, made of starched linen supported on a light wire framework; originating in Spain, it soon spread to most of Europe, becoming a basic part of the dress of the time, both for men and women. Its prime purpose was to prevent the silk and velvet clothes from coming into contact with the hair, which was fairly long and greasy (hygiene had hardly been discovered in those days).

Miniature adults

Other aspects of social life are also revealed by dress. Why, for example, were children in past centuries dressed to look

ROMANTIC PERIOD
(France: 1800)

ROMANTIC PERIOD
(England: mid 1800s)

MODERN PERIOD
(Italy: early 1900s)

174

PERIOD OF LOUIS XV
(France: mid 1700s)

PERIOD OF LOUIS XIV
(France: late 1600s)

PERIOD OF THE DIRECTOIRE
(France: late 1700s)

NAPOLEONIC PERIOD
(France: 1800)

EIGHTEENTH CENTURY
(Italy)

HTEENTH CENTURY
(England)

These illustrations cover eight centuries of European history of clothing, from the Middle Ages to the beginning of our century, in a parade of characters who often remind us of famous paintings of the time. They show that in the Middle Ages, the men wore their clothes long like the women; during the Renaissance, very bright colours were preferred and instead of trousers long stockings were worn; in the early seventeenth century, clothes were severe, but with big lace and embroidered collars. However, the most amazing and cumbersome clothes, especially for women, were those of the following century, the eighteenth. This was a triumph of French fashion, with wigs, ribbons and bows. Only at the beginning of the twentieth century did clothes start to resemble those of today. Of course, only a small minority could afford such refined and complicated clothes. The dress of other people did not change very much from one epoque to another, and national costumes worn at traditional popular festivals have remained almost unchanged through the ages.

EIGHTEENTH CENTURY
(France)

These different styles of dress all come from the present time, but show different traditions (the Scots and their kilts) or local customs (in China, India and Japan).

In the photographs below are three very different examples of modern dress: a group of Arab women, a native of the Mentawa islands (Indonesia) and a Lapp woman. The Indonesian, in spite of his contact with twentieth-century progress (he is listening to the radio), retains the typical costume of his people, consisting chiefly of tattoos.

like miniature adults? In a picture painted by Velazquez, portraying the young girls of the court, the Infanta, or royal princess, is a girl of five. Yet she is wearing a low-cut neckline, tight bodice, flowers on her bosom and her movements hampered by the enormous skirt, held out by a rigid frame of the crinoline type so that she looks a strange, unreal, ageless figure. The young prince, Baldassarre Carlo, does not fare any better in another painting by Velazquez, seated on a horse, with his sash, velvet, boots and big hat throwing a shadow over his childish face. At that time, a child was considered simply as a smaller copy of an adult.

Only in this century has it been understood and accepted that a child is very different from an adult, with different needs, likes and dislikes. Now children are dressed simply, so that they can move freely. In fact the opposite to what used to be the case has happened: now it is often the adults who copy the children, wearing jeans, T-shirts and practical pullovers.

Two basic discoveries

A discussion of dress, however, does not only involve the clothes and their wearers but also those who make them. Originally clothes did not take long to make; animal skins only had to be cut up and cleaned

with stone and bone tools. However, when primitive man changed from his nomadic life to a more settled existence and learned to cultivate the land and raise animals, he made two sensational discoveries: the raw material with which he could make clothes (wool, linen, hemp and cotton) and the way to produce them by spinning and weaving.

Once he had learned this secret, he then had to develop and improve his performance. The results depended not only on the skill of the craftsman, but also on technology, that is first instruments and then machinery. The first instruments were the spindle and distaff for spinning, to convert the fibrous mass into thin, strong threads. Then came the loom for weaving, interlacing these threads in an ordered and regular manner. Carding combs to make the fibres soft, needles with eyes and of course scissors, an essential tool, also appeared. With these basic instruments, man continued to make clothes for thousands of years, without any substantial differences except in the raw materials used.

Linen, wool, silk, cotton

The Egyptians used mainly linen, sometimes interwoven with gold threads for the pharaohs, priests and nobles, and with leather and other plant fibres for the people. They were so good at working with linen, that they could make it transparent for the veils of the princesses or thick and very strong for the bandages of mummies. The Greeks alternated between linen and wool, depending on the season. They added sea-silk, obtained from a sea mollusc in the same way as silk is obtained from the silk worm. The Chinese had a monopoly in the production of silk, as they were the only people who knew how to produce it. In spite of the expedition to the Orient of Alexander the Great three centuries before Christ, and that of the Romans over a century after Christ (specially organized to discover the secret of silk), it was not until around AD 550 that its use was introduced into the West in the time of Justinian. He persuaded two Persian monks who had lived in China to return there and smuggle silkworms to Constantinople in the hollows of their bamboo canes. These were the beginning of all the varieties that supplied European raw silk until the nineteenth century.

As a result of lack of trade, even linen became rare until about the year 1000, but matters improved after the Crusades (which were not only carried out for religious purposes but also for economic and political reasons). The Arabs, who had settled in Spain, became very skilled at dying and producing fabrics. They were among the first to become involved in the production of silk and revived the weaving of cotton on a grand scale.

Machines: a revolution

Machinery arrived in the eighteenth century, when the two operations of spinning and weaving were mechanized. Machines no longer assist man in making cloth; this is done by the machines on their own. Today we are so used to machinery that this seems normal, but in the eighteenth century it was an enormous turning point. Using a machine meant producing much more material in a shorter time and using fewer workers, and so at greatly reduced cost. As prices were lower, more people could buy the cloth and so the demand increased. Machines were subsequently improved to produce more and more and so the price fell further and the number of buyers multiplied.

This system still works today, so that we are called the industrial society. Life changed radically with the coming of machines in the eighteenth century which became known as the period of the "Industrial Revolution". This affected many sections of society.

The mid-nineteenth century saw the invention of the sewing machine and the cutting machine, which cut out layers of material. These led to another great innovation, the manufacturing industry, which has developed further in this century with the flood of synthetic fibres. Some artificial fibres worth remembering are rayon, the production of which started in 1891, and acetate, first developed in 1865, and widely used for clothing and household furnishing. Nylon was first introduced commercially in 1938 to make bristles for toothbrushes, and next as hosiery. Synthetics score over natural fibres first of all because they are more economic (the costs of manufacture are lower and there is less waste); also they are light in weight and do not go out of shape when washed; lastly, they can be dyed more easily and with more stable results than natural fibres since the dye can be included as part of the preparation of the raw material.

The Arts
and
Entertainment

Alphabet
Signs and words

The alphabet takes its name from the first two letters of the Greek alphabet, alpha and beta. We call our own alphabet the ABC in the same way. In fact many years ago, children learned the letters of the alphabet from a book called an abecedary, a word which sounds like the first four letters.

What really is the alphabet? It is a system for transcribing spoken words as written words. It did not come into use at the same time as the art of writing itself. That was invented just before 3000 BC. The oldest written material so far discovered is from the Sumerian city of Uruk. This writing was called "cuneiform" which means "wedge-shaped", because it was inscribed on tablets of soft clay by an instrument which left wedge-shaped marks. The alphabet came later, or rather alphabets for there are a number of different ones, almost one for each language, even if the differences are slight. With the invention of writing, man began to indicate by means of symbols and pictures what certain words signified. Life was very simple in those times and it was not considered necessary to be able to write. The words needed to communicate were relatively few.

Typewriters and similar equipment for writing Arabic characters, such as the teleprinter in the photograph, are more complicated than those for other languages because the letters of the Arabic alphabet change their form according to their position: at the beginning of a word, within it, or at the end. They are not written separately, but are almost always joined together. They are set out from right to left because Arabic is read in the opposite direction to our writing. The hieroglyphs of ancient Egypt are also read from right to left.

English		Greek		
A	a	Α	α	a
B	b	Β	β	v
C	c	Γ	γ	gh
D	d	Δ	δ	dh
E	e	Ε	ε	e
F	f	Ζ	ζ	z
G	g	Η	η	ee
H	h	Θ	θ	th
I	i	Ι	ι	ee
J	j	Κ	κ	k
K	k	Λ	λ	l
L	l	Μ	μ	m
M	m	Ν	ν	n
N	n	Ξ	ξ	ks
O	o	Ο	ο	o
P	p	Π	π	p
Q	q	Ρ	ρ	r
R	r	Σ	σ	s
S	s	Σ	ς	s
T	t	Τ	τ	t
U	u	Υ	υ	ee
V	v	Φ	φ	f
W	w	Χ	χ	kh
X	x	Ψ	ψ	ps
Y	y	Ω	ω	o
Z	z			

Arabic

letter	central letter	final letter	
آ	‍	إ	a
ب	‍	‍	b
ت	‍	‍	t
ث	‍	‍	th
ج	‍	‍	g
ح	‍	‍	h
خ	‍	‍	kh
د	‍	‍	d
ذ	‍	‍	dh
ر	‍	‍	r
ز	‍	‍	z
س	‍	‍	s
ش	‍	‍	sh
ص	‍	‍	s
ض	‍	‍	dh
ط	‍	‍	t
ظ	‍	‍	dh
ع	‍	‍	glottal stop.
غ	‍	‍	gh
ف	‍	‍	f
ق	‍	‍	g
ك	‍	‍	k
ل	‍	‍	l
م	‍	‍	m
ن	‍	‍	n
ه	‍	‍	h
و	‍	‍	w
ي	‍	‍	y

Hebrew

letter	sound
א	a
ב	b
ב	v
ג	g
ד	d
ה	h
ו	v,w
ז	z
ח	h
ט	t
י	y,j,i
כ	k
כ	kh
ל	l
מ	m
נ	n
ס	s
ע	glottal stop.
פ	p
פ	f
צ	s
ק	k
ר	r
ש	sh
ש	s
ת	t

Finali

letter	sound
ך	k
ם	m
ן	n
ף	p
ץ	s

Russian

letter	sound
А	a
Б	b
В	v
Г	g
Д	d
Е	ye
Ё	yo
Ж	zh
З	z
И	ee
Й	y
К	k
Л	l
М	m
Н	n
О	o
П	p
Р	r
С	s
Т	t
У	oo
Ф	f
Х	kh
Ц	ts
Ч	ch
Ш	sh
Щ	shch
Ъ	—
Ы	i
Ь	—
Э	e
Ю	yoo
Я	ya

Even the blind can read, thanks to the alphabet invented in 1829 by the Frenchman Louis Braille, who was himself blind. Each letter is made up of a group of between one and six small dots which are arranged in different ways. The dots are raised up from the paper, and are "read" by being touched gently with the finger-tips. The photograph shows a book in Braille writing.

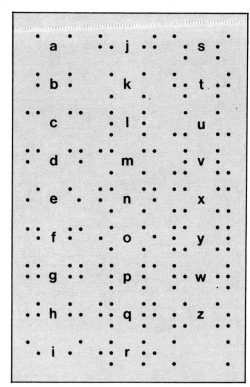

One hundred and forty-two letters in five alphabets

The main alphabets in use in the world today.

English: the Latin alphabet which, with some small variations, is used by almost all European languages.

Greek: apart from being used in Greece, Greek is still used in scientific and mathematical names.

Arabic: this consists of consonants. There are only three vowels ("a", "i" and "u") and these are indicated by supplementary signs.

Hebrew: a language which was dying out (confined to religious texts), but which has returned to life in the State of Israel.

Russian: it is the Cyrillic alphabet, the most recent of all. It is used by the Russians and other Slav peoples: Ukrainians, Serbs, Bulgarians.

181

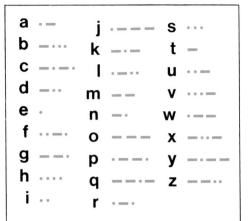

The picture

Why do animals not need a complex language and still less the ability to write? The answer is that their lives are simple, made up of only a few basic sensations like danger and hunger, and as they do not use objects such as tools and utensils, they can get on very well without giving them names. The men of 6,000 years ago were certainly no longer "animal-like" but they were still fairly primitive and there were few matters that they thought were worth writing down. If a king believed himself to be as beautiful and strong as the sun and wanted to write it down, all he had to do was have cut into a stone the special sign for the king and the special sign for the sun.

This type of writing, which still could not really be called writing proper, is known as "pictograms" (*gramma*, in Greek, means "writing") and is easily seen to be based on the idea of a picture or diagram.

Simple pictograms gave way to ideograms, that is signs which denoted thoughts that were more difficult to illustrate. To say, or rather to write, that the king is beautiful may be easy, but to write that he is also intelligent and good is more complicated. How does one depict intelligence and goodness? It is at this point that writing incorporated new signs to represent abstract ideas. The writing of the ancient Egyptians, the hieroglyphs, consisted of pictograms and ideograms which even then managed to express a fairly large number of ideas.

But obviously it was not enough: it was easier to invent new words than new signs. Only the Chinese have succeeded (and only the Chinese with their proverbial patience could have succeeded) in devising a large enough number of different ideograms to be able to write down any word. In fact the Chinese "alphabet" contains about eighty thousand symbols but only a very few are committed to memory by the Chinese themselves. With good luck they succeed in making themselves understood very well by using only two or three thousand.

We have been more fortunate because there must once have been someone who grew tired of having to invent new ideograms which were becoming more and more obscure and complicated, and so devised a series of signs to show the various sounds which the word contained, instead of showing the meaning of a word.

It is not known who had that brilliant idea. Perhaps the Egyptians themselves, while increasing and improving their hieroglyphs; perhaps the Phoenicians, who made long voyages and, as a trading

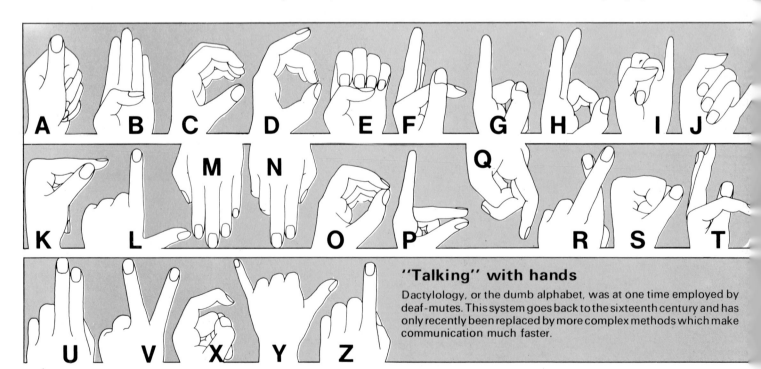

"Talking" with hands

Dactylology, or the dumb alphabet, was at one time employed by deaf-mutes. This system goes back to the sixteenth century and has only recently been replaced by more complex methods which make communication much faster.

h i j k l m

u v w x y z

Semaphore is a signalling system where a flag is held in each hand, at arm's length, and in varying positions. Below, a ship dressed overall.

people, faced the practical problems of writing and had little time to waste.

The Greeks

It is at any rate certain that the first people to take this invention and from it to create a simple alphabet which could be used by as many people as possible, were the Greeks. This took place about 500 years before the time of Christ. The Greeks were also the first to write as we write to-day, setting out the letters from left to right. The Arabs, however, always wrote in the opposite direction, from right to left.

In the meantime, other civilizations had begun to compile their alphabets. Syllabic alphabets, or syllabaries, with one sign for each syllable, were developed. These were a great improvement on ideograms but they always needed a large number of letters, and in addition were alphabets consisting solely of consonants and so were only useful for languages in which vowel sounds play a relatively small part.

Many minor alphabets have virtually disappeared. The most recent one to be developed and which is still in use, is the Cyrillic which was devised in Bulgaria at the end of the ninth century, and is used by the Russians and Bulgarians. It is so named because its invention is attributed to St. Cyril, who would have used it to translate the Bible into the Slavonic languages. Indeed, thanks to Christianity, the Latin alphabet (our own) has become the most widely known and used in the world. It is also the alphabet of the peoples who in the past conquered and subjugated half the world: the Spanish, French and English. However, even the Latin alphabet cannot be perfect and complete for everyone. The English and the French, for example, put two or three letters together to represent certain sounds or else pronounce one sound in several different ways.

Yet the alphabet has changed little in nearly 3,000 years. It is the most convenient and adaptable form of writing. Children learn it easily and it can be passed from one language to another.

Cinema

When photography broke into a run

One day in 1895, in Paris, a group of journalists and theatre directors were present at an unbelievable spectacle: an apparatus threw onto a screen a series of moving pictures. Thanks to the work of the Lumière brothers, the cinema was born.

The idea was not, as we shall see, entirely new, but the moment when the cinema began was without doubt 28 December 1895, when Auguste and Louis Lumière presented at the Grand Café, Boulevard des Capucines, the extraordinary machine which made photographs ''run''.

Inventions are strange things. The rewards often go to the person who puts the finishing touches to the hard work of somebody else. And so in this case, the exploratory work which made the Lumière brothers' creation possible is ignored. This preliminary work goes back, according to some experts, to the time of ancient Egypt or, according to others, to a Jesuit of the seventeenth century. To the latter is attributed the perfecting of the ''magic lantern'', a simple but fascinating device: a closed box containing a source of light which can project a magnified image onto a screen.

With the invention of photography, towards the middle of the nineteenth century, and then with the use of celluloid film covered with a soft gelatine, further progress was made.

Among those who worked on the problems of reproducing movement was the French-born Louis Le Prince, who used a camera patented in Britain to take the first motion pictures in Leeds in the autumn of 1888. Le Prince disappeared mysteriously while on a train journey in 1890. So it fell to Thomas Edison and William Dickson, who had been working on similar apparatus in America, to give the first public demonstration of motion pictures. This was at the Edison Laboratories on 22 May 1891, when representatives of the National Federation of

184

A group of film actors at work (right): before each take is begun, there is always a tumult of actors rehearsing their words, technicians adjusting the lights and film cameramen trying to get the perfect shot.

"Behind the scenes" in the film industry's world of pretence: here we can see sets which faithfully copy a terrace (above), or an actor, hanging in mid-air, who experiences the movements of the science fiction hero whom he has to impersonate (left). In the cinema, watching the film, we will not notice these tricks: it will seem to us that the actor really is flying in the sky and that the terrace gives on to the roofs of old Rome.

The cinema has travelled along many roads from the old machine of the Lumière brothers in 1894 (below) to the modern cine cameras (right). The films used today have various sizes. The smallest is 8 millimetres wide and is used in amateur film-making; the largest is 70 millimetres wide and is used for films to be shown on a panoramic screen.

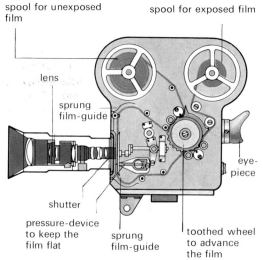

spool for unexposed film

spool for exposed film

lens

sprung film-guide

eye-piece

shutter

pressure-device to keep the film flat

sprung film-guide

toothed wheel to advance the film

Let us look at the main parts of a cine camera which are found both in the cheapest and the most expensive models. First the system of lenses which make up the objective; then the diaphragm which serves to control the amount of light to suit the ambient light conditions and the sensitivity of the film; then the shutter which determines the exposure time. Forming part of the secondary mechanisms, we find the "film-guides", the pressure-device which feeds the film through and keeps it always in the correct position relative to the lens, and the eye-piece or view-finder to "frame" the scene to be shot. Lastly, of course, there is the film, which is wound from one spool to the other.

As soon as the potential of the cinema show had been demonstrated, industry decided to take a hand in the persons of Léon Gaumont and Charles Pathé, two unforgettable names. Independently, these two provided the cinematograph with the commercial organization and means of distribution which it needed. Their trade-marks (a daisy for Gaumont and a cockerel for Pathé) were symbols of quality for many years.

Public interest grew rapidly from the time of the first demonstrations. Wherever a film was to be shown it was certain that there would be a large audience and that many tickets would be sold, so very soon the number of projection halls multiplied. In Britain, the first film show before a paying audience took place at the Regent Street Polytechnic on 20 February 1896. For the sum of one shilling (five pence) the audience saw a programme of Lumière films. The first feature film was shown publicly in Britain in 1908. It was *The Story of the Kelly Gang* which had been made in Australia in 1906.

Silent films in black and white

At that time films were in black and white only and were silent. The performance was "accompanied" by a pianist hired for this purpose by the hall in which the film was shown. A few words of dialogue and explanatory phrases appeared as writing on the screen between scenes. The actors were compelled to mime in a very exaggerated way.

These limitations did not prevent the cinema from creating its own demi-gods. The absence of sound in fact helped to create an atmosphere of mystery around the actors and especially around the actresses. These mute creatures took on the seductive personality of the roles they played, heroes and heroines of love stories, of adventure stories and epics from history and literature. The worship of screen idols was born. In Europe, Asta Neilson of Denmark and the German Henny Porten were the first international "stars". Meanwhile the film industry in the United States had learned that if it fed the curiosity of the public about the leading performers, its profit increased.

The "star system" soon bore fruit. The passionate interest in Rudolph Valentino, Pola Negri, Mary Pickford and other assured enormous receipts for any film, good or bad, in which the stars appeared.

But the cinema was not purely commercial: it had already become an art. This was demonstrated during the era of the silent films by both actors (for example, Charlie Chaplin) and directors (for example, the Russian, Sergei Mikhailovitch Eisenstein, the American

Women's Clubs were able to look through a hole in the top of a box, called a kinetoscope, and see moving pictures. It was, however, the Lumière brothers who first publicly projected a moving film onto a screen, and whose film first moved fast enough to avoid jerkiness.

Without a plot and without actors

These short films of the Lumière brothers had no plot and no actors. The brothers confined themselves to showing, for example, some workers leaving their factory, a family eating a meal, the arrival of a train and the waves on the sea, but each film seemed then like a miracle. Another of their films showed a gardener "being watered" (as from a watering-can) by his own pump: a trifling incident but enough to go down in history as the first comic film.

The Lumière brothers had no idea that the cinema would later become a "spectacle". On the contrary, they thought of it as a possible aid to scientists and researchers. It is said that when a conjuror, Georges Méliès, offered to buy their apparatus from them they refused and advised him not to waste his money, as the cinematograph had no future.

But the conjuror did not give in easily and bought a similar apparatus from an Englishman, R. W. Paul. Cleverly and with persistence, Méliès modified it so as to be able to realize his dream: to amuse the public as well as himself. He built in his garden the first theatre for showing motion pictures, a large hall in which fantastic tales with titles such as *Cinderella, The Impossible Voyage* or *Voyage to the Moon* were shown.

If the Lumière brothers were the inventors of the cinematograph, Méliès was without doubt the inventor of the cinema show. He was a genial, extravagant man with bizarre habits, around whom strange stories grew up. He had a total lack of business sense and died in poverty in an institution.

David Wark Griffith and the Dane, Carle Theodor Dreyer). During the early twenties while films were largely silent, the pictorial side of the art was perfected, as were facial expression, gesture and technique.

The long period of silent films allowed the visual aspects of the cinema to mature, but the advent of sound brought a crisis. The stars found themselves suddenly confronted with the need to speak. Until then, it had been enough to know how to move and how to express oneself with gestures and looks. Suddenly one had also to be able to declaim, to have no trace of dialect in one's speech and to have a pleasant voice. Dubbing was far from perfect. Many actors were forced to retire.

The first spoken words

The first sound films to be shown commercially were produced in the early 1920s. Most of these were "shorts", or had only music and sound "effects". For this reason, the film which is always remembered as the first "talkie" is *The Jazz Singer*. This was produced in 1927 and the star, Al Jolson, actually spoke a few sentences as well as singing. The cinema had at last uttered its first words.

It was progress, although there were some who held that it was a backward step. Chaplin declared: "I detest talking films. They destroy the great beauty of silence." It was not until 1940 that the great "little man" of *Modern Times* reconciled himself to sound in *The Great Dictator*.

The silent cinema survived for a few more years, until the technology of sound-recording, which consisted of registering or "photographing" the sound on the film itself (sound-track), was perfected. Once that was accomplished, the cinema underwent a great expansion everywhere.

In the United States, Hollywood, already the capital of the film world, attracted the most famous European directors and actors. One of the first to cross the Atlantic was the Frenchman, Maurice Chevalier, who played the lead in numerous minor films opposite Jeannette MacDonald. Sound gave a boost to the musical film, just as the silent film had made the fortunes of comic actors possessing the gift of self-expression.

Hollywood became unbeatable for the ostentation of its musicals: beautiful women, dancers such as Fred Astaire, singers such as Bing Crosby, created a type of cinema with which the poorer European cinema could seldom compete. The song and dance film was the only genre not attempted by the silent films, which had already tackled love stories,

horror stories, science fiction, thrillers, stories with a social or political background, comedies, satires and even animated cartoons, which in the thirties reached their maximum popularity with the full-length films of Walt Disney.

Gangsters, cowboys and empresses

It was, however, inevitable that with the perfecting of its technique the cinema should once again take up its old themes. In comedy (more precisely American comedy) performers such as Clark Gable, James Stewart, Jean Arthur, Katherine Hepburn and Cary Grant and directors such as Frank Capra and the elderly Ernst Lubitsch were triumphant.

The gangster films had their own stars in Edward G. Robinson and George Raft, who created across the world a very

Further moments in the making of a film: left, getting ready for an outside shot, during work on the film Jaws; below, an inside take; above, a film-cameraman prepares to shoot.

different image from that of the sparkling musicals – a picture of a violent America, entirely lacking in moral sense.

During the silent era, the most popular cowboy star in the westerns had been Tom Mix. His successor was John Wayne, who in John Ford's *Stagecoach* (1939) achieved a popularity which was to last until his death, four decades later.

History and literature provided many female roles: for example, *Cleopatra* with Claudette Colbert, *Marie-Antoinette* with Norma Shearer or *The Scarlet Empress* (Catherine of Russia) with Marlene Dietrich, who had migrated to Hollywood from Germany as a result of the fame she won in the film *The Blue Angel*.

But it was above all the Swedish actress Greta Garbo, goddess among the deities, who was to bring to the cinema screen fascinating historical and literary per-

sonalities. From Queen Christina to Marguérite Gautier and from Maria Walewska to Anna Karenina, she played with such power as to merge her own personality with those of the mysterious and dramatic women she portrayed.

Films with a theme of terror continued to be popular. *Frankenstein*, *Dracula* and *King Kong* are now cinema classics. Thrillers established themselves firmly at the same time. Comedy thrillers, which cleverly combine shudders with entertainment, were at least as popular.

Films aimed at a family audience became commercially successful and ousted the more artistic films. A typical example is *Gone with the Wind* starring Vivien Leigh and Clark Gable, considered a masterpiece to this day, because of the success it had and still has with the public throughout the world.

The Hollywood stars

The stars (a term which includes both men and women) were essential to Hollywood. They were "built up" according to the tastes of the time. The cinema blonde was represented over the years by Jean Harlow, Carole Lombard and lastly the unforgettable Marilyn Monroe.

The *femme fatale*, to whom there had been little alternative in the silent days, was represented in the 1930s by Joan Crawford, Greta Garbo and Marlene Dietrich and later by Rita Hayworth, Lana Turner, Ava Gardner and Elizabeth Taylor. The "girl-next-door", whose archetype was Clara Bow, was personified at various times and with varying success by Deanna Durbin, Doris Day, Debbie Reynolds and many others.

There were also child prodigies. Shirley Temple was an historic example. And among so many there are a few whose magnetism still comes from their personalities rather than their looks: Bette Davis and Katherine Hepburn, for example. Of course, to be "type-cast" in certain roles did not help the actresses and in fact

The film is not completed when the shooting is over: there are still many things to be done. The various reels of film are developed, mounted and viewed on special equipment (above left); at this stage special effects are also added. The film then goes on to mixing (above right), and the insertion of the sound-track which has already been recorded (above). Usually there are three sound-tracks (dialogue, music and sound-effects) which are fused or "mixed" together. This makes it possible for only the dialogue to be dubbed if needed, leaving the other two tracks

intact. Now the whole film is ready for developing (below left, drums containing the chemicals used). Then the film is put through the projector and a technician carefully checks the quality and looks for possible defects (below right).

imposed constraints on them, but it did strengthen the film industry. Even men could not escape from this conditioning. Actors like Gary Cooper, Henry Fonda and Gregory Peck always seemed to be firmly linked to kind-hearted characters with sound principles, while other actors have had to play ne'er-do-wells and unscrupulous Don Juans throughout their lives.

This, then, was the industry dominated by the directors: for example, Cecil B. De Mille, who specialized in epics, and John Ford, famous for his cowboy films. It is impossible to say where artistic vocation ended and the commercial needs dictated by the producers, that is, the financial backers, began.

During the late 1920s and early 1930s, the colour film was developed. By the late 1950s, colour films were more common than black and white. All things considered, it was perfectionism which was the basis of Hollywood's success, for Hollywood knew how to transform all sorts of ideas into great commercial successes and represented for years the final objective of all kinds of artists. But this was also the cause of its decline. However, since the 1950s, television ever more widely available, has presented a formidable challenge to the cinema, which has been compelled to defend itself by concentrating on quality, on technique and on the production of lavish spectacles. Cinemascope, stereophonic sound and fidelity of colour reproduction have been the weapons with which the cinema has armed itself, especially in America, in order to survive.

The rise of a new wave of European film-makers also contributed to the decline of the old capital of the cinema. However, after only a few years the American film industry is renewing itself, having acknowledged that the European cinema had meanwhile established new methods and obtained outstanding results.

The European cinema reawakens

In the period 1930 to 1945, it was the French who staked a claim to artistic merit (at that time in Italy, Germany and Russia the cinema was politically controlled). A film like *The Great Illusion* by Jean Renoir is still regarded as a masterpiece. Such directors as René Clair, Marcel Carné and Julien Duvivier could easily stand comparison with the great names of Hollywood.

It is difficult to describe all the "trends", "schools", stars, talented people of the period from the end of the Second World War to the present day. Foremost among

them was the Italian cinema and its "neo-realism". This term implied an insistence on showing the world as it really is, and the use of actors, as was said at the time, "taken from the streets". Such directors as Roberto Rossellini, Vittorio De Sica and Luchino Visconti completely revolutionized the smiling world of pretence and became the creators of a new style.

This did not prevent an eventual crisis in neo-realism. The star system took root again even in Cinecittà (the "Hollywood of Rome"), with stars such as Gina

The film is at last ready: its arrival in the cinemas is proclaimed by attractive publicity posters; below, a French poster advertising one of the most famous stars.

Lollobrigida and Sophia Loren, and the film industry there called a halt to the exploitation of new ideas, though there were exceptions. Federico Fellini explored the worlds of nostalgia and fancy, while Michelangelo Antoniani with his psychological portrayal of human loneliness, gave the cinema a new language. Luchino Visconti, who with the end of neo-realism had found fresh strength in images from memory and from the past, also contributed to making Rome the new centre of the world cinema industry.

Other countries have won attention through their talented writer-directors: Sweden with Ingmar Bergman, Spain with Luis Buñuel, Japan with Akira Kurosawa, to mention only a few. In addition, starting in the sixties, there has been a revitalization of the German cinema with such directors as Alexander Kluge and Werner Herzog.

Meanwhile the English cinema continued to struggle against the danger of dominance by Hollywood, which arose from the use of a common language. Directors such as Carol Reed, David Lean, Tony Richardson and Ken Russell managed to maintain their independence.

The French cinema had its own *nouvelle vague* (new wave). The dedication of its directors and the quality of its performers have kept it both flourishing and innovative. The star system, however, has had in Brigitte Bardot a notable, and perhaps final, representative.

And the American cinema? It has now aligned itself with the new ideas, and stands ready to reconquer its former power. With its money, its perfect technique and its system of building up stars, it can certainly present a fine show.

Jazz
Unique rhythm

Jazz is a relatively recent type of music but is so intense and so much alive that any attempt to provide a general definition would prove extremely difficult. It is, therefore, best to keep to its traditional meaning which associates its basic characteristics with its Afro-American origin. These characteristics are its unique rhythm and constant improvisation which may be played by a solo instrument or a group. An even better approach is to examine the series of styles which have marked the development of jazz by looking at music produced by the "greatests". These styles have mingled with each other and a classical school of jazz has now been established.

The origin of jazz

The word "jazz" was first noted at the end of the nineteenth and beginning of the twentieth centuries in the poorer districts of New Orleans, Louisiana, USA. It was used to indicate the set of percussion instruments given to juggler-musicians, the ancestors of our modern drummers, and later to the music that these strange artists performed. However, the merging of African music and popular and classical European music, which all critics agree are at the basis of jazz, started much earlier, at the beginning of the seventeenth century when the first black slaves were deported to Virginia.

These men, who were born in various African countries, brought with them immense despair but also their own musical habits, their own ideas on the magical and religious value of music and, often, their own instruments: marimbas or balafons (from which originates the vibraphone used by modern orchestras) and banjas or banjars (the first banjos, which are stringed instruments whose sound box is like a drum).

Top left, a picture of the Creole Jazz Band taken in 1921. The group was led by the cornetist Joseph "King" Oliver, one of the main representatives of New Orleans jazz and teacher of Louis Armstrong. Centre left, a picture of Louis Armstrong with his New Orleans River Boat Jazz Band (Armstrong is the one holding a trumpet on the right). Bottom left, Edward Kennedy "Duke" Ellington (piano) leading his band. Top right, Billie Holiday (her real name was Eleanor Gouch McKay) and her wonderful voice. She sang with the most prestigious bands and was at the top of her success in the forties. Bottom right, Erroll Garner: he never learned to read a single musical note, but was a first-class pianist.

The impact with the country which was to become the homeland of their great-grandchildren was tremendous for these black slaves, and the shock was seriously worsened by the cruel and oppressive conditions to which they had to adjust. Music, therefore, became a comforting rite, a nostalgic memory of a brutally wiped-out lifestyle and an expression of their religious beliefs which was more than ever necessary now that they were so far from their native lands. Every day's work was accompanied by songs and their free time by instrument playing, in the same way as music accompanied all their activities as part of a ritual in the distant tribes.

However, the African form of the music gradually faded away when it came into contact with music of European origin. The black population started to change their religious habits, although not totally and not overnight. They began to sing in Methodist and evangelical churches, to adopt ceremonies and observances more suited to their new condition, to assimilate musical themes and to learn the language of their new country. They came into contact with other oppressed people such as Italians, Scots and Spaniards who had their own native folklore. The typically religious gospel songs and spirituals were heard and their theme was introduced into the work songs. These are at the basis of the blues still heard nowadays.

The blues and ragtime

During these years at the beginning of the nineteenth century, the word "blue" (which meant "bad" or "sad" in addition to the colour "blue") was used to describe a particular style. When singing church melodies based on the diatonic scale (our scale of seven notes) black people, used to other sound sequences, found the third and seventh (and sometimes the fifth) notes difficult and these ended up slightly lower, or falling as musicians would say. However, the effect was particularly eloquent, and, even more so when combined with an American accent, it still today characterizes songs performed by blues singers and may be described as a vocal type permeated by extreme sadness.

Blues have played an extremely important role in the history of jazz. Their very simple, melodious backgrounds have always been used as a basis for improvisations.

Among the other forerunners of jazz is ragtime, a dance music of West Indian origin which was very popular among white people who transposed the skipping and syncopated rhythms, playing it in the saloons on pianos or mechanical

Top, another leading jazz artist, Ella Fitzgerald at the Montreux International Festival in Switzerland. Top right, the extraordinary pianist, William "Count" Basie, organ player and band leader, in 1968 in Milan, Italy.

Right, a photograph of John Birks "Dizzy" Gillespie and his trumpet. Gillespie was one of the leading representatives of be-bop, the first type of modern jazz which started during the first years of the Second World War. The word "be-bop" derives from vocalizations and meaningless words used by singers to imitate solos played by instrumentalists.

pianolas. The first type of jazz showed signs of many other influences and these were as varied as the number of races in the south of the United States. There were French dances, Spanish music, Italian operas and even Schubert's songs. New Orleans, near the mouth of the Mississippi and the biggest city in the area, was the centre of this musical excitement, and it was here that the official birth of jazz took place and where the fame of "black music" became worldwide.

The "king": Buddy Bolden

The first and most amazing jazz soloist was Buddy Bolden who was already well-known in 1893. His life story appears to be blurred by the clouds of myth. He started off as a cornetist with Billy Peyton's group, then soon became the king of New Orleans' musicians. This title was won in regular public competitions at the end of which the audience selected the winner by throwing coins. The story goes that

when the King played in Union Park, black people danced as far as one and a half kilometres away. He ended his reign as uncontested sovereign (only Emmanuel Perez, a Creole cornetist, now and again tried vainly to challenge him) in a mental hospital.

Whatever the claims that have been made, Buddy Bolden, however great he was, cannot be considered as the creator of jazz, as this was the result of collective contributions. However, in those days, the brass groups of New Orleans were more like bands which all had managers and whose players wore uniforms. Moreover, their music, in the same way as in string bands, was probably still affected by the rhythmic rigidity of the ragtime. Bolden certainly helped to break this down by introducing greater freedom and the "swing" which is the beat that characterizes jazz.

People played everywhere in New Orleans, on trucks loaded with musicians

Three jazz players who had three different styles. Left, Stan Getz, saxophonist and representative of cool jazz which was the opposite of be-bop and which was particularly important to white musicians. Right, another white saxophonist, Gerry Mulligan. He also started with cool jazz but later created a more commercial version, the West Coast jazz. Bottom, Miles Davis, a trumpet player who was always at the forefront and played hard-bop, another type of be-bop.

and while wandering along the streets of the city, as well as for weddings, christenings and funerals. But the real home of jazz continued to be the poorer areas and nightclubs where the most famous musicians played and passed on ideas in a rather strange racial sequence: from blacks to Creoles who were, at the beginning, less oppressed socially, from Creoles to Anglo-Saxons and then to the whole world. Jack Laine, a white musician, was the first to start a standard quintet formation (trumpet, clarinet, trombone, double-bass and drums) and the Creole, John Robichaux, to improve the rhythmic section by taking on a drummer who played with felt-covered drumsticks. However, Buddy Bolden was the first to improvise in a melodious blues.

The music of the South started moving to New York in 1910. The black Jim Europe opened a club dedicated to the spiritual and blues and on 29 December 1913 his band recorded "Too Much Mustard" for a French record company which re-named it "Tremoutarde". In 1917 a white band, the Original Dixieland Jazz Band, prepared the second record of the history of jazz.

The great soloists

At the outbreak of the First World War, black musicians of the South emigrated to northern cities where the armaments industry required more and more labour. The new music reached Chicago. The jazz recording era started in the twenties, the golden years of singers like Gertrude "Ma" Rainey and Bessie Smith. The piano was introduced into jazz with music written by Ferdinand "Jelly Roll" Morton and players of boogie woogie which was a type of rapid blues with repeated bass figures.

In 1923 record companies introduced Louis Armstrong, the second trumpeter of Joseph "King" Oliver's Creole Jazz Band. Jazz was still collective and contrapuntal (each player improvised his melody) but the first soloists now came onto the scene although always with a band whose role was to accompany them. These were typical of the classical jazz era. This trend, strangely enough, also became a feature of bands hired for balls and dances. Great soloists like "Satchmo" Armstrong and Coleman Hawkins (one of the first saxophonists in the history of black music) had to take on the task of defending authentic jazz in the noisy commercial world.

Small groups specially suited to the virtuoso, like Armstrong's "Hot Five" came into being, but the orchestra features of jazz emerged and became more and more refined, thanks to the appearance of a man who became a myth, Edward "Duke" Ellington.

In the meantime jazz caught on among whites: the commercial success of Benny Goodman and Paul Whiteman were assured, but more serious white musicians came onto the scene, like Frank Teschemacher, a clarinettist, and Bix Biederbecke, Armstrong's admirer and rival.

Behind the most famous white bands, the artistic value of black bands increased considerably. Among these the most famous were the bands of Jimmie Lunceford, Chick Webb (with Ella Fitzgerald as singer) and in particular Count Basie's band (with Billie Holiday). Count Basie's band perfected a balanced style with a soloist and group interventions that be-bop followers later used. This new style started in 1940 in New York's cellars as a reaction to the disfigurement of "swing". It was an attempt to make jazz far less a dance music and more a listener's music.

Charlie Parker, a top saxophonist in the same way as Armstrong was the top trumpet player, was the most brilliant member of the new jazz movement which was characterized by its soloists, greater harmony and broken rhythm influenced by South-American percussionists' contributions.

During these years, John "Dizzy" Gillespie explored the possibility of using the higher notes of the trumpet and became one of the most assiduous collaborators of Charlie Parker, with whom he worked as "showman" and singer. The great saxophonist was later accompanied by musicians like the be-op pianists, Thelonious Monk, and Earl "Bud" Powell, and by Miles Davies, the

trumpet player who more recently led one of the greatest changes in jazz: the beginning of jazz-rock music.

White musicians such as Lennie Tristano, Lee Konitz and Gerry Mulligan, tried to imitate this and started the cool jazz which quickly degenerated into the West Coast's commercial version. Blacks came back with funky jazz, black jazz and with "soul" music, which were based on the original gospels and spirituals and were re-introduced with rock and roll.

Protest jazz

Racial problems again became particularly serious in the United States in the fifties and the most politically committed musicians expressed their rebellion. John Coltrane, a leading saxophonist, together with Parker influenced the style of all their contemporaries by introducing a new type of music with a different rhythm. Thanks to Charlie Mingus, Elvin Jones, Cecil Taylor and Ornette Coleman, Afro-American music moved away both controversially and decisively from white traditional music.

The search for a true identity provided jazz with African ethnic elements, Indian classical music (the *ragas* of Ravi Shankar with improvisations on a single chord) and the new pop music of young European groups. So, next to the resonant explosion of the saxophonist Archie Shepp one finds Sun Ra's cosmic music.

Top, two leaders of free jazz. On the left, Archie Shepp with his tenor saxophone. On the right, Ornette Coleman, a saxophonist, violinist and trumpet player. Free jazz, also known as informal jazz, gives ample space for improvisation.

Monster box office

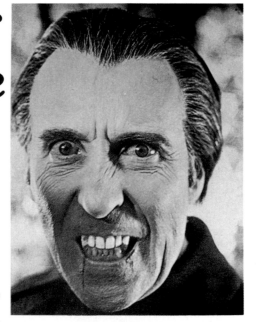

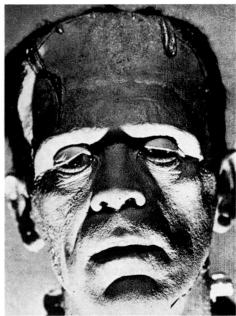

A monster can be defined as a being of very brutal appearance, often exceptionally wicked and with physical and psychological abnormalities which set him apart from other creatures. The word comes from the Latin *monstrum*, which means a prodigy or marvel. This implies that the brutality and the wickedness are such as to astonish us.

Monsters exist more often in fantasy than in nature. It is true that nature can play nasty jokes by producing, for example, donkeys with two heads or men of great cruelty, but these manifestations are always less horrific than the visions which can be conjured up by our imaginations.

Since time immemorial, man has made representations of his fears by creating terrifying monsters. Among those remembered from the days of ancient Greece are Argus with the hundred eyes, who slew Echidna, half beautiful woman and half serpent; the Harpies, grossly deformed birds; Polyphemus and the Cyclopes, giants each with a single eye; the terrible Medusa, whose head was covered with wriggling snakes in place of hair; the Minotaur, with the head of a bull and the body of a man. It would be possible to compile a long list of such horrible creatures.

Even traditional fairy-tales have given substance to fears, by devising witches, ogres and dragons. Thus the legends of monstrous beings have become very numerous. Today there are tales about the gigantic Yeti (or "abominable snowman"), which is alleged to live amongst the ice of the Himalayas, and, of course, about the Loch Ness Monster.

Literature also has created fantastic and terrible beings to which there has been an immediate popular response. This suggests that people have a need to express their obsessions in material form and to

A notable company of celebrities: Dracula, Frankenstein, King Kong, Nosferatu (below) and the Loch Ness Monster (immediately above). This last (it is said to appear in the Scottish loch from which it takes its name) is the only one not to have become a famous film star.

King Kong (left) captures a girl in a shot from the film of 1933. Above, in contrast, Frankenstein has his monstrous energy pumped into him while chained. Below, a scene from a Japanese film in which two prehistoric monsters are seen fighting.

free themselves from their fears by confining them to a tale in which the monster is frequently destined to be the loser.

Sometimes what we are really afraid of is the "monster within us"; that is to say, the worst part of our own selves. This is the hypothesis which Robert Louis Stevenson used when, in the last century, he wrote his famous story, *The Strange Case of Doctor Jekyll and Mr Hyde*. It is the story of a doctor who discovers a potion capable of splitting the personality of an individual into its two halves, the good and the bad. The philtre also transforms physically the main character in the story. The good Doctor Jekyll, after drinking the strange beverage, is turned into a deformed and repellant individual whose face reveals all the evil within him.

Stories of vampires

One of the most famous monsters in tradition, in literature and later in the cinema, is the vampire. In popular belief, the vampire is the dead body which emerges from its tomb by night to suck the blood of the living and thereby prolong its own existence. The roots of this superstition lie in the remote past, probably in the popular culture of Central Europe. This attributed to real people reputed to have engaged in sorcery during their lifetimes, the ability to continue their evil ways even after death. Terrible misfortunes were blamed on the vampires, and they were held responsible for many calamities: epidemics, drought and violent death. The means of protection against these fearsome beings was curious. It was to carry a clove of garlic on one's back. There were other devices, too, for keeping the vampires at bay: to

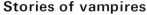

threaten them with a cross or to transfix them in their coffins with a stake through the heart.

Stories about vampires spread across Europe in the eighteenth century. The legend became attached to some historical figures noted for their cruelty and these were believed to be capable of living off the blood sucked from their victims' necks, so perpetuating their wickedness. Their monstrous characteristics were supposed to extend to their physical appearance: no one has ever imagined an attractive vampire. They are usually depicted with very long, fang-like, protruding teeth, eyes red with blood and yellow skin.

It was inevitable that sooner or later writers would take an interest in their exploits. And so it was. The first to write a work of fiction on the theme of vampires was Giovanni Polidori who lived in England despite his Italian name. His story, entitled simply *The Vampyre*, was published in 1819 and can be considered the prototype of a long series of stories of this sort. Around the same time, Mary Wollstonecraft Shelley wrote a romance under the title *Frankenstein*. This was the story of a man who discovered how to infuse life into dead matter and so created a horrible, frightening and inconceivably brutal monster. The cinema has dealt with this story in various ways, some of them comic.

However, it is the vampire which has continued to be the inspiration for most of the monsters of literature and films. Great writers like Gogol and Tolstoy wrote about vampires. The most famous vampire, Dracula, was dreamed up by an Irishman, Bram Stoker, who probably took his inspiration from the evil deeds of Prince Vlad III of Wallachia, who lived in the fifteenth century.

Cinema monsters

Monsters and vampires became popular subjects for the cinema. The best-known film monster is perhaps Dracula as portrayed by Bela Lugosi in 1931, closely followed in popularity by the monster created by Boris Karloff in *Frankenstein* (also 1931). In 1933, Merian C. Cooper and Ernest B. Schoedsack filmed *King Kong* with a gigantic gorilla as the main character. There were very many other full-length films which made a great impression on the public with creaking noises, wailing, weeping, sinister sounds and special effects. These are elements which the world of horror films has taken up again recently, offering, in spectacular new productions with new leading actors, the same titles which were used

In the books and newspapers of earlier times, there often appeared items about monstrous creatures which somebody, generally a sailor, swore he had seen with his own eyes. On the left, for example, we see an illustration taken from an eighteenth-century book showing a devil-siren reported from Peru. Above, a votive panel shows a sailing ship attacked by an octopus. Today, the "manifestations" tend to show beings from outer space.

years ago (*The Mummy*, *King Kong*, *Frankenstein*, etc.).

Recently our imaginations have been regaled with space monsters. These are presented by comic strips, animated cartoons, television and the cinema. Sometimes these monsters are merely strange: inhabitants of distant planets neither good nor evil and with scarcely any feelings. On other occasions they are designed specifically to terrify us. Today just as in the past, it is the function of these monsters to translate fear into entertainment.

Music
The art of
organizing sound

Like all the arts, music varies from one place and time to another and with the different genres which develop within a single culture. It is obviously not a simple task to trace the whole story and even less easy to explain it all, even in outline. We will confine ourselves, therefore, to music of one type: the "classical" music of western civilization.

Music is the art of organizing sounds and is common to all the peoples of the world, though at different levels of development and with differing underlying concepts.

The first European music of which traces still remain dates back to classical Greece: They were simple melodies, intended to be sung and accompanied, without "variations", by the flute or the lyre. The ancient Greeks used systems of notation based on letters of the Phoenician and Ionic alphabets. The notational system of European music first came from Jewish liturgical recitation signs and Greek grammatical accents. It was not until about 1600 that music was written down in the form we know today.

The Greeks used to compose their own music (or, more often, modify existing music) using as a basis different successions of four sounds in order from highest to lowest pitch. More interesting than such details, is their conception of music as a whole. According to their poets and to tradition, the art of making sounds

Two pieces of evidence about ancient music. Below, a Roman fresco from Stabia, in Campania, in Italy, shows a group round a lady lyrist. The lyre was the basic instrument of the classical world. Above, a page from a medieval book of plainsong or anthems. These compositions, usually religious, for choirs were taken up again in more recent times: similar works by Johann Sebastian Bach are famous.

was a magical art (Orpheus moved mountains with his songs; Amphion built the walls of Thebes by playing his lyre; Arion by singing summoned the dolphins who saved him from destruction. The philosophers asserted that music was able to affect the human soul and so was educationally useful. Plato and Aristotle speak of it while Aristoxenus, who was himself a musician, was among the first to try to study rhythm and harmony. Music became indissolubly linked with poetry: Homer was shown with a lyre in his hand.

The Romans had a more practical view of the art of music. They took over and adopted the musical knowledge of the nations they vanquished, passing it on to posterity together with the numerous musical instruments taken as war booty. Of these, the organ is particularly noteworthy, for it dominated an entire era in the history of music. Some maintain that it had been invented by the ancient Egyptians. The earliest surviving record is of an organ invented by a Greek engineer, Ctesibius, who lived in Alexandria in the third century BC.

The first Christians, with their prayers and canticles taken from the Hebrew liturgy, marked an important change in the development of music. Their melodies were based on a single note repeated at length (psalmody) or else on the interplay

of statement and response between priest and the worshippers (versicles and responses) or between two alternating choirs (antiphony). The text, always taken from the Scriptures, remained, however, the most important part of the chant.

Saint Ambrose of Milan, in the fourth century, collected together a series of hymns in which the melody broke away from the low first notes and rose in ever-bolder variations to the climax of the Alleluiah. Two centuries later, Pope Gregory the Great revised the plainsong of the Christian liturgy, turning once again to Greek models. The Gregorian chant, strictly monodic (meaning that one or more voices followed the same melody), was shaped by the rhythm of the words, the understanding of which was not to be modified by the music.

Little remains of the secular music of that period. Yet we know that often the chants of the minstrels were not pleasing to those in power. Passed on orally, they were later to influence the music of the troubadours. Music also accompanied performances of liturgical drama (the real forerunner of plays and opera).

Polyphonic music

The first experiments in polyphony (in which several voices sing different melodies at the same time) were made in about the ninth century. The harmonies used were fairly straightforward but further novelties followed in quick succession, culminating in the great development of the fourteenth century which was the so-called *Ars nova*, which made its greatest impact in France.

Guillaume de Machaut was the principal representative of the new development. His work was praised not only in France, but in Italy, Spain and much of the rest of Europe.

Musicians eagerly absorbed the new trends from France which had become more widespread following the return of the papacy from Avignon to Rome (1377). Italian polyphonic music, simpler

Above left, a beautifully decorated page of sacred music (the transcription of a Gregorian chant). It dates from the fourteenth century, a period in which the rift between religious and secular music was growing deeper. The former was strictly monodic, that is possessing only one melody which several voices sang in unison so that the words would remain perfectly intelligible; the latter had become completely polyphonic. Above, a group of musicians with "profane" instruments which would never have been allowed inside any church. The woman in the centre, who is playing a "portable" organ, represents the personification of music.

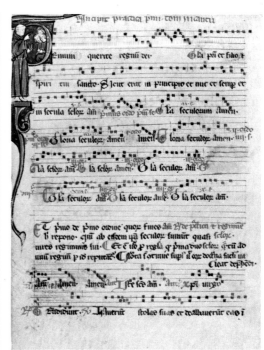

han the French, was expressed in three orms – the "madrigal" of poetic origin, he "ballad" based on popular songs and he *caccia* or hunting songs. The English vord "catch", a type of round, may be lerived from *caccia*.

During the fifteenth century, there was an explosion of polyphonic music everywhere in Europe with much intermingling of different styles – for example, between the music of the Flemings with heir interwoven melodies (for up to hirty-six different voices) and the maginative music of the Italians. During he century, there came about in Italy true fusion of the polyphonic techniques of the learned musicians and composers with the fresh and spontaneous popular music, a vast reservoir of inspiration and melodies.

The sixteenth century was the century of the Protestant reformation and the counter-reformation. Control by the Roman Catholic Church extended to all the arts and this included music; the Council of Trent proposed the re-introduction of the Gregorian plainsong in defiance of the flourishing polyphonic music which had revitalized even sacred music. The music of Giovanni Pierluigi da

Palestrina was very important as it formed a link between the two extremes. He was the greatest composer of the age of contrapuntal compositions for unaccompanied choruses. This was mostly church music but there were also a number of madrigals. He wrote a hundred and five masses in many styles. This great composer was excluded from the papal choir by the mere fact that he was married, but in his music he safeguarded the independence of the musical art, at that time drastically divided between sacred and secular, while still respecting the traditions of the Church.

In sixteenth-century Venice, the two masters of the organ, Andrea and Giovanni Gabrieli, uncle and nephew, brought to fruition their investigations into the timbre, or tonal quality, of the instrument. They achieved a contrasting effect by using brilliant sounds and other instruments which were banned elsewhere in Italy as being too "worldly".

Vocal music, still liturgical in origin, began to lose its hitherto undisputed supremacy and the first compositions written for instruments alone appeared. During the seventeenth century, especially as the result of work by Claudio Monteverdi, the complicated polyphony of the preceding years was being simplified. The bass vocal parts were relegated to the role of accompaniment to the principal part, which was played or sung so as to convey the maximum

expression. This practice, which was called *basso continuo*, spread rapidly and was provided by keyboard instruments and lutes.

This innovation cleared the way for opera, that is drama in a musical form and also for the concerto for solo instruments. Composers began to experiment with the remarkable possibilities of the violin, while in France François Couperin discovered the infinite shades of tone that could be obtained from the harpsichord.

combine constructively the different trends in German music (of both the austere northern school and the southern school), blending them with the influence of the French harpsichord players and the Italians' harmonic innovations. A musician by profession, and used to the habit of daily practice, Bach was also a great theoretician and a passionate student of the art of Vivaldi, Corelli and other important composers.

(continued on page 202)

Above, a musical gathering depicted in the style of the seventeenth century by the French painter and engraver Abraham Bosse, a careful documenter of his times. As you can see, secular music was practised and studied by women as well as men.

Below, two great Italian musicians: left, Giovanni Pierluigi da Palestrina; right, Arcangelo Corelli, violin virtuoso and one of the first exponents of the concerto for solo instruments.

The "tonal" scale

As a result of the work of Couperin, and even more that of the Italian violinists and composers Arcangelo Corelli and Antonio Vivaldi, the latter of whom is considered the greatest genius of harmony (the combination of sounds which go well together), there developed, at the beginning of the eighteenth century, a new awareness which was to lead to the "tonal" scale.

The scholarly work which set the seal on all this was *The Well-Tempered Clavier* by Johann Sebastian Bach, published in 1722. This consisted of two books, each of twenty-four preludes and fugues in all keys and known as the "Forty-eight". Bach was also one of the first composers to write harpsichord concertos. He was the universal genius who was able to

The men who transformed music

The composers included in this table have been chosen for their influence on the development of music: that is, only those who are acknowledged to have been great innovators or theorists. In keeping with this criterion, some famous and significant musicians have inevitably been omitted, such as Rossini, Bellini, Verdi and many others, even though they wrote a great deal of splendid music.

Guillaume de Machaut (c. 1300–72), Frenchman. Musician and poet, he was the most outstanding representative of the so-called French *Ars nova*. His *Messe de Notre-Dame* is the first polyphonic work complete in all its parts and written by a single person to come down to us.

Giovanni Pierluigi da Palestrina (1525–94), Italian. He spent the whole of his life in the service of the Church, composing mainly religious music, but distinguishing himself also in secular music, in which he used the most up-to-date techniques, at that time prohibited by the ecclesiastical authorities.

Monteverdi

Claudio Monteverdi (1567–1643). Italian. He greatly simplified the intricacies of polyphonic music, and in so doing gave prominence to the leading voice. He can be considered as the creator of opera, in which words and music achieve a perfect balance.

Arcangelo Corelli (1653–1713), Italian. A violinist and composer, he contributed to the recognition of the violin as a solo instrument of great expressive power. He also gave great encouragement to the three-part sonata form.

Antonio Vivaldi (1678–1741), Italian. Called the "red priest" from the colour of his hair, he wrote a great deal of instrumental and vocal music. In his compositions, he combined a perfect technique with a rich imagination, searching for the imagery which music could excite.

Johann Sebastian Bach (1685–1750), German. His contemporaries saw him mainly as a virtuoso of the organ and harpsichord: it was not until the nineteenth century that the value of his work as a composer was recognized. It was above all the musical form known as a "fugue" which he brought to perfection.

George Frideric Handel (1685–1759), German. He wrote many lyrical works, taking Italian compositions as his model. His genius was revealed most of all in the great oratorios he composed such as *Messiah*, and in his popular music for special occasions, such as the *Water Music* and the *Fireworks Music*.

Haydn

Franz Joseph Haydn (1732–1809), Austrian. Father of instrumental music (and considered as the first great exponent of the modern symphony), he laid down the present structure of the string quartet and for the first time produced complete interpretations of the sonata form.

Mozart

Wolfgang Amadeus Mozart (1756–91), Austrian. He began to compose minuets at the age of five and at six undertook an extraordinary series of concert performances. He applied his talents to every musical form and was one of the first to exploit fully the potential of the piano.

Ludwig van Beethoven (1770–1827), German. Born in Bonn, he worked throughout his life in Vienna as pianist, conductor and composer. His symphonies are immortal. We remember the Third (the "Eroica"), the Sixth (the "Pastoral") and the celebrated Ninth, which is scored in part for a choir.

Schubert

Franz Schubert (1797–1828), Austrian. He passed into history with his *Lieder* (songs) in which were revealed not only his own melancholy, but also the lyrical vein prevalent in music at that time and even the political delusions of his generation.

Richard Wagner (1813–83), German. Drawn into a search for an ideal fusion of all the arts, he was a leading composer of opera and creator of "musical drama", in which the singing is almost declamatory, with the music, faithfully following the words and in which the orchestra, from being a simple support for the voices, becomes a substantial element in its own right.

Johannes Brahms (1833–97), German. Composer, pianist and conductor, he returned to strict classical models in an attempt to counter the exuberance of the romantic music. He was a great admirer of Beethoven whose artistic heir he was considered to be.

Gustav Mahler (1860–1911), Austrian. The tormented complexity of his symphonies, which is revealed in violent stylistic contrasts or in the use of different genres (from the great German symphonic tradition to military marches) marked the passage from the nineteenth century to our own.

Arnold Schoenberg (1874–1951), Austrian. Fearless innovator of musical language, he defined a scheme of original composition based on the repetition of the twelve notes (dodecaphonic music).

Béla Bartók (1881–1945), Hungarian. Confirmed as a piano virtuoso, he sought to reconcile inspiration drawn from the popular music of his country with the western musical tradition.

Igor Feodorovich Stravinsky (1882–1971), Russian. After a period of research into new musical possibilities, whose impact on the public was often violent, he returned to themes and styles from the past, becoming the leader of the neo-classical movement. He also interested himself in other musical forms, such as jazz.

201

(continued from page 200)

Apart from opera, Bach handled every musical form with extraordinary results, but his most characteristic style, with which his name is now linked, is the fugue, a type of composition which is so called because its structure consists of sequences of themes following each other in rapid sequence (the word *fugare* in Latin means to put to flight or run away). Bach's name has become almost synonymous with fugue and with elaborate counterpoint in general. In fact, he wrote much less counterpoint than is usually thought.

George Frideric Handel is thought of as the "natural opposite" to Bach. Worldly where Bach was unworldly, receptive to every stimulus when Bach was loftily indifferent to every outside suggestion, famous, acclaimed and much-travelled while Bach remained home-loving and devout, Handel represented the face of that period of history and musical history in particular. He was also different from Bach in composing operas and oratorios for vast audiences.

The eighteenth century

Without doubt, the eighteenth century can be considered the century most richly endowed with musical geniuses and musical developments.

After Bach and Handel, came Haydn, Mozart and Beethoven, three more of the greatest names in music. It is in the eighteenth century, too, that the piano began to take its place in music and two important new forms, the sonata and the symphony, come to be pre-eminent.

The sonata form is a musical construction with a completely harmonic basis: the musical theme is announced and immediately followed by another in a different key, that is consisting of notes from a different tonal scale, and both are developed through a series of modulations to reappear in their initial forms in the finale (after which may come a coda, or tailpiece) in the basic key in which the whole piece is written. The symphony results from applying this principle to a full orchestra. The principle can also be transferred to the piano alone or to small instrumental groups.

The Austrian composer, Haydn, is considered by many as the father of great instrumental music. He exploits magnificently in his own works the conquests made by the German and Italian composers. His symphonies, sonatas and string quartets are, in fact, the first examples of total application of the sonata form.

Now we come to Wolfgang Amadeus Mozart. At the age of four he could play the clavichord and at six started to give public performances as a pianist, travelling across the whole of Europe to do so. As a result, he was able to hear the greatest musicians of his time and learn from them their different styles. At the age of fourteen, he himself conducted his first opera, *Mithridates King of Pontus*, and published a series of quartets. During his life, he wrote in every musical form, including a series of great operas, among them *Figaro*, *Don Giovanni* and *The Magic Flute*. Many believe that the music of western civilization reached its peak in the works he composed.

Many of Mozart's finest works were written after he left the household of the Archbishop of Salzburg and took the difficult course of an independent musician, no longer bound to the predilections of an aristocratic patron.

The "free masters" and romanticism

This new attitude on the part of musicians characterized the end of the eighteenth century and the early decades of the next. It was Schubert (of whom it is reported that he was in the habit of paying his bills to innkeepers by composing fragments of music on the spot) who succeeded in expressing both his own melancholy – he was a recluse – and the sense of disillusionment at political events (the

Below left, a string quartet. This instrumental formation arose in the eighteenth century, together with the sonata form. The first to make use of it was the Austrian, Franz Joseph Haydn, who was immediately followed by his compatriot, Wolfgang Amadeus Mozart. Below, a painting, exhibited in the Louvre in Paris, by the French painter, Joseph Duplessis. It shows a very young Mozart seated at the clavichord. By this time, he had already completed his first compositions.

Great names from the music of the nineteenth century. Left, Ludwig van Beethoven at his writing desk; above, Franz Liszt at the piano; below: left, another master of this instrument, Frédéric François Chopin; centre, Johannes Brahms, classical composer and ''heir'' to Beethoven; right, the Russian Petr Ilich Tchaikovsky, who sought to bring about a fusion of western music with the popular tradition of his country.

congress of Vienna and the restoration of the French monarchy) in his immortal songs, or *Lieder*.

Beethoven never submitted to public taste, though it is true that the public would have had the sense to approve of what the great man produced. He preferred to examine new aspects of music with the rigorous approach of a philosopher. He never hesitated, even when the answers to his problems were "scandalously" dissonant, provided that they expressed what he had in mind, neither refusing to adopt complex harmonies nor drawing back from breaking established conventions for sonatas and symphonies.

In the meantime, while romanticism was "setting Europe ablaze", the piano really established itself as a leading instrument. With a deeper understanding of its technical possibilities, the first great piano virtuosi appeared, seeking new types of "sound effect" and timbre. These composers "thought in terms of the piano": the foremost of them were Frédéric François Chopin and Franz Liszt.

Chopin was above all a master of the intimate, but his music was also influenced by the social conflicts of those years: the dismemberment of Poland (his mother country), followed by the Congress of Vienna, the Polish revolution of 1830 and the cholera epidemic which broke out in Paris where he lived in self-imposed exile. Chopin composed mainly for the piano, broadening its potential in an unprecedented way. Some of his works still remain among the most played and popular of all recital items.

Franz Liszt was acclaimed as a brilliant pianist. As a composer, he introduced new processes and was the inventor of the symphonic poem. His principal merit seems to have been that he put his own enormous popularity as a virtuoso at the service of illustrious colleagues like Wagner, Berlioz and Schumann.

Schumann wrote a great deal of highly expressive music whose melodic resources seemed inexhaustible. His wife, Clara, one of the most accomplished pianists of her time, was partly responsible for the popularity of her husband's works. Thanks to Schumann, total mastery of the sonata form was achieved.

There was a similarity of thought and feeling between his work and that of Johannes Brahms who, as a young man, became very friendly with Schumann and his wife. Brahms' work showed a greater instinct for form and proportion. He returned to the rigorous methods of Beethoven, developing the symphony. Later, he achieved original forms.

The improvisation of oriental music

European music is not alone in drawing on a classical tradition: Indian music, too, has the support of a very ancient school. We see above someone playing the sitar, a typical Indian stringed instrument, with a soundbox made out of a gourd. Based on improvisation and played according to fixed models, called *ragas*, Indian music is written in a system similar to that of the ancient Greeks. In recent years, thanks to the activities of Ravi Shankar, a sitar virtuoso, it has known periods of great popularity even in Europe.

The national schools arose from the wave of romantic sentiment, though the Russian Petr Ilich Tchaikovsky preferred to stay with the western tradition, and had no strong national aspirations. His work, in line with the precepts of romanticism, tended always towards a purity of expression. It became popular in Britain and America, where he was the first Russian composer to become well-known.

Music of the twentieth century

The transition from the romantic nineteenth century to our own is marked by the work of the Frenchman, Claude Achille Debussy, and the Austrian, Gustav Mahler. An unashamed anti-romantic, Debussy was preoccupied with tone and was the founder of the Impressionist School in music. Mahler, in contrast, welcomed the various forms of the romantic symphony, but considered it inadequate to express the realities of the times, leaving the problem unsolved for someone else to tackle. His great admirer, Arnold Schoenberg, decided to do just this and he succeeded. Schoenberg was the founder of the Vienna school and was followed by Alban Berg and Anton von Webern. What Schoenberg preached mainly was the freedom to use any tonal scale or none (atonal music) and in accordance with this developed one of his own, based on repetitions of the twelve tones (dodecaphonic music). Some forms of the earlier tradition remained intact: in his compositions (and more so in the work of Berg) rondos, arias and dance themes can be identified, but even these were totally eliminated by Webern, father of modern composers. In opposition to the school of Vienna, were the neo-classicists, "followers" of the Russian Igor Feodorovich Stravinsky.

Among these groups, a place can be found for the independent tradition represented by Béla Bartók, a Hungarian, and the Russians. Bartók first of all attempted to unite the popular tradition of his country with the language of the western avant-garde. His first-hand investigations into ethnic music were of great importance.

The Circus Clowns and Acrobats

In Roman times the circus was a spectacle of violence and ferocity. Now it has been completely transformed into the embodiment of simple, good-natured fun. However, since its earliest days, the risks its performers take have continued to thrill and terrify spectators.

In Latin, the word for a circle is *circus*, and a small circle is *circulus*. The origin of our word "circus" seems clear, yet in ancient Roman times the circus was not a circle, but a rectangle. This is a historical fact which connects the harmless spectacle of today to the blood-thirsty amusements of the ancient Romans. They went to the circus to watch chariot-races, the fights of gladiators and men pitted against wild beasts, and were not satisfied unless all the contestants were killed.

A rectangular arena gave more space for the chariots who strove, at break-neck speed (it would be the drivers' necks which would be broken, of course) to arrive first. The corners of the arena were curved and the spectators sat all around the arena on steps which served as seats. In the centre was a long low wall, called the *spina* or "spine" decorated with obelisks and shrines and set obliquely to give more room at the beginning of the race. Later the races were held in the Roman amphitheatres with their round arenas. The largest was the Colosseum, which was dedicated in AD 79 and is said

to have held between 45,000 and 50,000 persons.

It is a good thing our tastes have changed. The people of ancient Rome went mad with excitement when a lion devoured a Christian, but today we are happy to laugh at the antics of a clown. Of course, in the circuses of those days there were, as now, acrobats, jugglers and animal trainers, but it was the spilling of blood and the scenes of violence which gave the public their greatest pleasure. The device was used by the Emperors: give the people bread and circuses, and avoid revolution!

Though the centuries have taken away the ferocity of the circus, there still remains a taste for danger and excitement: the brave man who puts his head into a tiger's mouth is a descendant of the gladiator who faced the wild beast in unarmed combat, just as the acrobat who risks his life making double and triple leaps on the back of a horse, reminds us indirectly of the horse races which, in Roman times, bound man and beast together in a fight to the death.

Strolling players

Until AD 326, a man could be condemned to the wild beasts in the arena, but in that year the Emperor Constantine banned the practice. At about the same time, another type of circus emerged, poor and ill-equipped, relying only on improvisation and skill. Gipsies and vagabonds carried on the circus tradition to earn their daily bread: they attracted the public by their practical jokes and horseplay and then entertained them with gymnastic displays, acrobatics and tightrope walking.

To this tradition of the wandering players, successors to the horrors of the Roman circuses, was added the strength of popular traditions. During the carnival at Venice, for example, the young people took part in a curious game, "the labours of Hercules": the lighter ones climbed up on the shoulders of the stronger and formed a "human pyramid".

For centuries the development of the circus was determined by chance, necessity and country fairs. At length in the eighteenth century, the Englishman,

Old posters from the two large American circuses, the Cole Brothers and Barnum & Bailey, proclaimed as "the greatest show on Earth".

A museum piece: the fantastic parade carriage of the Barnum & Bailey Circus. Built in 1878, it was pulled by more than forty horses.

Philip Astley, a former sergeant major turned trick-rider, found that if he galloped in a circle while standing on his horse's back, centrifugal force helped him to keep his balance. He decided to give public performances and his success was enormous. Within a few years, he had increased his repertoire with acts which had previously been performed in the streets and market fairs. Clowns, trained dogs, balancing-acts, jugglers and acrobats were included and Astley and his wife performed an extremely difficult acrobatic act on horseback.

The memory of the Roman circuses was by now very faint and Astley's idea seemed new and original. Other circuses were opened, not only in London but also in Paris and other European cities. Astley travelled to France and performed his "daring feats of horsemanship" before the king and the French court. Even in the past, the skills of acrobats and jesters had not been confined to the market squares of country towns, for they had often performed in the palaces of kings and noblemen.

The circus worldwide

The wandering life was still a basic element in the life of the circus and one of its most intriguing characteristics: so much so that when, towards the end of the eighteenth century the Italian, Antonio Franconi, joined forces with Astley in France and then continued on his own, he decided not to give it a fixed headquarters. A traveller himself by instinct and sentiment, Franconi wanted to have a "travelling company" and so took his spectacular acts on tour across the world setting down his tents, marquees and caravans in many different cities.

Astley also travelled widely. In 1782, he went as far as Belgrade, visiting Brussels and Vienna on his way. He set up nineteen circuses during his lifetime.

It was Charles Hughes, who had been one of Astley's horsemen, who first introduced the circus to Russia. He took a company of trick-riders there in 1793, and Catherine the Great allowed him to set up a private circus in the royal palace at St. Petersburg. The Russian circus was later developed by a Frenchman, Jacques Tourniaire.

In Spain, Benito Guerre presented his feats of horsemanship, and in America, John William Ricketts opened the first circuses in Philadelphia and New York in 1793. By the end of the eighteenth century, the circus had spread throughout Europe and was firmly established in America.

It continued to flourish with such names as the American Barnum and Bailey's, famous for the grand scale and sensationalism of their acts. They introduced multiple-ring circuses and at one time had three rings and five stages surrounded by a hippodrome track.

By the end of the nineteenth and beginning of the twentieth century, the circus was still spreading to other countries. A British family, the Boswells, went to South Africa, and Frank Brown, whose father had been a clown at Astley's, toured South America.

In the 1920s, the circus in Britain declined, but it was revived by Bertram Mills who presented the greatest international circus stars at Olympia, in London. Some years later, Tom Arnold had a great success with circus acts on ice at the ice hockey rink at Harringay.

The circus became very popular in Russia in the 1960s and there were over one hundred permanent and travelling shows. The performances reached a very high standard, especially the high-wire and balancing acts, and some Russian circuses appeared in European capitals.

The coming of television had a great effect on the circus. Many circus acts have appeared on television and so have reached a much wider audience, but attendances at the actual circus performances have dropped.

The rise of the circus spectacular

In the past, the circus played mainly to adult audiences, but today it is considered mainly an entertainment for children. The programme, however, has remained much the same, although attempts are always being made to perform new and spectacular feats of increasing difficulty. The big "attractions" are usually put on as the climax to the first half or at the beginning of the second, and at the end of the performance there is always a grand parade in which all the performers appear, gorgeously dressed. Every act is proudly announced by the ring-master; the rolling of drums introduces it and accompanies its tensest moments. An orchestra, or rather a band, occupies a prominent position, often in front of the artistes' entrance.

It is the clowns that the children like best. Their major task is to fill the gaps between one act and the next and to distract the audience while the lions' cage is being erected or the apparatus being set up for a juggler. Sometimes, one of them may be so good that he becomes the principal attraction of the circus and even the symbol of it. Among the most famous clowns have been Grock, the three Fratellini brothers and the Russian, Popov.

Figures of fun yet down-hearted

The comic appeal of clowns is simple and straightforward, but it has an underlying element of sadness. It has inspired masques, plays in mime, actors and cabaret performers. The best known type of clown is the "Auguste" or "Toni", with his startling make-up, brightly coloured wig, big red nose, baggy costume, exceedingly long black shoes and untidy manners. He frequently works with a white-faced clown, often with a solitary black eyebrow, and always spoils the latter's tricks by appearing at the wrong moment and causing chaos. The best-known turns, classics by now of their kind, are when the two clowns stage a boxing match or when one of them is to be photographed by the other, but instead receives a jet of water in his face from the camera. Clowns are always a delight, whether they appear in the large, successful circuses or in the small ones.

Jugglers, animal acts and acrobats

Other much-loved turns in the circus are the highly trained horses, onto which ballerinas and acrobats vault with impressive ease. There is also trick riding in which the rider turns somersaults, pirouettes and balances on the horse's back, and high school which is a spectacular form of dressage. At first sight, the jugglers' act seems to be a

matter of purely manual skill, but to keep several objects in the air at the same time causes great physical fatigue and nervous tension. It also demands constant and dedicated training.

The moment when everybody holds his breath is the finale, when the lion-tamer comes in and confronts the savage animals, orders them to leap through a ring of fire, to stand on their hind legs or even to embrace him. Just as thrilling is the act of the trapeze artists who often risk their lives in perilous flights across the marquee where the smallest mistake can mean death.

Other turns are also very impressive: the contortionists, the illusionists, the dwarfs and the trainers of dogs, seals, elephants or even snakes and doves. There is often a conjuror in the programme too, who moves his fingers with such speed and skill that even the most attentive spectators are taken in.

It is difficult to say which are the best circuses in the world. It is also unfair, for those with the largest financial resources can afford international acts, many "attractions" numerous animals and the

Every self-respecting circus has its elephant "act". Carefully and patiently trained, these clumsy beasts resign themselves to performing balancing acts. Their mere presence is enough to fascinate the public.

best sites. Yet a small circus, travelling from one seaside town or village to another, is enjoyed and applauded despite its humble pretensions and manages to make a living, though sometimes only a bare one. There is no ostentation: the marquee is often worn and patched, and sometimes even the children join in with simple acrobatic exercises and all the artistes seem to belong to one big family. It is in this type of show, not very well off and wandering from town to town, where we see the immensely courageous survival of a very old and noble tradition of popular art.

By tradition, as in the theatre, the circus spectacle ends as the artistes file out saluting the audience, and often waving flags. Here we see the Moscow Circus, one of the largest in the world.

These splendid pictures of the circus speak volumes and tell a story of courage and skill, of enthusiasm and determination, but also of weariness, of dedication which takes people to the limits of their powers, of an uncomfortable life and, in most cases, of very modest financial rewards. Here are a few curious facts: the first "man on the flying trapeze" was the Frenchman, J. Léotard, who faced great danger on the trapeze in Paris in 1859, suspended above the ring of the Cirque d'Hiver. The first to enter a cage full of savage animals was the American, Isaac Van Amburgh, between 1820 and 1830. He is also reputed to have been the first man to put his head in a lion's mouth.

The Olympic Games
A 3,000 year old idea

The name Olympic Games is derived from Olympia, an area of Elis in Greece which in ancient times was dedicated to Zeus, the ruler of the gods. Every four years in summer, the Olympic Games were held there, between reaping and the grape harvest. These games consisted of sports and religious observances, and while they were going on, no war could be started and any war in progress had to be suspended.

There were several legends about the origin of the games. Some people said they were created by Hercules and others by Iphito, king of Elis. What we do know is that the first games of which we have an historical record were held in 776 BC. From that year onwards, Greeks started to count the years in groups of four and to refer to the four-year periods between two Olympic Games as "Olympiads". At the end of the four-year period, that is the Olympiad, the "sacred truce" was declared, weapons were returned and athletes of all Greek cities and colonies met in Olympia to hold the games.

The games of 776 BC were certainly not the first Olympic Games, as the event had

The Olympic flag is white and has five interlaced circles of different colours which represent the five continents: blue for Europe, yellow for Asia, black for Africa, green for Oceania and red for the American continent.

already justified the construction of a famous stadium in Olympia, with a seating capacity of 40,000. In those days there was only one athletic competition – the stadium run, around the 192 metres of the track. The stadium was later used in ancient Greece as a basic linear unit of measurement.

The Olympic Games started with one event (the first name on the winners' roll of honour was that of Corebo) but others were soon added. By 680 BC they included the *diaulos* (or double course), the *dolichos* (or long race), boxing, the pentathlon (long-jump, throwing of the discus, throwing of the javelin, wrestling and stadium run) and chariot-racing. As time went by, the Olympic Games became more and more important in the Greek world because of the links which they created between Greeks divided by the constant rivalry between cities and states. However, even in those days, the Olympic Games were affected by the corruption and dishonesty which accompany any major show. Professionalism, organization of paid athletes, betting and cheating progressively weakened the original force of an event in which amateurism had been an essential element.

Below, an old print showing the arrival of a marathon runner at the finishing line during the first modern Olympic Games.

The opening ceremony of the games in 1976 in Montreal (top right) and in 1896 in Athens (bottom right).

Since the first Olympic Games in 1896:

no.	year	place
1	1896	Athens (Greece)
2	1900	Paris (France)
3	1904	Saint Louis (USA)
4	1908	London (Great Britain)
5	1912	Stockholm (Sweden)
6	1916	not held
7	1920	Antwerp (Belgium)
8	1924	Paris (France)
9	1928	Amsterdam (Holland)
10	1932	Los Angeles (USA)
11	1936	Berlin (Germany)
12	1940	not held
13	1944	not held
14	1948	London (Great Britain)
15	1952	Helsinki (Finland)
16	1956	Melbourne (Australia)
17	1960	Rome (Italy)
18	1964	Tokyo (Japan)
19	1968	Mexico City (Mexico)
20	1972	Munich (West Germany)
21	1976	Montreal (Canada)
22	1980	Moscow (USSR)

As time passed, all peoples around the Mediterranean were allowed to take part in an event which originally had been strictly reserved for Greeks. Later still, during the centuries of Roman rule, the great success of circus games eventually relegated the Olympics to the status of one of the many agnostic events in which players and violence were more important than sport. The dislike of the Christian Church for this type of event gave the final blow to the Olympics. In AD 393, the year of the 294th Olympiads, St. Ambrose persuaded the Emperor Theodosius to suspend the games, which had been held regularly for almost twelve centuries.

The modern Olympic Games

Olympic myths and ideals were almost forgotten until the middle of the nineteenth century, when a young Frenchman, Baron Pierre de Coubertin, prepared an ambitious and fascinating project. He proposed restarting the Olympic Games by adapting the old ideals to con-

211

temporary European culture. In particular, he wished to encourage competitiveness and fairness; ambition to beat one's own record rather than that of an opponent; sports training as a means of achieving equilibrium between body and spirit; and the promotion of goodwill and fraternity amongst nations. De Coubertin was an idealist but was prepared to work hard to make his dream come true. Luckily the time was right for his project to become fact. On the one hand, numerous and successful archaeological excavations had brought to light significant evidence on ancient Greece and had awakened interest in the Hellenic world. On the other hand, athletic and combative sports had been standardized. Many sports clubs had emerged throughout Europe and had created central bodies to develop and supervize various sports.

In 1894, de Coubertin sent a circular to all athletic associations, putting forward his proposal and in June 1894, representatives of fifteen countries officially proclaimed the resumption of the Olympic Games. The first modern "edition" was to be held in Athens in the spring of 1896. A committee (the IOC – International Olympic Committee – which still exists today) was responsible for organizing the games. The chairman was naturally de Coubertin, who deserves our gratitude for his organization and his imaginative ideas, which, in an improved

Top left, an aerial view of Tokyo's stadium during the opening ceremony of the 1964 Olympic Games. Bottom, a giant "picture" achieved by using many coloured flags at the inauguration of the 1980 Olympic Games in Moscow.

The Winter Games have been held since 1924 (also every four years). Left, the inauguration of the games at Sapporo (1972): and below, at Innsbruck (1976).

form, are still the basis of more recent Olympic Games. For example, the Latin motto of the games *Citius, altius, fortius* (quicker, higher, stronger) is his.

In spite of the difficulties involved in the organization, the Athens Olympic Games proved particularly successful. Two hundred and eighty-five athletes (representing twelve countries) took part in nine different types of sports. Winners were given the Olympic title and received a medal at the end of the games in Athens' stadium, which was constructed to resemble the original stadium at Olympia. The Olympic spirit seemed to have been revived during the ten days of the games in Athens. However, subsequent games in Paris (1900) and Saint Louis (1904) were overshadowed by the World Fairs within which local organizers had confined them. De Coubertin's disappointment was immense and the great adventure seemed doomed. However, things changed drastically in London (1908). The British had a great sports tradition and were determined to organize the event properly. A special stadium was built which included a cycling track, athletics track, swimming pool, sports stand for 100,000 spectators and the first Olympic village. As a result, the games regained dignity, respect for their regulations and a large public. However, it was in Stockholm (1912) that the modern Olympics were finally established. All the knowledge gained from previous experience was put to good use in the organization of the fifth games. Since Stockholm, the organization, participation, showmanship and popularity of the games have constantly improved. One cause of this improvement was the final definition of the conditions under which

213

*On this page can be
seen two British gold
medallists, left, Robin
Cousins and above
Duncan Goodhew.*

athletes could participate, the number of
participants, the programme of events
and the development of the contests.
Only citizens of countries whose National
Olympic Committee (for Great Britain, the
British Olympic Association) is recognized by the IOC may take part in the
games.

In the modern Olympic Games, unlike
the ancient ones, women can also take
part. A women's event (lawn tennis) was
first introduced in 1900. In 1928, some
athletic events were organized for them
and at subsequent games the number of
women's events rapidly increased. Men
and women competitors must be able to
prove that they practise their sport as
amateurs and they must not resort to
stimulants.

The number of participants per country
is fixed by the IOC and varies for each
sport. For sports that require teams, only
one team per country is permitted. If there
are too many teams from the various
countries entering the same event, pre-
Olympic qualification tournaments are
held. These classifications by country do
not appear to keep within the Olympic
spirit, which should take into account
only the personal contribution of an
athlete and not his nationality.

Prizes given to the top three competitors in each event are purely symbolic and

consist of a gold, a silver and a bronze medal.

The games are held every four years. Those of 1916 (which should have been held in Berlin), of 1940 (which should have been held in Tokyo) and of 1944 (which should have been held in Helsinki) did not take place because of the two world wars. Games must be held in different cities capable of providing both the facilities and the organization required (so far only Paris and London have been used twice).

The programme

The programme always includes twenty-four sports divided into six main categories (athletic sports, gymnastic sports, combative sports, aquatic sports, equestrian sports and the modern pentathlon). Athletic sports include not only individual track and field events but also team sports and cycling. Only sports practised in at least twenty-five countries may be included.

The games' opening and closing ceremonies are now a traditional part of the programme. The opening ceremony is characterized by the promise made by the athletes and judges to comply with Olympic regulations and by the lighting of the flame which continues to burn during the whole games. The Greek tradition of

the flame was revived for the first time in 1928 in Amsterdam. The relay race which carries the torch from the temple of Zeus in Olympia to the city where the games are held, was introduced in 1936.

The closing ceremony is an invitation to return after four years, that is at the next Olympic Games. The flame is put out and the IOC flag with five coloured circles (blue, black, red, yellow and green, symbolizing the five continents) on a white background, is lowered. The flag is still the same one that waved in the wind in 1920 in Antwerp.

Winter games

The origin of the winter games is most certainly linked to the success of the summer ones and to the increased popularity of sports on ice and snow. However, the idea of Olympic Games on snow arose during the Antwerp games in 1920. The programme included an ice-hockey match and a figure-skating competition. The unexpected success that the two events had amongst the public and the members of the IOC led to a decision to organize special winter games in the future. The French Olympic Committee took advantage of the situation and organized (in Chamonix in 1924) a series of ski, skating and bob

Above, Steve Ovett and Sebastian Coe at the 1980 Moscow Olympic Games. Both of these British competitors won gold medals but the 1980 games were marred by political disputes.

competitions which were held in accordance with the Olympic regulations.

The success was tremendous, even on the organizational level, but it was only in 1925 that the IOC decided that tests held in Chamonix the previous year could be considered part of the Olympic Games and that they should be called the "First Winter Games". The Chamonix games, therefore, became Olympic Games retrospectively and today they are at the top of the list. The number given to the winter games depends on the number of games actually held, whilst for the summer games it is the number of four-year periods that have elapsed since the first games in 1896 in Athens that is taken into account. This explains why the Antwerp Olympic Games of 1920 are the seventh, not the sixth. The sixth four-year period since the beginning of our modern Olympics ended in 1916, during the First World War, which prevented the games from being held.

Pop Groups
A long way from string quartets

During the Middle Ages, instrumental music was considered greatly inferior to vocal music. Sacred or church music was generally sung by choirs that were not accompanied by musical instruments and with court music, such as songs performed by troubadours, the function of instruments was simply to accompany the voices. Dance music, whose origin is almost always popular, was the only type of music to be performed solely by instruments, usually viols. So, in the thirteenth century, groups very similar to our modern string quartets already existed.

Musical instruments were used more and more in churches during the fifteenth century. They were resonant instruments, such as organs, horns, various types of trumpets and trombones, the same as those used for official ceremonies to accompany royal processions or to announce a knightly tournament. On the other hand, receptions and banquets were enlivened by the more subtle sound of viols, harps and flutes.

Up to the end of the seventeenth century, most written music could be either sung or played. However, during the next century, composers started to indicate which instrument should be used, and instrumental music became more important.

Chamber music

Chamber music was intended for a small group and was performed by one or more "melodic" instruments whose aim was to provide melody. They included flutes, oboes, violas and violins together with a *basso continuo*, the instrument which provided the accompaniment. This was frequently a harpsichord, either on its own or backed by violas da gamba, violincellos or bassoons.

During the second half of the eighteenth century, harpsichords began to be replaced by fortepianos (the early type of piano) whose tone was more expressive. Keyboard instruments began to disappear or took on the same role as the other group instruments. Previously composers had provided the *basso continuo* with short-hand figures indicating where the player

Jazz bands

A jazz band at work. The rhythm is given by the drummer and double bass, while soloists generally play wind instruments like trumpets, trombones, clarinets, flutes and saxophones which were first introduced by Chicago jazz. The piano, violin and guitar are also used.

should improvise and fill out the harmony, but from the first half of the eighteenth century onwards, parts for the harpsichord and piano were clearly written in full.

Chamber groups were created in the days of Haydn and Mozart and their formation has remained the same. The most common formation was the violin-piano duet, the trio of violin, cello and piano, the quartet which included a piano together with violin, viola and cello, and the quintet which included a piano or a wind instrument. There were also many combinations for wind instruments only.

However, the most sophisticated chamber group was the string quartet comprising two violins, a viola and a cello, which reached its peak with Haydn and later Mozart. From the eighteenth century to today, many composers have used the string quartet formation for their most avant-garde compositions. For example, Beethoven's last quartets were extremely difficult and revolutionary for their day and were understood only a hundred years later.

Other composers of splendid quartets in the period include Franz Schubert, Robert Schumann, Felix Mendelssohn, Johannes Brahms, Gabriel Fauré, Bela Bartok and the twentieth-century composers Arnold Schoenberg, Alban Berg and Anton von Webern.

Jazz and rock groups

Current jazz and pop groups also make use of a section which has the same function as the *basso continuo* of earlier music, that is to accompany and give the *tempo*. This is the rhythmic section which consists of the double-bass or electric bass (in the case of pop music) and drums.

Other instruments vary. Jazz groups usually include a piano and wind instruments such as trombone, trumpet, saxophone, clarinet and flute. However, the violin, electric guitar and even the cello, which are not typically jazz instruments, are also used.

The main instrument in rock music is undoubtedly the electric guitar. Whilst the first groups invariably consisted of drums, electric bass, rhythmic guitar and soloist guitar, during the mid-sixties, the period that followed the sudden success of the Beatles, pop music tried out other instruments.

The most common was the electric organ, or electric piano, which groups like Pink Floyd, Emerson, Lake and Palmer, Van der Graaf Generator, Vanilla Fudge and many others used from the very

Some of today's most typical groups. On the left page, Pink Floyd. Top left, Sha-na-na, an American group. Top right, Premiata Forneria Marconi, a well-known Italian group. Bottom left, the "great four" of American music, Crosby, Stills, Nash and Young. Bottom right, an English "punk" group, the Sex Pistols.

beginning. Other instruments were included, like the flute (Jethro Tull, Genesis, Gentle Giant), African percussion instruments (Santana, Yardbirds) and wind instruments (Chicago).

Towards the end of the sixties, the two most famous groups, namely the Beatles and the Rolling Stones, also started to make wide use of oriental instruments such as the Indian sitar as well as flutes, pianos and harpsichords. From 1965 to the beginning of the seventies, groups continued to have an enormous amount of success. Then, as in fashion, the groups disappeared and the public started to prefer soloists.

Rock has become fashionable since 1976. Punk (a type of rock which is particularly rough and violent) groups have been formed with the same combination that existed five years ago, electric guitar, bass, drums and a lead singer.

217

Science Fiction Who invented the Alien

"Science fiction" is an expression made up of two words which seem to contradict each other: "science", which implies accuracy, reasoning and truth, and "fiction" which implies imagination and invention. Nevertheless, these two concepts are found in harmony in a particular type of novel – the sort which looks into the future. Some science fiction stories have even described events which actually took place years later.

The "grandfather" of science fiction, the French author Jules Verne, forecast in the nineteenth century discoveries that have been made in our own century. In his adventure novels, for example *From the Earth to the Moon* (1865) or *Twenty Thousand Leagues under the Sea* (1870), he anticipated expeditions which science made possible a hundred years later. Literature has always included exciting fantasies (even the myths of the ancient Greeks narrated events which could be defined as space odysseys), but it is one thing to imagine a voyage between the stars on a winged horse and quite another to imagine it being made with a vehicle or a spacecraft.

In the days of Jules Verne, there were already guns and cannons, and it was therefore possible to imagine a large projectile capable of containing people and of being fired to the moon. Such a voyage could not be made at that time, but it was possible to think about it. That was enough to allow writers to combine a large element of fantasy with the scientific and technological knowledge of their days. This is where the difference arose between fantasy literature and science fiction.

In those days, progress was seen as a source of hope for a better world, full of wonderful surprises. Only later, as we

An illustration by Moebius, a Frenchman who is one of the best-known science fiction cartoonists.

shall see, did science fiction also express the dangers of progress, by imagining a world distorted, not helped, by science.

The ancestors of science fiction

The most important fore-runner of science fiction writers (as of detective story writers) was undoubtedly Edgar Allan Poe, who lived during the first half of the nineteenth century. Poe revealed a scientific cast of mind in his stories. His novel, *The Narrative of Arthur Gordon Pym* (1838), relates a meeting with mysterious creatures hiding under icecaps.

However, the first real science fiction novel had been written twenty years earlier, in 1817, by a woman, Mary Wollstonecraft Shelley, the wife of the famous English poet. Her novel, *Franken-stein* (1818), narrates how a scientist uses

stills and electric machines to transform a dead man's body into a living monster. The story was so successful that it is still popular nowadays (especially in films and *Frankenstein* has remained the symbol of a particular kind of science fiction.

It is not clear whether Poe and Mrs Shelley had any influence on Verne, but there is no doubt that Verne influenced the first novels of H.G. Wells, an English writer who was born in 1866 and died in 1946. Wells is, amongst other things, the writer who invented "Martians". His most famous books are *The Time Machine* (1895, about a machine which makes it possible to move backwards into the past

"Classical" authors of the past

There is no doubt that Verne and Wells are the two best-known science fiction writers of the past. The pictures on the right show an illustration and a cover from two of their most successful novels: *From the Earth to the Moon* written in 1865 (with a spacecraft similar to a rocket which has open windows) and *War of the Worlds* written in 1898 (French edition). Verne first wrote a series of books for musical comedies but became successful only later when he started writing adventure and science fiction stories for children. These stories, and in particular those in the "Extraordinary Voyages" series, were also enjoyed by adults.

Wells was a biology teacher who gave up teaching to dedicate himself to literature (not only science fiction) and history.

and forwards into the future), *The Invisible Man* (1897) and *The War of the Worlds* (1898). In this last novel, he describes an invasion of the earth by extraterrestrial creatures, the famous Martians. In 1938, his novel was adapted for use as a radio programme in the United States, and the producer decided to present the programme as a live news report of a real invasion by extraterrestrial creatures. Pandemonium broke out as thousands of people who had not been warned of the nature of the programme descended into the streets, terrified.

Science fiction

By that time, science fiction was already very popular in the United States. Serial stories and novels had been published for ten years or so in widely sold monthly and weekly magazines. In 1929, one of these stories used the term "science fiction" for the first time. The first magazine to deal exclusively with science fiction (there were many others which published every type of adventure story) appeared in 1926. It was called *Amazing Stories* and its founder, Hugo Gernsback, defined science fiction as describing "events in which the plot gets tied up with scientific events and a prophetic outlook on the future."

Gernsback was also a science fiction author. He wrote a novel with the strange title *Ralph 124C41+*, in which he described with great accuracy both space flights and sophisticated equipment including radar, television, microfilms and a whole series of automatic systems which have still to be invented. Gernsback is considered one of the "pillars" of American science fiction even though his style was dreadful. The most prolific

(*continued on page 222*)

Above and left: two frames from Metropolis, *one of the first science fiction films. It was produced in the United States in 1926 by the German Fritz Lang and describes a hallucinatory future world controlled by robots.*

219

Science fiction has been a subject for films since the days of silent movies (sound films did not start until the late 1920s). Futurist films of those days, like more recent ones, were generally mediocre or poor because too much emphasis was put on the fantasy aspect. The first science fiction film which proved successful because of both the topic and the quality of the picture was 2001-Space Odyssey (above), produced in 1968 by the American director Stanley Kubrick and British scriptwriter Arthur C. Clarke.

Thanks to the progress achieved in film techniques, it was possible to create very imaginative scenes with astronauts who seemed real. However, another ten years passed before the most spectacular films were produced. The first was Star Wars (below), directed by George Lucas. It tells the incredible adventures which happen during a space flight between "good" and "bad" characters. As in a fairy-tale, there is also a beautiful princess who has to be freed. Among the main characters are two robots, one of which is small and fat and the other tall and thin.

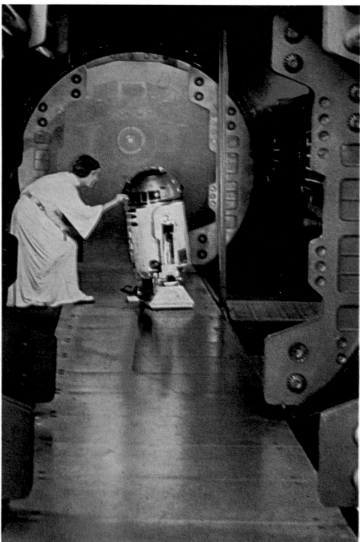

Another leading science fiction film which had a great success at the end of the 1970s was Close Encounters of the Third Kind *(left and below)*. The director, Stephen Spielberg, told the story of the arrival of an extraterrestrial being in the United States and the meeting between men and ''aliens'' who can communicate only through music. Amongst the most important science fiction films, mention must be made of Solaris, *produced by the Soviet Andrei Tarkovski (above) in 1972 and based on the novel of the Pole, Stanislaw Lem.*

(continued from page 219)

writer of the opening period was undoubtedly Edgar Rice Burroughs. He had millions of readers and has remained famous both for his numerous science fiction novels and for having created Tarzan.

From the boom to the crisis

In spite of the success of writers like Burroughs, science fiction became a well-defined literary genre only during the second half of the 1920s. We have seen that this was the time when magazines specializing in science fiction were successfully launched in the United States. It was much later that a series of books dealing exclusively with science fiction appeared there. The magazine stories were based on the pattern of adventure novels, where the main character or hero always wins. The authors of these fantasies were influenced not only by the need for scientific accuracy but also by the attitudes which were common in the 1920s. In most cases the "conqueror" (of new planets rather than lands) was praised in a way which was typical of those days. In fact, extraterrestrial creatures were seen only as "savages" to be destroyed or colonized, or as the "baddies" to be converted to civilization, preferably of the American variety.

Science fiction novels reached their peak, still in the United States, between the thirties and the first half of the fifties. The quality of the writers' style improved and topics started to change. There were not only extraordinary voyages between the stars and incredible fights with extraterrestrial creatures (aliens, mutants, humanoids according to the science fiction language), but also optimistic or pessimistic forecasts about the world, the progress of science and changes in the social life on earth. Mention was even made of good extraterrestrial creatures in love with human and galactic beings, and of races lost in the cosmos which were infinitely more advanced than the human race. It was during this period that there emerged writers of high literary quality, such as Ray Bradbury and Isaac Asimov.

However, science fiction encountered problems as soon as space voyages became reality. More than thirty out of forty science fiction magazines had to close down in the United States between 1957 (the year in which the first artificial satellites were launched) and 1965. The remaining ones saw their sales drop by half. The public clearly preferred real photographs and news reports on television and in newspapers to fictional novels.

The European school

At the end of the sixties, when space voyages achieved their greatest success with the first landing on the moon (1969), science fiction suddenly became popular again, presumably because of a further change in the content of the stories and because of the arrival of talented new authors. Special credit must especially be given to the "English school" (which had meanwhile come closer to and stimulated the American school) and to authors of the quality of James Ballard and Thomas Disch.

In addition, publishers re-launched a thirty-year-old type of fiction, known as "heroic science fiction", which was popular with the public. In these novels, astronauts were replaced by incredible characters who resembled knights of the old days and science was replaced by magic and occultism. In fact, these were epic and fantastic stories which had little in common with the classic type of science fiction and which in no way complied with the basic rules.

Science fiction was, therefore, created in Europe, but developed almost exclusively in the United States where there was a huge production of novels and stories as well as cartoons, films and finally television programmes. Very few European writers worked on this type of novel during the period before the Second World War and there were no specialized series of books or magazines, at least until the fifties. Nevertheless, the two masterpieces of science fiction, which are important particularly from the literary point of view but also go well beyond ordinary adventure stories, were written in Europe. These are *Brave New World* written by Aldous Huxley in 1932 and *1984* written by George Orwell in 1949 (when the year 1984 appeared a long way away).

Huxley and Orwell were both English and since their day the few recognized writers who have worked alongside Americans have also been English. We have to conclude that from *Frankenstein* onwards, science fiction has always "spoken" English, preferably with an American accent. The only well-known exceptions are the Frenchman Jules Verne, in the last century, and the late Stanislaw Lem in our own. Of the latter, the only novel known is *Solaris*, which has been made into a film.

The first science fiction cartoon story was published in 1934, when the character of Flash Gordon, created by Alex Raymond, first appeared. The idea proved extremely successful all over the world and was immediately copied. "Space heroes" have since multiplied and become more varied. Stories of Jeff Hawke, drawn by Sidney Jordan, have been widely read since 1954. It is interesting to see in the "strip" below how American characters were given Italian text. The seventies also witnessed the arrival of cartoons which may be described as "artistic". Among these are the cartoons of the French designer, Philippe Druillet, a strip of which can be seen on the next page. (The strip is taken from The Fantastic Voyages of Lone Sloane.)

Jeff Hawke BY SYDNEY JORDAN

SÌ, LA SPEDIZIONE HA TROVATO L'OGGETTO MISTERIOSO NELL'ORBITA DI GIOVE... ORA SI TRATTA DI CREARE UNA BRECCIA NELL'INVOLUCRO PROTETTIVO!

LONTANO, SULLA TERRA, HAWKE USA I POTERI CONFERITIGLI E ...

... PROIETTA LA SUA MENTE NELLO SPAZIO!

Sport
Competing
for fame or money?

The word "sport" has undergone a curious change, since it derives from the old French word *desport*, of which the English equivalent is "disport". So the word was first used in Latin countries, where it meant something done for amusement, but is now a common English word with a somewhat different meaning. In particular, it means an activity where man makes use, either individually or in a group, of his own physical, mental and technical capacities to prevail in competitive games carried out on the basis of well defined rules.

Physical exercise is as old as mankind, and the competitive spirit, which is the basis of games involving two people struggling to prevail against each other, is just as old. However, in the past, establishing a winner was not the final aim but a means of reaching a different

goal. It served to determine who was the leader; who should be head of a hunting party or an army; or who should have the right and privilege of acting as intermediary or representative to the gods.

In the old days, religion always played an important part in competitive physical games. Even the well-known Hellenic games (Olympic, Pythian, Isthmian, Nemean and others), which had many of the characteristics which we nowadays associate with a sports competition, were linked with the desire to offer to the gods physical effort, technical capacity and the competitive spirit. The greater the effort, the better the result and the greater the offering. Greek civilization just missed that extra step which would have changed the games from solemn religious rituals to sports events in the modern sense.

Even though the Romans continued to hold Greek games, they directed their physical exercise to useful purposes (for example, military training and circus performances). Team games became a popular hobby, and in these physical effort, observance of pre-established rules and competitiveness were aimed at victory for its own sake, a symbolic concept, but one no longer linked to religion. Even when Christianity suppressed what had remained of the Hellenic sports (ideologically linked to paganism), the Roman type of games continued to exist in all regions of the empire.

Popular games, with different characteristics depending on the area, were created during the Middle Ages. They gave rise to lively competitive contests between villages and towns and led to

the partisanship which is still found in modern sport.

During the Renaissance, physical exercise and activity were regarded as basic elements in developing a person's character. In 1423, the educator Vittorino da Feltre founded the "merry house" in Mantua. This was a school where study and physical training, good behaviour and awareness of one's own capacity were considered as basic essentials.

This particular project was copied elsewhere and further developed, leading eventually to the education system used in English public schools. In fact, the first "modern" sport was noted in Great Britain during the early years of the eighteenth century. English schools encouraged classic athletic activities and many popular games were "purged" by replacing violence and brute force with more and more sophisticated rules.

During the second half of the nineteenth century, sports became widespread throughout the world and the Olympics were re-established when the first modern Games were held in France in 1896. Since then, the Olympics have provided an opportunity to compare the best performances in many sports.

Amateurs and professionals

The concept of amateurism was im-

Spectacular pictures of various sports. Left-hand page, a horse race. Above, a cycle race. Below, the start of the rowing competition.

portant in the creation of modern sports. The British wanted a clear distinction between sportsmen competing for the satisfaction and honour of achieving a good result and those who did it for financial reasons. The Baron de Coubertin and his friends laid down that athletes who wanted to take part in the modern Olympic Games had to be amateurs. Rules prepared by international and national sports federations for the various disciplines have always been extremely clear about the definition of amateurism. However, the problem was not solved satisfactorily right at the beginning. Rules penalized less wealthy athletes (some rules still lay down that professional seamen cannot take part in rowing competitions and that people over twenty-one years of age who have been caddies cannot take part in golf championships) and limited the spread of sports throughout the population. On the other hand, some rules allowed a kind of disguised professionalism, with payments established by the governing bodies of the federations. In addition, because of their highly spectacular and competitive content, some sports (for example, boxing, basketball, football) involved large commercial elements in which it was extremely difficult not to implicate the athletes. Other sports (such as rowing, running, cross-country racing and weight-lifting) were subject to very strict amateur rules.

Because of the high standards in most sports today, athletes must dedicate themselves almost entirely to training and preparing for competitions if they want to achieve any significant result. Therefore, they must either find sufficient means to survive while practising a sport on a full-time basis, or dedicate themselves to something else and regard sport as a "spare time" activity in which they will achieve only mediocre results. This is a problem to which nobody has yet found a solution, although the governing bodies of various sports have made differing attempts to find a way around it. In general, the rules that define the term "amateur" are extremely inadequate. This is the case, for example, with tennis players, who are considered amateurs when they play for their national team in the Davis Cup, but who are handsomely paid when they take part in international tournaments. The recent introduction of "open" championships, in which both amateurs and professionals compete for a cash prize, may be considered as an attempt to solve this delicate problem, but it is also an expression of the general malaise to which the distinction gives rise in almost all sports.

Classification

As a result of the large number of sports practised nowadays, it has been necessary to classify them, that is group them according to one or more characteristics. The first classification, which is the most general, distinguishes between "individual" (for example, wrestling and weight lifting) and "team" (for example, football, basketball, etc.) sports. Some sports can belong to both categories, as, for example, tennis which is an individual sport in singles but a team sport in doubles. Similarly, running competitions are usually individual events but become team ones in the case of relay races. Another major division is that which groups sports into Olympic and non-Olympic events.

An important system of classification is concerned with the technical and

This table shows some of the most common sports and hobbies subdivided according to the environment in which they are performed. There are so many sports disciplines that it would be extremely difficult to classify them on the basis of a single criterion. An important distinction can be made between individual and team sports. However, in this case too, there are many exceptions. For example, tennis includes singles and doubles championships and athletics includes individual races as well as relay races. The table also gives curling which is an unusual game similar to bowls but which is played on ice.

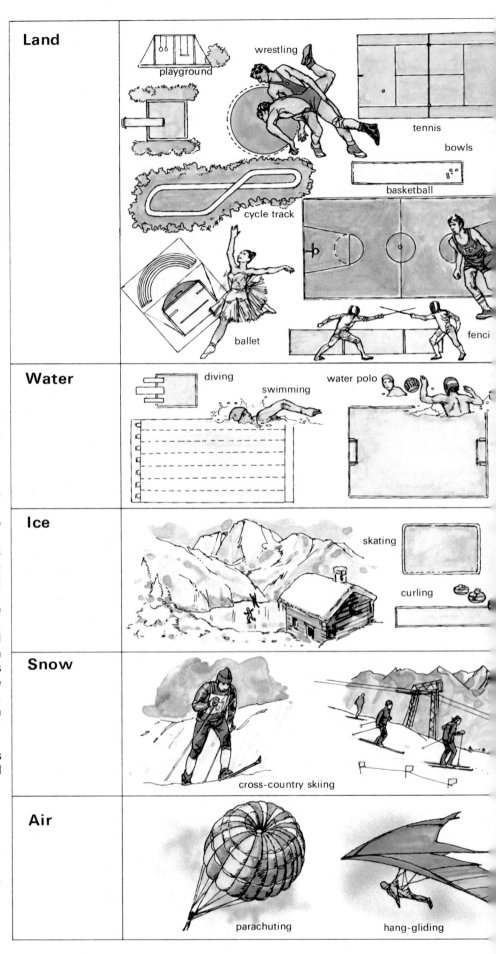

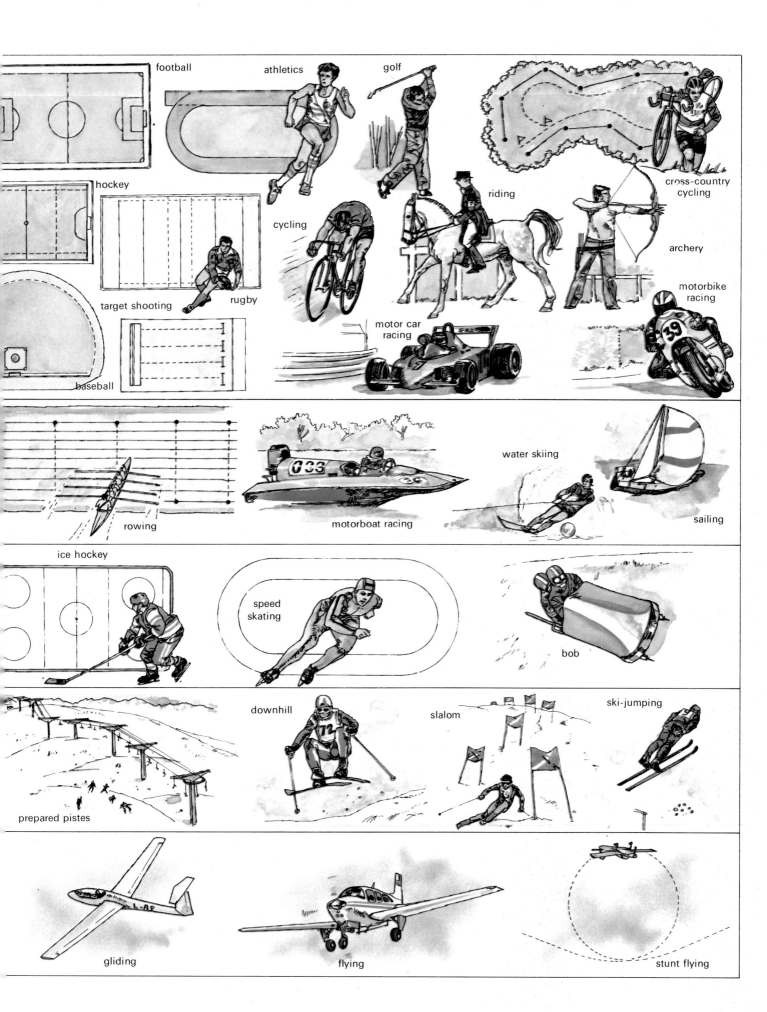

football

athletics

golf

cross-country
cycling

hockey

riding

cycling

archery

target shooting

rugby

motorbike
racing

motor car
racing

baseball

rowing

motorboat racing

water skiing

sailing

ice hockey

speed
skating

bob

downhill

slalom

ski-jumping

prepared pistes

gliding

flying

stunt flying

Ice hockey (above) is one of the fastest team sports as players can move at up to 45 kilometres per hour in an "attack". Above right, a match between two American basketball teams. Below, in spite of its many fans all over the world, boxing is a rather controversial sport. The violence in some bouts makes it almost comparable to a brutal fight.

environmental characteristics of each speciality. The most common subdivisions are: athletic sports (track and field events, weight lifting and gymnastics); water sports (swimming, diving, sub-aqua, surfing); nautical sports (sailing, rowing, canoeing); ball games (football, rugby, basketball, volleyball, handball); small ball games (tennis, table tennis, field hockey, track hockey, baseball, softball, cricket); equestrian sports (three-day events, show jumping, cross-country races, dressage, hunting, polo); mechanical sports (cycling); motor sports (car racing, motorbike racing, motorboat racing, aeronautic racing); mountain sports (climbing, alpine skiing); snow and ice sports (skiing, bob, ice hockey, ice skating); combat sports (boxing, wrestling, fencing); weapon sports (target shooting, archery); and mixed sports (decathlon, pentathlon).

In spite of all the efforts which have been made, it is difficult to classify each sport individually. Some sports have not been classified (roller skating, for example, cannot be included in a specific group), and other sports are put first into one group and then into another (for example, should water polo be considered as a water sport or a ball game? And should wind surfing be amongst water or nautical sports?)

Organization

The process of classification began a century ago but only now can sports be said to be well organized on an international level. Nowadays, each speciality is organized and controlled by an international federation which is linked to national federations which in turn are often associated with continental bodies (European, American, Asiatic, etc.). A particularly important role in the world organization of sport is played by the IOC

Gymnastics (whether free standing or apparatus work) is a very common sport, particularly amongst young people as it is included in educational programmes. Above, an athlete performing an exercise on the rings. Right, parachuting is a sport in which it is much more difficult to participate.

(International Olympic Committee). The IOC organizes the Olympic Games as well as controlling and encouraging "Olympic" sports (those which are included in the Olympic programme). It does this through two groups of bodies, the national Olympic Committees (in Great Britain, the British Olympic Association) and the international federations of individual sports.

Each country has, on a national level, created different structures. In Great Britain the organization of sports is controlled largely by the various sporting associations (the Football Association, the Lawn Tennis Association, the Amateur Athletic Association and the Jockey Club, for example). However, other bodies have an important part to play.

Amongst public bodies, mention must be made of the important role played by schools. In spite of the numerous problems encountered, schools aim at incorporating a wide range of sports in children's education. Both state and private schools organize competitive sports within the school and full fixture lists of matches with neighbouring schools. From the primary school through all the stages of secondary school, a child can expect the opportunity to take part in local and area championships. When a school is in a built-up city area, it will have access to playing fields and transport to take the children there.

Public bodies, such as local councils, aim at ensuring that every citizen has sports facilities available. They try to encourage sport which they consider a social asset and a healthy way of spending spare time.

Sports Centres

Modern sports have become so numerous, as well as so technically sophisticated, that it has been necessary to develop large sporting complexes which can sometimes change the appearance of the area quite significantly. This is true of the Sports Centres in large cities (and in particular cities where there have been Olympic Games), which include stadiums, swimming pools and every possible type of facility. In addition, there are centres for golf, rowing, riding and skiing which cover hundreds of hectares and affect the scenery.

Sports Centres are becoming ever more numerous and are found even in small communities. In fact, they are the answer to the increasing wish to practise sport as opposed to watching it. The development of sport and its role in the future depends on the number of centres that are built and the possibility of their meeting the requirements and wishes of the community they serve.

The Theatre
Behind the curtain

The stage is the part of a theatre where the performance takes place and usually makes us think of lighting effects, colours and movement. The curtain is like a door to a new world.

Let us imagine, however, that the curtain is raised when there is no performance: the area behind it is very large and empty, much deeper and higher than it appears to be from the auditorium. Sometimes the stage is on a rising slope to increase the perspective effect, and signs may be marked on the floor for the actors and stage furniture. In larger theatres, there are impressive pieces of equipment or machinery and systems incorporating stage effects and supports for wings.

Most of the stage work takes place not on stage, but backstage, where activities essential to the performance are carried out without the audience actually being aware of them. At the rear of the stage, there may be a room or space for keeping furniture and fittings. Above, out of sight of the audience, there are the "flies" from which lights, scenery and ropes are operated. Below, is the "understage" which allows actors to pass from one side of the stage to the other without being seen by the audience. There are also trapdoors for special effects. The understage may house machinery for raising sections of the stage or enabling a section to revolve.

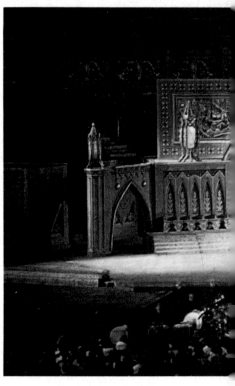

With individual variations, this is what a typical stage looked like from the seventeenth to the beginning of the twentieth century. Stages have, in fact, changed quite significantly with time.

How have stages changed?

Actors who performed in the open-air theatres of ancient Greece, could be seen by the audience not because they were higher up, but because they were below the audience. Seats were arranged in a huge semi-circle on a hillside or a building which had a similar slope. They were in tiers, rising upwards and outwards from a central area known as the orchestra. This was used by the actors and the chorus which also took part in the play by performing dances. The chorus remained in this area in later Greek and Roman days, when a small stand was built for the actors. As the ancient pagan civilization declined, the large stone theatres with their stage scenery representing arches and palaces, remained unused and were sometimes looted for building materials.

During the Middle Ages, theatre stages were of timber and could usually be dismantled. They were raised up, with a curtained area beneath as a room for the actors who reached the stage by climbing up a small ladder. There were often several stages, each representing a different setting, and during the performance the actors moved from "heaven" to "hell" or from "home" to the "tavern". The audience stood around the raised stages, leaving space for the actors to perform on

the ground if need be.

From the sixteenth century onwards, two types of stages were used. In England, during the Elizabethan period, the stage consisted of a platform which projected out into the audience and of a small structure at the back, the "tiring house" or "house of the actors", which was used by the actors when they were not performing and by musicians who played during the performances. A sketch of the Swan Theatre, built in London in about 1580, shows us what the inside of

Left-hand page, a nineteenth-century painting entitled, Stage preparations in a theatre. *Above, the inside of the Scala Theatre in Milan, built in 1778. The stage is 31 metres high and covers 1,308 square metres.*

Below, an open-air performance of Otello *by Giuseppe Verdi. Performances sometimes take place in ancient amphitheatres or arenas, as at Verona in Italy, and scenery is specially built for the production.*

these early Elizabethan theatres was like. Later the tiring house was altered to contain a curtained inner room, doors of entry onto the stage and a balcony, which could be used by the actors for upper scenes. A famous example of this is in Shakespeare's *Romeo and Juliet*, where the lovers talk to each other from a garden and a balcony. There was no curtain separating the actors and audience in

those days and this is why the Shakespearean characters who died on stage were taken off with a solemn funeral procession: obviously they could not have walked off the stage, thereby ruining the effect of a tragic death.

The other type of stage was found in Italy where temporary stages were erected in the courtyards and halls of palaces: it was only later that buildings

used specifically as theatres were constructed. At the beginning, the stage was based on those of the Greek and Roman theatres, but it gradually changed and acquired a number of mechanical "miracles". The structure of the building remained the same: the stage was in front of the stalls and circles and the curtain concealed any change in scenery. However, as stage designing became more and more complex, the dimensions of the stage increased and areas for housing machinery and equipment were created or extended. The stage of the theatre designed by Andrea Palladio for the Olympian Academy at Vicenza at the end of the sixteenth century, was 6.70 metres deep but the Tuileries' Machine Room in Paris, built by Vigarani between 1659 and 1662, measured at least 46 metres.

Changes and tradition

This type of "Italian-style" stage became widespread in Europe and was used till the beginning of the twentieth century when experiments in drama influenced both style and acting and had a marked effect on the stage.

In fact, although the traditional type of stage is still used, other styles have been studied and developed as a result of more and more sophisticated techniques.

The drawing above shows the main structures of a traditional stage seen from the rear. On the left and right, are the wings and platforms from which cables, projectors and other equipment can be operated. Left, a revolving stage with which the scenery can be rapidly changed (for example, from the inside of a house to a garden).

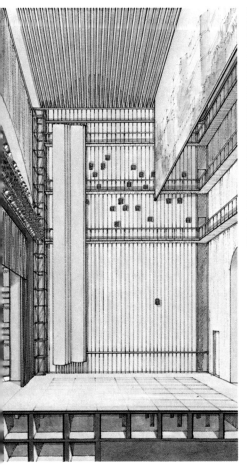

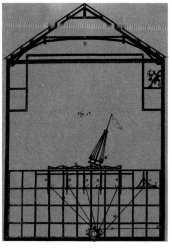

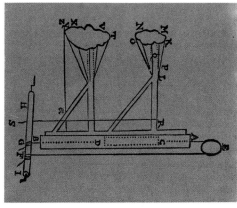

The top part of the stage is used for the backcloths for the different scenes of a play. These backcloths are lowered when required, as can be seen in the drawing on the left. Top left, a page of Diderot's and D'Alembert's Encyclopédie, *showing the movement of a ship and waves on a stage. Top right, a simple device to give the same effect. Right, a machine for "moving" clouds, designed in the seventeenth century. Below, the auditorium and stage of the seventeenth-century Pergola Theatre in Florence.*

Flexible theatres have been designed where the audience and stage areas can be changed depending on the requirements of the play. The stage can be raised or lowered or seats arranged in front of or around the actors. An example of this is the "total" theatre designed by the well-known architect Walter Gropius in 1927. He conceived a building that was completely mechanical and could be used for any type of performance.

As well as the increased use of sophisticated equipment, contemporary theatre also takes advantage of places where it is possible to gather a large audience and perform plays in squares, courtyards, gynmasiums, warehouses and canteens. In these cases, the stage consists of any type of platform that enables the actors to be seen (for example, a terrace, the steps of a church) or simply of a raised platform that can be easily dismantled and re-erected.

In this way, the stage goes back to its original form: it is said that a legendary Greek actor went round the villages of Attica with a cart which he used both for travelling and reciting. For many centuries, wandering players travelled from place to place, putting on their shows in the barns of taverns, courts of noble houses and fairgrounds.

Gold
What unleashes "gold fever"?

"Gold fever" used to spread rapidly whenever the precious metal was discovered in some faraway place. Groups of prospectors, hoping to become rich, would flood into the area. Today gold causes quite different "epidemics".

In California, on 24 January 1848, a certain James W. Marshall, working on the construction of a saw-mill not far from San Francisco (which was then a small settlement of a few hundred inhabitants), found gold in the gravel of a tributary to the Sacramento river. This set off the so-called "gold-fever" (or "gold rush"), an important moment in the history of the United States, which brought repercussions throughout the world. In only eighteen months, the hunt for gold attracted to California about 100,000 men and soon San Francisco became one of the most important American cities.

Three years later, in 1851, a veteran miner of the United States gold rush discovered a deposit in the Blue Mountains in Australia and here, too, within a few months men arrived from all parts of the world and new towns rapidly sprang up. The same thing happened again in Alaska when, at the end of the century, a gold-bearing area was identified, though here the gold "rush" became a frenzy because of the terrible climatic conditions in those regions.

These are only some examples of the great importance men may attribute to gold. There are many others, like the myth of a fantastic Eldorado, which gained wide currency in the sixteenth century when the Spanish "conquistadores" began to colonize South America. Eldorado was thought to be a fabulous city, wholly paved with gold and precious stones, which was believed to be situated in the territory of present-day Colombia. Despite frequent and extended searches, nobody ever succeeded in finding it.

Everywhere but in small quantities

As gold does not easily combine with other substances, it is frequently found in nature in the pure state, or else as veins of gold in the rock, associated with (but not

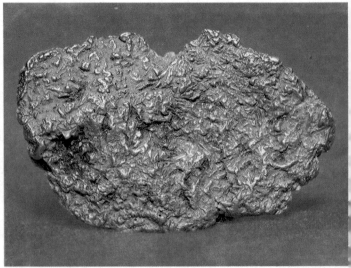

Above, a large nugget of native gold found in California. Left, an old illustration showing the trek of the gold prospectors towards Ontario territory (in Canada) where, towards the end of the nineteenth century, a rich gold-bearing area was identified.

On the page opposite, some pictures which recall the "gold fever" period in Canada. Above: left, typical wooden hut in the Yukon territory; right, "plant" for the extraction of gold. Below, two photographs taken in the vicinity of the township of Carcross, where the gold-seekers built the boats in which they made their way up the Yukon river in search of nuggets: left, the bridge for the railway and, right, the strange cemetery where some of the prospectors are buried.

chemically bound to) sulphides, like iron pyrites, the yellow disulphide of iron. More frequently it is mixed with sand in alluvial deposits (deposits left on the bed or banks of rivers by running water). Over thousands of years, the rock in which the gold originally occurred was broken down and exposed to the effects of the atmosphere and carried down to the valleys by rivers. The gold, which is a very inert material, keeps its characteristics unchanged and is laid down by currents in the form of dust or small grains or as larger lumps, called nuggets. Even in sea-water, there are very tiny quantities of gold: one gram for every two thousand tonnes of water.

Gold, then, is never found in large quantities; it is a rare metal and this is partly responsible for making it precious. A few years ago, it was calculated that all the gold refined by man in the course of history would amount to no more than a cube with fifteen-metre sides. It is, however, fairly widely distributed in every continent and has been worked by civilizations as different as the European and the American Indians. Perhaps it was the first metal which mankind used; small golden beads and decorative objects dating back to prehistoric times have been recovered in France and Egypt. Certainly it was one of the seven metals known to the ancient world, in company with copper, lead, tin, iron, silver and mercury

Extraction and refining

At the present time, the principal places where gold is extracted are the Transvaal, a province of the South African Republic where it was discovered in 1884, in Siberia (USSR), in the United States, in Canada, in Australia, in the Philippines, in Colombia, in Mexico and in India. It is possible that in ancient times deposits of gold were found in Western Asia, too, and certainly there were some in Southern Europe (the province of Asturias, in Spain, was particularly famous). These deposits are now worked out.

The procedure for extracting gold from alluvial sand (also used sometimes on gold-bearing rock after crushing) was at one time very simple. It is even recorded in inscriptions discovered on Egyptian monuments dating back to 4000 BC and the stories and comic strips set against the background of the American Far West have since made it familiar: it was universally adopted by the near-legendary American gold prospectors. The sand was collected a little at a time, in containers through which a current of water was made to flow. By shaking the container, the sand, which is much lighter than the gold, tends to stay at the top and

After extraction from the various deposits, the gold is subjected to a special ''cleaning'', then melted down and turned into ingots (above).

be washed away by the water. It was a long and tiring procedure on which prisoners of war were employed in Roman times in areas that had gold-bearing sands. These days, the sand is collected by mechanical dredgers capable of sifting thousands of cubic metres of material per day. Pure gold is not obtained as a result of the washing process, but only very concentrated gold-bearing sand: together with the gold powder there are granules of other minerals still present. The next step is to make an amalgam of the gold with mercury. The gold-rich sand is passed across a level surface sprinkled with liquid mercury. The mercury amalgamates with the gold and leaves the other minerals behind. The amalgam is then filtered and the mercury distilled off. A lump of almost pure gold is obtained in this way.

Cyanidization and electrolytic refining are the two most modern methods. In the first, the mineral containing the gold is treated with a dilute solution of sodium cyanide; in the second case, the separation is done by a chemical process called electrolysis.

Ductile and malleable

Gold is a yellow metal which does not oxidize in the air, but always stays shiny. Very few chemical agents attack it: only chlorine, bromine, *aqua regia* (a mixture of hydrochloric acid and nitric acid) and cyanide in the presence of oxygen (from which comes the method of extraction called cyanidization). Gold is also the most malleable and ductile of all metals: it can be made into very thin, almost transparent sheets and into gold thread which weighs only half a milligram per metre. It is, therefore, particularly suitable for making necklaces and similar items. In the archaeological excavations made on the second level of the city of Troy, there have been found, together with other precious objects (the so-called Treasure of Priam), a diadem consisting of thousands of pieces, attached to numerous very fine subsidiary chains hanging from a principal chain fifty-two centimetres long. Such a refined piece of work (using the far-from-perfect techniques of those days) would not have been possible using less malleable metals.

Gold is also very dense and heavy and this makes it very suitable for coinage,

On this page we see the mining town of Kalgoorlie, in Western Australia, which became the centre of the gold rushes of 1892–4. Above, an aerial view of the area. Below: left, some of the machinery and right, deposits of sludge.

because any attempt at counterfeiting using lighter metals can easily be discovered. It is even heavier than lead, with a specific gravity of 19.3 grams per cubic centimetre (against 11.34 for lead). In addition, its thermal and electrical conductivities are amongst the highest of any metal, but its mechanical strength is low and it is not a very hard metal. For these reasons, it is nearly always used alloyed with other metals. Alloyed with copper, for example, it assumes a reddish or pinkish colour, with silver it becomes greenish and in conjunction with nickel or palladium it becomes very hard and white: it is then called white gold, which is often used in place of platinum.

The chemical and physical properties of gold, and specially of its alloys, suggest its use in many applications. Whenever possible, however, other, less expensive metals are substituted for it.

In dentistry, it is used (in the form of alloys with other metals) to make replacement teeth and fillings since it does not corrode and is chemically inert. Contacts in many electronic circuits are also made from gold, as are conductors and the internal contacts in the most sophisticated miniaturized integrated circuits. In this last case, the soldering of the gold wires is done under the microscope, using laser beams. At certain times in the past, gold has been considered as a medicament and even until the end of the last century a gold-based preparation was prescribed as an antidote to tuberculosis.

Jewellery and works of art

Beautiful, shining, easily worked and rare, gold has been used in all ages especially to make jewellery and decorative objects. The most beautiful of objects have been made from it and are still made to this day, including some artistic masterpieces. Sometimes, in the form of gold wire, it has the simple function of supporting precious stones, but often whole objects are made of it. Even in architecture and sculpture, gold has played an important part. Many monuments and statues were at one time covered by sheets of the precious metal. Unfortunately, only a very few of these decorations have survived to our own day. Many precolombian objects (the term used for American civilizations before the arrival of Christopher Columbus) were made of gold and here, too, the desire for riches outweighed the appreciation of artistic value, so most of these objects were melted down and sent back to Spain by the conquerors.

The goldsmith's art often employs gold alloys in which case the surface of the article is given its characteristic yellow

Gold is a ductile and malleable metal: for this reason, since ancient times, it has been possible to work it so as to make precious decorative objects. On the left, is a golden cup which dates back to the fifteenth century BC. Below, two other ancient golden objects: left, a chalice of the seventeenth century with precious stones inset and, right, an Etruscan brooch of the seventh century BC.

colour by special processing as a final touch, although sometimes the natural colour of the alloy is left unchanged. In the last century, for example, red gold obtained by alloying gold with copper was very much in fashion. The percentage of gold in the alloy is indicated by a number of "carats". It has been established by convention that pure gold has twenty-four carats. Thus an alloy, for example, of eighteen carats contains eighteen twenty-fourths of pure gold, or seventy-five per cent.

Symbol of wealth

On account of its chemical and physical properties which render it almost unalterable and impossible to counterfeit and also on account of its rarity, very early in human history gold became a unit of value for exchange of goods as well as a symbol of wealth. It still has a great importance today in international commerce. In fact, it is accepted as a repository of value by every country in the world and each nation keeps a reserve of it.

In the past alchemy, the forerunner of chemistry, saw in gold a symbol both of nobility and of the sun, and many alchemists tried to discover the formula for "transmuting" it, that is transforming "base metals" into gold. Modern chemistry shows us that this transformation is not possible; probably some of these investigators succeeded in extracting small quantities of gold present as an impurity from other metals, but they certainly did not succeed in transforming it totally.

Gold has long been the subject of songs and poems. One of the best-known traditional songs, by a nineteenth-century writer Percy Montrose begins:

"In a cavern, in a canyon,
Excavating for a mine,
Dwelt a miner, Forty-Niner,
And his daughter, Clementine."

A direct reference to "Gold fever" of 1848–9.

Painting
The oldest art

Man started to draw and paint and so to express himself through pictures, a long time before he invented writing and when his language was still rather primitive.

Painting has been an essential as well as spontaneous means of expression since man's first days on earth and the evidence which remains is much older than any of the inscriptions so far discovered. The first inscriptions do not go beyond the fourth millennium BC whilst paintings and engravings (incisions in stone) dating back to tens of centuries before have been found in many prehistoric caves, such as the pictures of animals in the Lascaux caves in Southern France, or those in the Altamira caves in Northern Spain. This type of painting is known as "rock-drawing" because it was done on the rocks of the caves in which prehistoric men lived. Although they date from such distant times, some of them have only been discovered quite recently. The famous Lascaux cave paintings, for example, were found in 1940. They date from between 15,000 and 10,000 BC, and are thought to relate to hunting rituals.

Real documents

Primitive artists drew pictures with pointed stones, and then coloured them with sap or crushed minerals mixed with animal blood or fat. They first started to apply colours with their fingers, but later used pieces of stick flattened at one end, sponges made of moss and lichen and finally the first paintbrushes, consisting of tufts of animal hair fixed to a stick.

As civilization spread around the Mediterranean, painting became more important. Pictures of gods, warriors and heroes decorate the temples and tombs of ancient Egypt, evidence of artistic ability as well as documents on real life.

More sculptures than paintings have come down to us from the ancient past. This does not mean that the people of those days preferred to sculpt rather than paint, but simply that paintings are more difficult to preserve. Those that have

reached us, had been kept in closed or sealed areas such as the Egyptian tombs and the prehistoric caves which were blocked up for centuries by rocks or landslides. Similar environmental conditions have preserved some Etruscan paintings in tombs that remained hermetically sealed for many years. On the other hand, the effect of air and light, damage caused by weather and human negligence have destroyed a great deal of the Persian, Assyrian, Babylonian, Phoenician and Greek civilizations.

Our knowledge of the paintings of ancient Greece is limited to the names of such painters as Polygnotus, Zeuxis, Parrhasius and Appelles who lived during the golden years of Hellenic civilization, between the fourth and sixth centuries BC. Their names and works are mentioned by ancient writers, but the works themselves have been lost. The only trace of their art is found in the paintings on vases and amphoras.

Roman painters found inspiration in Greek models, but became more realistic. No names are known, but a few works were preserved by a natural disaster which paradoxically created similar conditions to those which preserved the Egyptian pictures. The disaster was the eruption of Vesuvius, which destroyed Herculaneum and Pompeii in AD 79. Men and animals died, but houses and buildings remained intact under the huge flow of lava, ash and stones. Excavations started at the end of the eighteenth century and discovered paintings which had decorated the walls of the houses. Pompeiian painters used tempera and encaustic paint. Tempera was prepared by mixing powdered pigments with gelatine, casein glue, fig latex or, more usually, egg yolk. For encaustic painting, the colours were first mixed with molten beeswax to which a little resin had been added. When the picture was finished, it had to be burnt into the wall, and a hot iron was passed over the surface of the paint.

The same techniques were used in catacombs, the underground burial places where the first Christians met during the persecutions. These paintings are rather primitive and naïve, but are nevertheless important because they introduced new subjects which were

Cimabue lived in Florence during the second half of the thirteenth century and is known especially for his splendid crucifixes. The Painted Cross of San Domenico ad Arezzo (left) was one of his first paintings and shows an intense dramatic force quite different from the stiff medieval pictures.

used during the next period, the religious period. During the whole of the Middle Ages, paintings dealt almost exclusively with subjects taken from Christian doctrine and the Bible. At first, there were mosaics which are decorations made up of small natural stones or enamels and prepared according to a technique which was very common among Romans and was later developed by the Byzantines. Later, there was a return to traditional painting and, in particular, tempera painting on wood, or directly on walls as frescoes.

Frescoes

From about the fourteenth century, fresco painting was very popular. This method was extremely difficult as it allowed for no interruption and mistakes could not easily be rectified. Workers prepared the wall or ceiling by applying a layer of lime to it and covered this with plaster. The artist painted onto the wet plaster, so that the colours mixed with the plaster and dried with it. The effect was soft, luminous and durable. There were special problems: once the plaster was dry, it was almost impossible to correct the work. If a mistake were made, the plaster had to be cut out and the work done again.

During the Middle Ages, drawings to be incorporated in a fresco were made directly onto the wet plaster. Later, in the middle of the fifteenth century, a cartoon (a careful preliminary drawing) was used. This consisted of a set of paper sheets on which the picture was traced with a charcoal pencil. It was then marked on the wall by "dusting", that is by making a number of very small holes along the lines of the pictures and filling them with carbon dust which deposited on the plaster. The picture was later coloured.

Medieval paintings generally strike us as unnatural and stiff: figures appear flat and have no expression; faces with the same features are sometimes repeated indefinitely; perspective does not exist: the size of the characters does not depend on their position in the painting, but on their importance.

Medieval painters, who were often anonymous and belonged to monasteries, interpreted art in general as a series of fixed rules and formulas. They passed these on to their pupils together with methods of preparing colours, which, in those days, each painter did himself. However, at the end of the thirteenth century, signs of an artistic revolution occurred in Italy. The Tuscan Cimabue and his pupil, Giotto, gave a new sense of truth and dramatic force to the painting.

Giotto (approx. 1267–1337) is the most important painter of his century. He

Giotto, Cimabue's pupil, is the most important painter of the Middle Ages and gave a new feeling of imagination and passion to painting. Left, The Resurrection of Lazarus from the Arena Chapel in Padua which Giotto designed and decorated with frescoes. Simione Martini's works, such as the Young St. Augustine (below) at Siena, can also be compared to Giotto.

is particularly known for his frescoes in the Assisi Basilica and the Arena chapel in Padua. His ability to control volume and space, which had previously been ignored by fresco painters, can be widely noted in his scenes. Giotto was followed by other important innovators during the fifteenth century: first of all, the Tuscan group, which included the mighty Masaccio; the "father of perspective", Paolo Uccello; Andrea del Castagno who painted heroic figures; and Fra Angelico, famous for his angels and saints. With these artists, a marvellous era of painting started in Italy and reached its peak during the Renaissance between the mid-

sixteenth century and the mid-seventeenth century.

Italian supremacy

The Renaissance is a "return to life" of classical art, that is Graeco-Roman art. Famous schools of painting were created throughout Italy. These schools found their inspiration from models of ancient times (which were much more frequent in Italy than elsewhere) and developed it on the basis of past experience. The most outstanding are the Tuscan and Venetian schools. The former excelled in dazzling colour effects whilst the latter was famous for the force of its drawing and elegance of style. In northern Italy there were artists like Vittore Carpaccio, the Bellinis, Mantegna (the Gonzagas were his patrons and his masterpieces filled the royal palace of Mantua). In central Italy, whose arts capital was Florence (this title went to Rome in the sixteenth century), there was a very large group of talented painters around the court of the Medicis. It included the two Lippis, Botticelli, Ghirlandaio, Verrocchio and the two Pollaiolos. Other major painters were, in Umbria, Luca Signorelli and Perugino, masters of the young Raphael; at the court of Urbino, the genius Piero della Francesca; in Sicily, Antonello da Messina. The use of oil colours, which replaced the old tempera techniques, was attributed for a long time to Antonello. However, the development of this new technique (still used today) was due to Flemish painters, although Antonello was among the first to promote it in Italy.

Italy was at the forefront of art in Europe throughout the whole Renaissance. Its supremacy was unquestionable. Some of our most famous and popular paintings were created during this period: Sandro Botticelli's *Spring*, Raphael's *Wedding of the Virgin* and Leonardo's *Last Supper*. The choice of subjects, which was no longer limited to religious themes, became very wide: mythological scenes were painted (such as Botticelli's famous *Birth of Venus*) as well as scenes of court life such as those which inspired Mantegna when he decorated the bridal bedroom in the ducal palace at Mantua.

From the fifteenth century onwards, portraits became popular. An abyss separated old paintings of "donors" from the strong, masculine heads of Antonello da Messina or from the arrogant profile of Federico di Montefeltro painted by Piero della Francesca, which now appears next to a portrait of his wife on two panels in the Uffizi Gallery in Florence. Another portrait, the most famous in the world, was about to be painted: Leonardo da Vinci's *Mona Lisa*.

As far as painting is concerned, the sixteenth century in Italy was an era of "giants" which started with the well-known Leonardo – Michelangelo – Raphael group (the first two are Tuscan and the third from the Marches) and finished with the Venetian group of Titian, Tintoretto and Veronese. These were the greatest painters of their time. Their works included unequalled masterpieces, such as Michelangelo's frescoes in the Sistine Chapel, Raphael's Rooms and Galleries in the Vatican Palace or Leonardo da Vinci's already mentioned *Last Supper* in Milan's convent Santa Maria delle Grazie. The three Venetian artists left their individual

Perspective is the great revolutionary discovery of Renaissance painting. Above, Masaccio's Crucifixion, *interpreted in a deeply human and dramatic way. Perspective lines used by Andrea Mantegna (right, St. George) converge on the spectator, drawing him into the painting. Piero della Francesca used pale, soft colours and arranged his figures to give a feeling of timelessness and serenity (below, the* Triumph of Frederick of Montefeltro, *painted on the back of the duke's portrait).*

240 (continued on page 245)

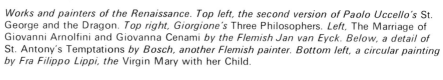

Works and painters of the Renaissance. Top left, the second version of Paolo Uccello's St. George and the Dragon. *Top right, Giorgione's* Three Philosophers. *Left,* The Marriage of Giovanni Arnolfini and Giovanna Cenami *by the Flemish Jan van Eyck. Below, a detail of* St. Antony's Temptations *by Bosch, another Flemish painter. Bottom left, a circular painting by Fra Filippo Lippi, the* Virgin Mary with her Child.

Painters of various Renaissance styles. Raphael became famous for his paintings of the Virgin. Left, the Virgin Mary on a Chair. Above and below, two versions of the same episode, Ecce Homo, painted by two famous Venetian artists of the sixteenth century, Tintoretto and Titian.

Top left, Portrait of a Sultan *by the Dutch painter, Rembrandt. Above, a version of the* Supper at Emmaus *by Caravaggio, a master of light and shadow effects. Left,* St. Maximus and St. Oswald *by Giambattista Tiepolo, a Venetian painter of the eighteenth century.*

Above, a detail from Portrait of Two Young Men *by the Flemish Anthony van Dyck; he was taught by Rubens, was influenced by Italian art and in turn influenced English portrait and landscape painting. Left,* La gamme d'amour *by the French Antoine Watteau, whose hazy and almost blurred style left a strong mark on the whole of the eighteenth century.*

The great innovators

The following biographical notes cannot include all the greatest and best-known painters, and even some of the most famous and popular artists have had to be omitted. Our criterion has not been perfection, but innovation. Each painter mentioned below broke away from the traditions of the past, stimulated his contemporaries, or showed a new direction for painting to take. Some gave rise to resentment and scandal. Others were not understood until long after their death or were rediscovered after periods of obscurity. It is through their efforts and achievements that art is alive, finding new forms of expression and creating works of beauty and perception.

Giotto (approx. 1267–1337). The son of Florentine peasants, he created a type of painting which, as his contemporary Petrarch pointed out, shocked scholars and left the ignorant cold. He turned away from the stereotyped forms of the medieval tradition and created in his paintings scenes of dramatic reality with solid, natural figures. Painters of the late fourteenth and fifteenth centuries were influenced by him and he is generally regarded as the founder of modern painting.

Paolo Uccello (1397–1475). It is said that the Florentine Paolo di Dono, also known as Paolo Uccello, was so obsessed by perspective that he used to utter in his sleep, "What a nice thing perspective is", and that he almost went mad. His most famous painting the *Deluge* (which was previously lost, but has now been restored) shows his ideas on perspective. They are also seen in the three *Battles* paintings, where men, horses and arrows create a succession of lines whose aim is to achieve depth, which until then was unknown.

Masaccio (1401–28). Tommaso Guidi, also known as Masaccio, was born in San Giovanni Valdaino in Tuscany. His masterpiece, the frescoes in the Carmelite Church in Florence, are in a realistic, grand and solemn style which is typical of the avant-garde style of the fifteenth century. The pictures are compact and vigorous with a very strong spiritual force.

Bosch (approx. 1450–1516). A Flemish painter from Brabant, Hieronymus van Aeken, also known as Bosch, created a style which was a challenge to conventional painting, current models, good sense and even good taste. In his most famous works, such as the *Earthly Paradise* and *St. Anthony's Temptations*, the daring and disconcerting symbols and grotesque representations show both an incredible fantasy and strong awareness of the anxiety of his days. He is often considered the greatest master of fantasy who ever lived and modern surrealists consider him as their forerunner.

Leonardo da Vinci (1452–1519). Son of a Florentine notary, he lived a wandering life during the Renaissance, staying for a time with various Italian noblemen, and died at Amboise when working for Francis I of France. The inimitable attraction of his painting is found in the "haziness", an effect created by light and shadows where the edges of the faces appear softened and circled by a twilight which accentuates the mystery.

Albrecht Dürer (1471–1528). Born in Nuremberg in Germany, he should be called the first "modern painter" of central Europe. He combined northern traditions with lessons from classical antiquity and the Italian Renaissance. His famous painting, *Madonna of the Rose Garlands*, carried out in Venice, marked a change in German art from the Gothic to the Renaissance world.

Michelangelo Buonarotti (1475–1564). Son of a Florentine magistrate who opposed his artistic vocation for a long time, Michelangelo was considered first and foremost as a sculptor. He used to say that painting and sculpture were the same thing and that colour was, in fact, of minor importance to him as he only resorted to it to accentuate the "mighty profile of human beings". He is considered by many to be the greatest sculptor, painter and draughtsman who ever lived, as well as a great architect and poet.

Giorgione (approx. 1478–1510). Few works remain of the Venetian Giorgio Barbarelli, also known as Giorgione, but *Venus*, the *Tempest* and the *Three Philosophers* were among his best-known paintings. Compared to previous Venetian masters, he used colour in a revolutionary way, no longer considering it as something to cover the picture, but as a means of expression capable of creating characters and forms.

El Greco (1541–1614). Born of a wealthy family in Crete, his real name was Domenikos Theotocopoulos. He studied Italian art, but found his spiritual home in Toledo, Spain. His most famous painting, *Burial of Count Orgaz*, still shows some classical features, but his next work (*Opening of the Fifth Seal*) broke away from reality and preceded the audacity of modern expressionists by more than three centuries.

Caravaggio (1573–1610). Recent studies have shown that Michelangelo da Merisi, also known as Caravaggio, was born in 1571 and not 1573. Son of a Lombard architect, he started the legend of the painter as a rebellious and dissipated young man by his chaotic and violent life. He made important changes to Italian painting, broke off all dealings with the past, rejected "ideal beauty" and depicted traditional themes with great reality, simplicity and intensity.

Diego Velazquez (1599–1660). He was the descendant of a noble family of Seville (Spain). His skill as a portrait painter made him Court Painter to Philip IV. His early work followed the trend of Spanish realism and reached its peak in *Las Meninas* which combined realism with atmosphere and characterization. His work also showed extraordinary anticipation of the future, as in the *Rokeby Venus*, the most modern nude of the seventeenth century.

Rembrandt (1606–69). Born in Leyden in Holland, the son of a miller, Harmenszoon van Rijn Rembrandt became famous when he was still young. His style developed magnificently, rejecting classical themes (he was known as the first "heretic of painting") and attained powerful original effects with his use of light and shade (chiaroscura). His output was prodigious: he produced about six hundred and fifty paintings as well as about three hundred etchings and nearly two thousand drawings.

Leonardo's Mona Lisa *and a detail from Michelangelo's paintings at the Sistine Chapel. Some experts consider these the greatest painters the world has known.*

(continued from page 240)

Francisco Goya (1746–1828) A poor boy, born in Saragossa in Spain, he succeeded through his own determination, in entering the world of official culture. A long illness left him very close to death and completely deaf, and changed his outlook. His paintings. drawings and engravings showed nearly every aspect of contemporary life, reflecting the political and social upheavals. His later work had a great effect on French artists of the nineteenth century.

Eugène Delacroix (1798–1863). Brought up in Paris, the son of an ambassador, he had a brilliant and stormy career during the Romantic Period and is the most prominent of the French Romantic painters. In spite of his genius, he was criticized to the end of his life: contemporary critics attacked a number of his masterpieces, such as the *Massacre at Chios*, calling it the "massacre of painting", or *Death of Sardanapalus* which gave rise to a great deal of scandal.

Edouard Manet (1832–83). A Parisian of bourgeois family, he caused an upheaval in the artistic and critical circles in the French capital with the *Déjeuner sur l'herbe*, which was seen as "revolutionary evidence" of a new style of painting. The same reaction was given to his *Olympia* and *Balle aux Folies-Bergeres*. By his handling of colour and light and his individual method of creating realistic impressions with large luminous spots, Manet opened the way to Impressionism.

Henri Toulouse-Lautrec (1864–1901). The descendant of a very old, noble family, he broke both his legs as a child and this stunted his growth. He influenced artistic avant-garde ideas on painting. He chose themes from the dance-halls and cafés of Montmartre, such as the Moulin Rouge, and from cabarets and circuses, and these provoked violent reactions from the public. Toulouse-Lautrec also designed a number of brilliant posters with simple lines and large areas of flat colour, and was the first to recognize their future importance.

Pablo Picasso (1881–1973). Born in Malaga in Spain, he left his middle-class family at the age of twenty to lead the Bohemian life of Paris artists. He spent the rest of his life in France. Picasso was at the forefront of twentieth-century painting, and his works show examples of a number of contrasting styles. His most famous painting, *Guernica*, is a huge canvas prompted by the Spanish Civil War and shows the artist's hatred of the violence and horror of war.

Amedeo Modigliani (1884–1920). He was born in Leghorn of an Italian-Jewish family, but went to Paris at an early age and died there of tuberculosis, misery, drink and drugs. As a painter and sculptor his style was influenced by African sculpture, Cézanne, Picasso and, most of all, medieval Italian painting. He was a superb draughtsman and painted figures with elongated forms and lines limited to the barest necessary, reflecting a strong psychological understanding and awareness of the human condition.

mark on three different aspects of painting: Titian in the field of portraiture (Europe's sovereigns queued to be immortalized by his brush); Tintoretto with his paintings of magestic Biblical events; Veronese with his huge pictures of sacred, allegorical and historical subjects, containing vast crowds of people such as the frescoes of the Villa Maser or *The Feast in the House of Levi*.

Before the end of this great century, another personality emerged, the Lombard Michelangelo da Merisi, known as Caravaggio (1573–1610) who influenced significantly the whole of the seventeenth century in Europe. On his canvas he depicted dramatic characters with a wealth of detail, strong light and shade effects and vivid realism. Caravaggio's earliest works were still-life subjects, inanimate objects such as flowers, game, foodstuff, musical instruments and books. An early example of this work is his *Fruit Basket*.

Spain and Flanders

The artistic era in Italy reached its peak in the sixteenth century and continued during the next century in Spain and Flanders. Flemish painters, who had rivalled Italy since the end of the fifteenth century, distinguished themselves from Italian painters by their more realistic representation of everyday life, as can be seen, for example, in the peasants' worlds depicted by Pieter Bruegel the elder (1530–1569), also known as "Peasant Bruegel".

The most important Flemish painter of the seventeenth century was Peter Paul Rubens. His imposing works are influenced by Italian painters, in particular Titian and Caravaggio. In nearby Holland he had a rival, Rembrandt, famous for his use of light and shade (chiaroscura). Among his greatest masterpieces are *The Night Watch*, painted in 1642, and a series of self-portraits from youth to old age.

Titian's (and Tintoretto's) influence can be seen in Spain in Domenikos Theotocopoulos, known as El Greco, of Cretian extraction. He lived at the end of the sixteenth and beginning of the seventeenth century and created majestic and disturbing scenes with sharp contrasts of colour, blue, green, yellow and pink. His work shows signs of Impressionism, a style which appeared two centuries later. Spain's golden century triumphed with the remarkable characters of Velazquez, the Court Painter, and of Esteban Murillo and Zurbaran, who evoked very moving religious scenes.

Jean-Auguste Dominique Ingres was one of the main representatives of the Classical Movement in French nineteenth-century painting. Above, his Portrait of Madame Moitessier. *Left, Claude Monet's* Impression, Sunrise, *painted in 1872, gave its name to the group of Impressionist painters.*

245

Spanish painting, rich in expression and colours, later included two great painters of genius: Francisco Goya, who lived from 1746 to 1828, was known for his fervour and inexorable realism (two paintings called *2 May* and *3 May 1808* show the atrocities and horrors of war); and, during the twentieth century, Pablo Picasso, who died in 1973, and was the greatest exponent of contemporary art.

The French eighteenth century

French painting was supreme in Europe during the eighteenth century. At first, painting was gentle and light-hearted, suitable for pastoral and court scenes and splendidly represented by Jean Antoine Watteau, François Boucher and Jean Honoré Fragonard, who often used a new technique, pastel. During the nineteenth century, Neoclassicism became important with Jacques Louis David, Napoleon's painter. It was followed by the Romantic Movement whose major painter was Eugène Delacroix and finally, at the end of the century, the splendid and inimitable Impressionism.

This movement took its name from a picture by Claude Monet, *Impression, Sunrise* which represents the effect of the sun rising over the sea. It tried to show how appearances change under the movement of light. Artists like Monet, Edouard Manet, Edgar Degas, Camille Pissarro and many others made Paris the arts capital of Europe and this supremacy lasted until the end of the Second World War. It had no rivals: at the end of the Renaissance in Italy, the only schools of painting that aroused international interest were the Venetian school of the eighteenth century (with painters like Tiepolo, Guardi and Canaletto) and that of the Tuscan painters who were partly influenced by Impressionism and included Giovanni Fattori, Silvestro Lega and Telemaco Signorini.

The most important German painter was Albrecht Dürer (sixteenth century) but he was an individual painter and not part of a school. In England, there were a number of superb portrait painters, like Peter Lely (seventeenth century), Joshua Reynolds, Thomas Gainsborough and, finally, Thomas Lawrence (nineteenth century). The landscape paintings of artists as different as John Constable and Joseph Mallord William Turner were extremely important and Turner was, in fact, the forerunner of Impressionism. In his later paintings, he thought in terms of coloured light, or, as Constable called it, "tinted steam". When he died in 1851, he left nearly 300 paintings and nearly 20,000 watercolours and drawings to the Nation.

Modern art

In Paris, the nineteenth century ended with a group of internationally famous painters (Paul Gauguin, Vincent van Gogh, Henri Toulouse-Lautrec, Paul Cézanne) who started with Impressionism, but dropped all forms of tradition in pursuit of new ideas.

Since the beginning of the twentieth century, painting has seen a variety of styles (Cubism, Fauvism, Expressionism, Synthetism, Surrealism) most of which started in France, but were influenced by the art of other races and periods. Two names stand out: that of Pablo Picasso (1881–1973), a Spaniard living in Paris, who painted in many styles during his long artistic life; and that of the Italian Amedeo Modigliani, who also emigrated to Paris and who, during his tragically brief life (1884–1920) revolutionized the art of portrait-painting by his avant-garde style. However, artists today are conscious of the contemporary significance of painting, which is the oldest form of their art.

During recent years, many artists have tended to abandon traditional subjects and materials, incorporating everyday subjects into their work and using such materials as metal packing cases, old doors or household utensils instead of paint and canvas. Painters are experimenting with a variety of styles. Some are now using acryllic paints in place of the traditional oils.

Among the most famous artists alive today are David Hockney, Lucien Freud, Francis Bacon and Andy Warhol. Their portraits often present an accurate social commentary without words. Artists help us to look at things afresh, seeing new relationships between art and reality.

Twentieth-century paintings. Left, the Fall of the Angel by Marc Chagall, who was of Russian origin and viewed the world between reality and fantasy. Bottom left, Portrait of a Young Woman by Amedeo Modigliani, one of the most important painters of our century. Below, the Lovers' Cry by the Spanish Joan Miro. The lines and colours in his paintings evoke dreams and imagination.

Precious stones
The riches
of the Earth

The clearness and brilliance of gems are only fully apparent when the stones have been cut and polished. In its uncut state a fabulous diamond could easily be mistaken for an ordinary piece of stone.

There are many stones, but only those of outstanding beauty are precious and of all the qualities that give beauty to gems, colour is the most important. However, their beauty is not their only characteristic: they must also be durable and rare. There are many problems involved in finding them, treating them, polishing them, cutting them and revealing their beauty. This work is assessed in financial terms, that is money. Since ancient times, precious stones have been among the rarest and most expensive objects owned by man.

There are semi-precious as well as precious stones, but naturally the more precious ones are most highly valued. Gems are usually cut with many facets to bring out the transparency and shine of the stone. Semi-precious stones are often opaque and their attraction lies in their colour. These may be cut and even carved (for example jade statuettes) but if they are used in jewellery, they normally have curved and highly polished surfaces.

Not only are precious stones worth more financially than other precious materials such as gold and silver, they are also a sign of wealth or social status. Men and women have been attracted to gems since ancient times and have often used them as an obvious sign of their wealth and importance. Deep red rubies, green emeralds, blue sapphires and diamonds as brilliant as stars, have been used to adorn crowns and sceptres, both symbols of power. Precious stones also have a purely aesthetic and decorative value and this can be seen particularly in medieval jewels where highly valued gems are set next to ordinary pieces of coloured glass purely to achieve a good colour effect.

Diamonds, corundum and beryl

A gem is a mineral. To be more precise, there are three types of minerals which correspond to gems: diamonds, corundum and beryl.

A diamond is pure carbon which has crystallized under great pressure and at high temperature. It is the hardest natural substance known to man. Its great

When they have been cut, precious stones are set in gold, silver or platinum to form jewels. Top left and above, a ring and brooch based on a flower pattern and forming a precious parure of diamonds and valuable Burma rubies. Flowers were used also as the basis of the unusual mosaic of hard stones shown below.

hardness and brilliance make it the chief of the precious stones. Most diamond mines are in the southern areas of Africa and in Siberia. Corundum, which is found mainly in Sri Lanka, Burma and Thailand, is given different names depending on its colour: if it is red it is known as ruby, but if it is blue, a sapphire. There are also yellow and green corundums, the latter are known as "oriental emeralds" and cannot be mistaken for real emeralds. In fact, real emeralds are deep green beryl. Pale green is the usual colour for beryl, but it may also be deep green, blue, yellow, brown, colourless or pink. Special names are given to the different colours: aquamarine, is pale blue-green; morganite is pink; golden beryl is yellow. Emeralds are very rare and, therefore, very expensive.

Diamonds, rubies, sapphires and emeralds are the best-known gems and their fame has given rise to legends and superstitions over the years. The largest diamond in the world was the Cullinan which was found in a South African mine in 1905. It was cut into 105 gems, the largest, a pear-shaped diamond weighing 530.20 carats, is known as the Great Star of Africa and is the largest cut diamond in the world. Both it and the second largest, known as the Cullinan II, are part of the Crown Jewels. The most unlucky diamond is the Hope as the story goes that whoever owned it was dogged by ill-luck

The picture shows a ruby crystal in a block of calcite. Right, uncut diamonds. The nine topaz below (three uncut and six cut) illustrate the different colours of this precious mineral.

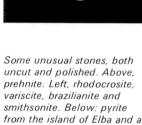

Some unusual stones, both uncut and polished. Above, prehnite. Left, rhodocrosite, variscite, brazilianite and smithsonite. Below: pyrite from the island of Elba and a calcopyrite cabochon.

or died a violent death. The most beautiful diamond is the Koh-i-noor, which was given to the Empress of Russia, Catherine the Great, by one of her lovers.

Rubies, sapphires and emeralds also have their stories of love or violence, so that we might well doubt the wisdom of owning gems of so much beauty. In any case, the largest and most famous stones are now kept in museums and are, therefore, protected against disasters and thefts. In addition to these "royal" gems, there are others which are less well-known and less expensive. They include topaz, garnets, tourmalines, zircons and others which are less common but just as beautiful. For example, Alexandrite, which has an incredible green-red colour, the honey-yellow titanite or sphene, pale blue cyanite and vermilion crocoite.

The cut

The value of a gem depends on its brilliance, the absence of flaws and impurities and on the cut. By increasing its brilliancy, the cut transforms a piece of bright, irregularly shaped stone into a fabulous gem with many facets. The cut of a gem is particularly important for its market value when it is sold as a jewel. This is especially so with diamonds, as they are colourless and transparent and their brilliancy is greatly increased when they are properly cut and polished.

The most common cut is the brilliant (this same name is also given to diamonds cut in this way) but there are others too, such as the rose, the baguette and the step or trap cut. The last is used particularly for emeralds and is often called the emerald cut. It is also used for rubies, sapphires and larger diamonds while the brilliant and rose cuts are used for diamonds in particular.

If a gem is cut *en cabochon*, it has no facets but is smooth and rounded, usually with a flat underside. If both the upper and lower surfaces are domed the cut is known as double cabochon. Sometimes the transparency of the stone is emphasized by making an incision in the lower surface. Cabochon stones were greatly used in jewels until the late Middle Ages and were also mounted in the leather binding of valuable books.

An expert's eye is needed to distinguish between real gems and synthetic ones. A gem has five main characteristics: density, hardness, refractive index, pleochroism and internal structure.

The density is calculated by instruments and is the first test carried out to distinguish a real gem from a near-perfect reproduction. The hardness is the capacity to resist abrasion. The diamond is very much harder than its nearest rival, the

rectangular or elongated diamonds

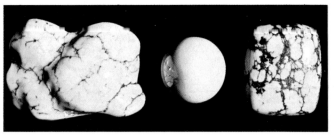

Persian turquoise

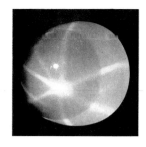

starred quartz

Brazilian tourmaline

Madagascan beryl

Burmese sapphire
(330 carats)

two Ceylonese sapphires and a Kashmir sapphire (right)

Ceylonese starred ruby (140 carats)

moonstone

zircon (top) and opals

uncut and cut South-African and Brazilian garnets

249

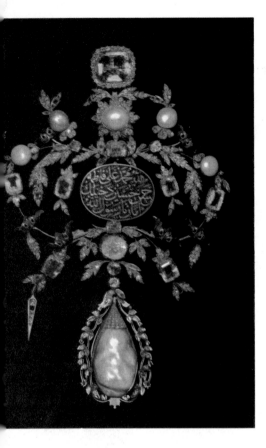

Above, a Turkish pendant of the eighteenth century with pearls, diamonds and emeralds. Right, the largest diamond in the world, the Great Star of Africa (530.20 carats) has been mounted on the sceptre of the British royal family. Each carat (the unit of measurement used for precious stones) equals 200 milligrammes. Bottom right, on the crown, the famous Koh-i-noor (mountain of light). Below, a Mexican jade statuette.

corundum (ruby and sapphire), which is followed by the topaz and emerald. The refractive index determines the stone's capacity of deflecting light and so creating the marvellous colour effects which are the greatest attraction of a "brilliant" diamond. Pleochroism is the quality of various gems to show different colours if they are viewed from different directions. This quality is tested with a special instrument known as a dichroscope. Finally, internal structure: synthetic stones are sometimes so similar to real ones that results of the above tests can be inconclusive. The final and decisive test is to examine the stone's internal structure. A gem formed over millions of years will never be the same as one of similar composition that has been manufactured in the space of a few days or months. Very accurate instruments are often required to determine any difference which cannot be seen with the naked eye.

Semi-precious stones give marvellous decorative effects even if they are not particularly expensive. The most common are quartz, jasper, chalcedony (such as the agate, bloodstone carnelian and onyx), opal, the legendary jade used in the East in ancient times, the moonstone so-called because of its milky colour, the yellow sunstone, the deep blue lapis lazuli with its fascinating specks of golden-yellow pyrite, the bluish turquoise which has given its name to the colour, and many others which have been used for decoration over the centuries. In ancient times, stones were used primarily as jewels but they were also used as seals and even charms, as special and even magical signs or symbols could be engraved on their surface.

Very popular presents

Not everyone can afford to buy precious stones, but many people buy as presents the so-called birthstones. These are the stones popularly supposed to bring luck to people born in the relevant month, corresponding also to the signs of the Zodiac. Although they sometimes vary, the usual stones and months are: January, garnet; February, amethyst; March, aquamarine; April, diamond; May, emerald; June, pearl; July, ruby; August, sardonyx; September, sapphire; October, opal; November, topaz; December, turquoise.

Birth stones have been popular since antiquity, but the stones now associated with each month bear little relation to those of ancient times, for the list has changed with availability and cost. In some cases, even the names have changed: the sapphire mentioned in the Bible is more likely to have been lapis lazuli than what we know as sapphire.

UFOs
Do they exist?

UFO: how many times has this acronym appeared on the front pages of the world's newspapers during the last thirty years? These three letters, which stand for "unidentified flying object", have lead to very heated discussions, been the subject of numerous articles and books and aroused the interest of authors and poets, politicians and military people, scientists and visionaries. And what has been concluded after so many discussions and articles? Nothing. UFOs are still what they have always been, namely a mystery. The only thing that has been established is what Willy Ley, popular writer on space topics and friend of Wernher von Braun, wrote: "the outbreak of flying saucers seems to have progressed in exactly the same way as a contagious disease". Ley spoke of "flying saucers" because the mysterious objects that had been sighted had almost always been in the shape of a saucer. Nevertheless, whether we call them flying saucers or UFOs, the outbreak mentioned by Ley is certainly not a recent problem. Apart from the old Indian and Chinese legends in which mysterious flying machines called "ships" and "celestial vessels" have been compared to UFOs, there has been plenty of evidence in more recent periods.

Flying dragons and cigar-shaped vessels

A French document written in 1608 mentions "terribly frightening objects that were seen near Nice and at sea in front of Genoa" in that year. The document also tells of "three carts each pulled by six flaming-like dragons which were seen on 15 August at sea in front of the port of Genoa . . . and which produced such a noise that the mountains trembled and many people died because of fright and deafness".

On 21 April 1897, Alexander Hamilton, a wealthy farmer in Kansas, USA, made a sworn testimony (which was therefore legally valid) that he saw on his farm "a vessel consisting of a section shaped like a large cigar, about one hundred metres long and with a kind of wherry under it". In fact, 1897 witnessed many mysterious "flying ships" all over the United States. Another wave of UFOs was noted in 1910 (a "cigar" appeared over Chattanooga for three consecutive days, from 12 to 14

January 1910, and captured the attention of all the inhabitants as well as the front pages of newspapers). After that, there was almost nothing for two years.

Frank Edwards, an American UFO expert wrote: "the first well-documented report of a saucer-shaped UFO that I have been able to find dates back to 1926 and is signed by the Roerich expedition of the American Natural History Museum. Members of the expedition witnessed an extraordinary object shaped like a saucer in the Himalayas sky in 1926."

After this official "birth", flying saucers were not mentioned in news articles for twenty years or so. During the Second World War, the Germans and Allied Forces were a little concerned after seeing strange objects which could have been terrible secret weapons. The Americans christened various luminous balls that were noted on the western front "Flying Sauerkrauts". After the war, however, they were no longer mentioned.

The outbreak of flying saucers

Kenneth Arnold, a wealthy American businessman, was flying in his personal aeroplane near Mount Rainier in Idaho on 24 June 1947 when he saw nine strange "aeroplanes" which he at first thought were secret prototypes of the United States' military Air Force. In an article which was widely published in the newspapers, Arnold used the forgotten words of the 1926 Roerich report: in his account of the flying objects that he was certain he had seen, he declared that "they were flying like saucers that had been made to bounce on the surface of the water". This is how the outbreak of flying saucers started again.

On 7 January 1948, Thomas Mantell, a pilot of the American Air Force, created a stir in the United States. On that day, he and three colleagues set out to chase a large luminous ball seen in the early afternoon over Madisonville, Kentucky. He flew his P.51 fighter towards the mysterious object and after a few minutes called the control tower saying: "I have sighted the object. It appears to be made

Optical phenomena, special effects or reality? Nobody has yet provided a complete answer to the question. In the meantime, strange "unidentified flying objects" continue to be photographed all over the world.

of metal and is huge . . ." A few words followed and then nothing. Mantell's body was later found next to the aircraft which had crashed to the ground at about 150 kilometres from the base. There was no sign of fire and the aircraft seemed to have disintegrated for no apparent reason.

Mantell's case led to a series of sightings all over the world, some of which were reported by reliable witnesses such as, for example, two American scholars, the meteorologist, Seymour Hess, and the astronomer, Clyde Tombaugh, who discovered the planet Pluto. Then, when space voyages started, various astronauts joined the list of those "who had seen something". "An incredible object with arm-like projecting parts" was sighted on 4 June 1965 by the astronauts Edward White and James McDivitt. However, NASA, the American space agency, later disappointed them by declaring that it was the American satellite Pegasus which in fact has two large, long "arms" which are solar cells.

Further sightings

Flying saucers have also been sighted in Egypt, Chile, Australia, Argentina and Vietnam. On 17 March 1950, a group of six Italians in a game reserve near Crescentino, Piedmont, sighted a luminous body travelling through the sky at great speed. A "tail of bright red sparks and a cloud of smoke of the same colour" (as reported in a newspaper article) sounds more like a meteorite. Four years later, on 17 September 1954, strange, luminous, cigar-shaped objects were sighted over the airports of Ciampino in Rome and Linate in Milan.

The sighting over Ciampino was confirmed by radar of the Ministry of Defence and that over Milan was witnessed by two aeronautical engineers.

Sightings of UFOs increased and were very often supported by reliable evidence. This is the case, for example, of the twelve flying objects which were seen on 30 November 1973 and were also picked up by radar at the Italian military Air Force base in Gambolo near Mortara. Twelve luminous balls (this is what they looked like to the naked eye) crossed the sky in jerks, reaching a speed of 1,370 kilometres per hour. A few days later, on 4 December 1973, another ten mysterious "marks" were picked up on the radar screen. One of these marks was travelling at a speed of 1,870 kilometres per hour.

Discussions on the nature of UFOs still continue but as we have already said, no definite answer has yet been found. Official surveys carried out in the United States and the Soviet Union have settled the problem by declaring that the phenomenon is "non-existent" or at the very most contains some element of doubt. To those who believe that flying saucers do exist and that they come from another planet somewhere in the universe, a report of the United States Air Force in 1969 based on the study of seven thousand sightings states that "there is still some doubt on a few cases but that it is in any case clear that even if UFOs do exist they are not extraterrestrial". The same opinion is expressed in a report published by the University of Colorado.

Electrical phenomena or unconscious yearnings?

Many scholars have tried to find an answer to the problem in physical or atmospheric phenomena. Mention has been made of clouds of ionized gas with an electrical charge which could be

Two photographs of UFOs taken in the United States. The one on the left was taken on 22 November 1966 in Oregon and the one on the right on 3 August 1965 in California.

picked up by radar. Another hypothesis (which is generally preferred) is that UFOs are electrical phenomena, the so-called "globular lightnings" which dart at very high speed and look like luminous balls.

Psychologists have also examined the problem and have declared that UFOs are the materialization of some of man's unconscious yearnings and above all of his hope that he is not alone in the universe. This hope clearly inspired Hermann Oberth, an important space scientist and astronautical pioneer, when he wrote: "I believe that extraterrestrial intelligences observe the earth and have been visiting us for millions of years". However, a German journalist has written that even if there were any truth in flying saucers, nobody could now be certain of how much has been obscured and altered by hallucinations and projections of the observers' own personalities.

Index

Acknowledgments

Aaron, R.E. 217d: Action Press: G.A. Rossi 45a: Action Press: Rusniewski 32; 33a–d: Adverphoto 112: Aerofilms 19a: Alinari 172: G. Allegretti 25b; 25c: All sport/Tony Duffy 214a: All sport/Steve Powell 214b: All sport/Don Morley 215: Anas 9c; 72: F. Arborio Mella 136a, b; 203b, c: B. Archive – 135d, e; 136c; 137d; 141a: A. Ballo 171b: G. Barone 49b: Beaujard/Titus 161a: F. Bernini 156c: C. Bertinetti 24a; 38a; 160b; 161b; 204; 235b–e: M. Bertinetti 110; 111b; 115; 121a, b: C. Bevilacqua 122c; 134b–d; 135a; 136d, e; 138b, f; 146a; 147a; 247c; 249a–e, g, i, l, n; 248a, c–f; 250a, b, c: A. Biber 129: Biblioteca Ambrosiana Milan 199b: BIPNA 111: Blauel Photo 124a: Bona 109b: British Crown 250d: Bulloz 170d; 244a: Bolova UK Ltd; 153a: California Inst. of Technology 234: M. Carrieri 8; 142b; 165; 237b; 240b; 241a, c; 243a, b; 246: Casiraghi Archive 194a, b, c, e; 195a–c; 219c, d; 220; 221: Casnati 55b; 127c: CEDRI 143a: Cesati 95: Chomon 118: J. Ciganovic 85: C. Cigolini 39; 41b, c; 231a: N. Cirani 89; 143b; 148a; 156a; 158a; 159b; 176c, e; 236: Citroen 38b: Colour Library International 28: A.C. Cooper 43a, c–e; 116b; 139a; 243e; 245: G. Costa 43b; 71a, b; 91a, b; 113b; 126c; 137a, c; 138d, c; 139c; 140b–e; 141b–e; 186b; 194d; 196a, b; 219a, b; 233a, b: A. Dagli Orti 42c; 54; 88; 99b; 116e; 146b; 147b; 151d; 154c; 164a, b; 197b; 200c; 201a, b; 202b; 203b, c; 230; 240a: G. Dagli Orti 108a–c; 113a; 119a; 120a; 124b; 128; 142a; 143c; 150a; 156b; 170b, c; 180b; 189b; 202a; 241e; 242b: C. Dani 138c; 140a: Dargaud Editore 223: D.B.L. Photo 47c: A. De Antonio 237c: De Beer 248b: De Gregorio 18a; 42a, b; 44a, b; 197a: E.P.C. Armees, Paris 63: E.P.T. 147c: Explorer/Delu 186: Farabola Archive 211b: Fristedt-Ostman Agency 20a: Gardin, B. 157f: G. Giansanti 184a, b; 186a, 187b, c; 188a–e; 189a: G. Giavonetti 217b: A & O Gogna 83: M. Going 206a, b, c: W.L. Hamilton 102b; 205a; 207b; 209b: Hamlyn Photo Lib. 14b; 71: C. Hicks 146c: I.C.P. 16: IGDA 27c; 31b; 55a; 64b; 122a, b; 123; 127; 132a, b; 135b, c; 139b; 158b; 190a, d, e; 191b; 206d; 231b; 239a; 247a, b: IGDA/O. Langini 92a: JACANA/VARIN 30b: J.M. Jarvis 66a–d:

Lauros/Giraudon 200a: M. Leigheb 20b; 21b; 77b; 82c; 149c; 157d; 171a; 176d; 213a: Libri Edizione Milan 218; 222: Magnum 82; 176b:/B. Glinn 15b; 17b: /E. Hartmann 15a: /M. Silverstone 82a: /Bruno Barbey 82b: /R. Buzzi 82e: Marka 15c; 34; 45b; 70; 78a, b; 80b, c; 89a–e; 104c; 114a; 185; 193c; 205d; 207a; 208b, c, e; 212b; 217a: /Mauri 35: P. Martini 86b: Marzari 233c: R. Masotti 191c; 192a, c; 193a, b: Max Mara 167a: Meyer 241b; 242c: S.P.A. Missoni 166a; 167b: Museo di Stato/G. Munden 203d: N.A.S.A. 133b: Nat. Maritime Museum Greenwich 58: Nat's Photo 138g: Neri/Bishop/Contact 31a: Neri/Pino 191a: P. Nigris 228b: G. Nimatallah 14a; 37b; 52; 53; 56a; 64a, c; 71c; 99c; 125; 126b; 127a; 129; 150c; 151a–c, e; 154a, b; 157e; 176a; 201d; 203e; 237a; 239b; 241d; 243c, d: C. Novara 9b; 108: Olivetti 180a: Olympia 210; 211a; 213b: Orbis 92b: Ostman 157c: P2 Archive 27f; 49a; 109a; 116; 157a: Paskall 75: Pasteur Museum 150a: F. & M. Papetti 155b, c: R. Pedicini 198b; 201c: M. Pedone 80a: Pellegrini 103a–d: Photri 62, 68c; 76a–f; 190b, c; 251; 252: G.B. Pineider 126a; 198a: R. Portolese 150b: C. Pozzoni 150a; 151a–d: S. Prato 157b: Publi-Aer-Photo 48a, b; 76: Publifoto 73: Quéméré, E. 40a: D. Redfern 216a, b: Redfern/d. Ellis 217c: R. Redicini 114b: A. Rizzi 27a–d; 138a; 150d; 153c, d; 155a; 181: Roger Viollet, H. 91c, d: G.A. Rossi 37a; 37c; 38c; 40b; 62b, c; 63a, b; 86a; 93; 94a, b; 120b; 183; 187a; 205c; 235a: G. Routhier 245b: Royal College of Surgeons 99a: St. Mary's Hospital 100a: A. Sabbatini 205b; 208a:Salmer 26: /E. Baumann 224; 225; 228a, b; 229: Sandak 148b: G. Sappa 77a; 78c; 97b: Scala 81; 238; 240c; 242a; 244b: Seemuller 87a, c; 88b; 102a; 131a–c; 133a; 173a–c; 199a: Seiko Ltd. 153b: Signorelli 209a: G. Sioen 29; 56; 62c; 97a; 170a: Smithsonian Institute 249f, h: SNCF 68a, b: S. Spini 83b: Technofrigo 36: A. Tessore 159a: Titti 137b; 212a: Titus 49c; 149b: Tomsich 200b: Tony Stone Ass. 100; 101; 208d: G. Vandystadt. 46a, b: Varin/Visage 30a: A. Vergani 9a; 17a; 24b; 25b; 26a; 36; 47a, b; 111a; 119b; 160a; 176g: P. Verni 116c, d: Verri 116b: M. Wolfe 192b.